G000037856

PALAEOLIMNOLOGY AND LAKE ACIDIFICATION

PALAEOLIMNOLOGY AND LAKE ACIDIFICATION

PROCEEDINGS OF
A ROYAL SOCIETY DISCUSSION MEETING
HELD ON 25 AUGUST 1989

ORGANIZED AND EDITED BY
R. W. BATTARBEE, SIR JOHN MASON, F.R.S.,
I. RENBERG AND J. F. TALLING, F.R.S.

LONDON
THE ROYAL SOCIETY
1990

Printed in Great Britain for the Royal Society
by the
University Press, Cambridge

ISBN 0 85403 394 7

First published in *Philosophical Transactions of the Royal Society of London*,
series B, volume 327 (no. 1240), pages 223–445

British Library Cataloguing in Publication Data

Palaeolimnology and lake acidification.
1. Palaeolimnology
I. Battarbee, R. W. (Richard W.) II. Royal Society 560.45

ISBN 0-85403-394-7

Published by the Royal Society
6 Carlton House Terrace, London SW1Y 5AG

PREFACE

The Surface Water Acidification Project was established in 1984 with several aims. Prominent among these was the key question: to what extent are the biological and chemical characteristics of catchments being affected by the acid deposition itself? Changes in the chemistry of the surface waters had been clearly demonstrated, and from a knowledge of the biology of many of the organisms the qualitative and quantitative changes in the biota could reasonably be regarded as a consequence. But why had the features of the surface waters changed over the last few decades? The acidity of rainfall had changed, though it was possible to question the calibration and accuracy of measurements made decades ago. Furthermore it was pointed out by Professor I. Th. Rosenqvist and others that there had been many other changes, more particularly in land-use. In many of the affected areas, maturing conifer plantations were now more widespread, occupying land previously used for grazing. Wood was much less important as a domestic fuel, so the amount of alkaline ash spread by man's activities would have fallen. It was argued that with so many variables it was not possible to identify, from the knowledge then existing, any particular factor as the cause. In addition it was known that as conifer plantations aged, the characteristics of the soil changed, perhaps the present acidification was simply a phase in a natural cycle with a long return time?

There are two basic approaches to answering such questions about a complex biogeochemical system. One, sometimes called the intensive approach, is to follow the putative cause and effect chain step by step, to make precise measurements of each component in particular field sites and, ideally, demonstrate experimentally that the change in one is a direct consequence of the observed change in the previous component. This is the traditional methodology of scientific proof, its structure analogous to that of a geometric theorem. A further step is to develop a numerical model of the sequential chain, the sensitivity of the outcome to variations in particular parameters can be tested. Unfortunately, in complex environmental situations, it is often difficult both to be sure that the chain is complete and to make the appropriate experiments. The consequent model may then contain too many uncertainties.

Another approach is to widen the field of observation, either in time or in space or both. This extensive method is essentially that of the epidemiologist, it involves correlation and relies for its insight into causation on a high frequency of association. With most complex environmental problems these two approaches are not alternatives, they are complementary and both are needed to give a conclusion in which one can have confidence.

In planning SWAP, the management committee adopted both approaches and the palaeoecological work described in this volume constitutes the major part of the extensive approach programme. Taken together, the two approaches in the overall programme have allowed definitive answers to be given to the original questions. In my view the palaeoecological work has been quite vital and, as is apparent from the papers in this volume, it has given particularly clear answers to those questions posed above. It has also demonstrated many complexities; from these one can see how unrepresentative conclusions could have been drawn if the scope of the studies had been restricted and, by chance, certain particular sites had been selected.

The success of these studies, the robustness of the conclusions, depends on several features.

Those I would like to highlight are: (i) the broad geographical coverage, (ii) the wide range of organisms and physico-chemical indicators used, and (iii) the care the different research workers have taken to ensure that their 'measures' are exactly comparable (intercalibration). This has been especially important with the diatoms, which have provided the dominant indicator. It is interesting to note that this piece of work, which has such important economic implications, has depended on and resulted in good taxonomic work on a superficially obscure group of organisms.

No introduction to this volume would be complete without drawing attention to another outstanding feature – the level of international cooperation. Under the leadership of Dr R. W. Battarbee and Dr I. Renberg, those involved in these studies have worked together to produce a truly integrated programme, sharing sites, expertise, material and findings. As in all good scientific projects a final line will not be drawn, but beneficial repercussions will spread out like the ripples in a pond.

February 1990 T. R. E. SOUTHWOOD

CONTENTS

[One microfiche in pocket inside back cover]

CONTENTS

PAGE

Phil. Trans. R. Soc. Lond. B **327**, 227–232 (1990)
Printed in Great Britain

The Surface Water Acidification Project (SWAP) Palaeolimnology Programme

By R. W. Battarbee[1] and I. Renberg[2]

[1] *Palaeoecology Research Unit, Department of Geography, University College London, 26 Bedford Way, London WC1H 0AP, U.K.*

[2] *Department of Ecological Botany, University of Umeå, S-901 87 Umeå, Sweden*

Improvements in techniques of lake-sediment analysis over the last two decades have enabled palaeolimnologists to reconstruct changes in water acidity and atmospheric contamination with high resolution. In the Surface Water Acidification Project (SWAP) Palaeolimnology Programme these techniques have been used to trace the history of a range of specially selected study sites and to evaluate alternative causes for lake acidification. At the same time further improvements in some of the techniques, especially diatom analysis, have been made.

Introduction

Palaeolimnology is concerned with the study of lake history as recorded by lake sediments. In the past two decades palaeolimnologists have developed sampling, dating, and analytical approaches that now enable the sediment record to be deciphered with precision and accuracy over timescales of relevance to contemporary environmental problems, taking advantage of the relatively rapid accumulation rate (1–10 mm a^{-1}) of most recent lake sediments.

Lake sediments also contain a record of catchment and atmospheric history (figure 1), and

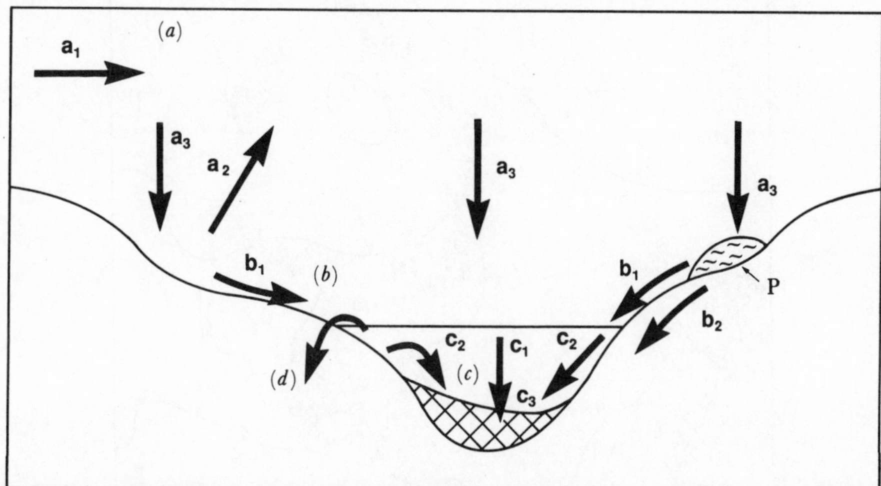

Figure 1. Diagrammatic cross-section of sources and pathways for lake sediment. (*a*) Atmospheric inputs; a_1, sources outside catchment; a_2, sources within catchment; a_3, wet and dry deposition to lake and catchment surface (radioactive nuclides, S, PAH, trace metals, fly ash and carbonaceous particles, pollen and spores). (*b*) Catchment inputs; b_1, inflow streams (silts, clays, organic detritus, pollen and spores, solutes); b_2, groundwater (precipitates, e.g. Fe, Mn). (*c*) Lake inputs; c_1, plankton (diatoms, chrysophytes, cladocera); c_2, littoral flora/fauna (diatoms, macrophyte spores and pollen, chydorid cladocera, chironomidae); c_3, benthic flora/fauna (diatoms, chironomidae). (*d*) Outflow losses; (P, peat bog.)

comparisons of these with records of lake history through time and between sites often allow the causes, as well as the timing and rate, of historical changes to be inferred.

Unlike other sources of historical scientific information, lake sediments usually provide a record that is continuous, covers a full range of timescales, is available at all sites and is amenable to standard methods of analysis. At some sites difficulties with dating, sediment conformability and fossil preservation are encountered but such problems can be recognized and poor sites avoided.

Palaeolimnological techniques are hence ideally suited to problems of lake acidification. Initial claims that these problems were caused by acid deposition were poorly supported because of the lack of high quality historical data and the need to differentiate between naturally acid and recently acidified waters. Almost all countries with acid waters and high S deposition have now adopted palaeolimnological methods to address this issue. Papers in this volume by Kingston & Birks, Davis *et al.*, Meriläinen & Huttunen and Charles are examples of such studies.

The palaeolimnology programme

When the Surface Water Acidification Project was set up in 1983 the Management Committee identified palaeolimnology as a key area of research with a dual remit.

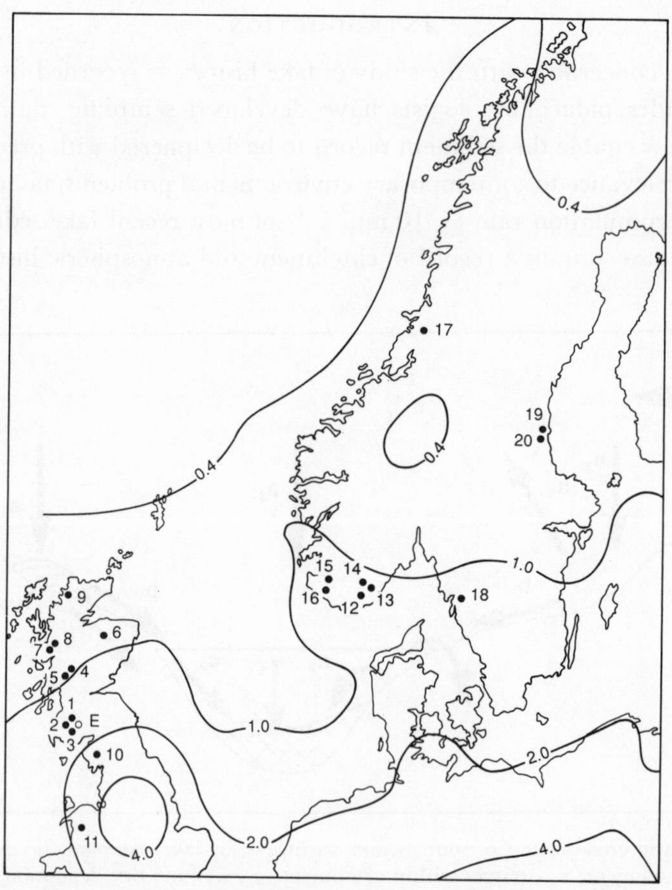

FIGURE 2. Map of N.W. Europe showing location of sites (table 1) and isolines of S deposition (g m^{-2} a^{-1}) (from Eliassen *et al.* 1988). 1, The Round Loch of Glenhead; 2, Loch Grannoch; 3, Loch Fleet; 4, Loch Tinker; 5, Loch Chon; 6, Lochan Uaine; 7, Loch Doilet; 8, Lochan Dubh; 9, Loch Sionascaig; 10, Devoke Water; 11, Llyn Hir; 12, Verevatn; 13, Gulspettvann; 14, Holmevatn; 15, Holetjörn; 16, Ljosvatn; 17, Röyrtjörna; 18, Lilla Öresjön; 19, Sjösjön; 20, Lill Målsjön; E, Ellergower Moss.

1. To carry out detailed integrated studies of lakes in areas of high and low acid deposition, choosing sites that had similar catchment characteristics and that were adjacent to the instrumented stream catchments studied by others in the main SWAP programme. For example, Verevatn (figure 2) was chosen because of its proximity to the Birkenes catchment study in southern Norway. Other sites in this category include Round Loch of Glenhead and Lochan Dubh in Scotland, Röyrtjörna in Norway and Lilla Öresjön in Sweden. Cores from each of these sites were subjected to diatom, chrysophyte, cladoceran, chironomid, pollen, trace metal, sulphur, carbonaceous particle, magnetic mineral and polycyclic aromatic hydrocarbon (PAH) analysis. The cores were dated by ^{210}Pb analysis and land-use history surveys of the catchments were made. The results of these studies are presented by Berge *et al.*, Jones *et al.* and Renberg *et al.* (this symposium).

2. To evaluate a range of alternative hypotheses for lake acidification. Although by 1983 there was already abundant palaeolimnological evidence available to support the acid deposition hypothesis, the role of long-term acidification and changes in land-use and land management was unclear. In this programme the long-term acidification question has been addressed by Atkinson & Haworth (this symposium) and Renberg *et al.* (this symposium) by using data from Loch Sionascaig, Devoke Water and Lilla Öresjön (figure 2, table 1), and various versions of the land-use hypothesis have been considered by Patrick *et al.* (this symposium), Birks *et al.* (this symposium), Anderson & Korsman (this symposium), Renberg *et al.* (this symposium)and Kreiser *et al.* (this symposium), by using data from many sites, including Holetjörn, Ljosvatn in Norway, Sjösjön and Lill Målsjön in Sweden, and Lochs Tinker, Chon, Doilet and Lochan Dubh in Scotland (figure 2, table 1). The palaeolimnological evidence supporting the acid-deposition hypothesis is presented by Battarbee (this symposium).

Techniques

To fulfil the objectives of the programme, many techniques have been used. The bases of the techniques and examples of their application to problems of lake acidification are also presented. The biological techniques used include diatom analysis (Birks *et al.*, Munro *et al.*, Round and Smith, all this symposium) chrysophyte analysis (Cronberg, this symposium), chironomid analysis (Brodin, this symposium) and cladoceran analysis (Nilssen & Sandøy, this symposium). Of these techniques, most developmental work has been devoted to diatom analysis, the central method for pH reconstruction. A SWAP calibration data-set of over 160 sites from Norway, Sweden and the U.K. has been created by using a standard approach to diatom taxonomy and water chemistry (Munro *et al.*, this symposium). New methods of pH reconstruction and error estimation have been developed from the data-set (Birks *et al.*, this symposium) and have been applied routinely to all sediment-core sequences within the project.

Techniques used to trace atmospheric contamination include trace metal, sulphur and PAH chemistry (Rippey, this symposium), carbonaceous particle analysis (Wik & Natkanski, this symposium) and mineral magnetic analysis (Oldfield & Richardson, this symposium). Clymo *et al.* (this symposium) describe a study evaluating the atmospheric deposition record of an ombrotrophic mire. The chronological framework for most studies has been provided by ^{210}Pb dating (Appleby *et al.* and El-Daoushy, this symposium) although ^{14}C wiggle-match dating has also been used (Clymo *et al.*, this symposium).

TABLE 1. SWAP SITES WITH MAJOR LAKE AND CATCHMENT CHARACTERISTICS

	United Kingdom										
	(1)	(2)	(3)	(4)	(5)	(6)	(7)	(8)	(9)	(10)	(11)
name	Round L. of Glenhead	L. Grannoch	L. Fleet	L. Tinker	L. Chon	L. Uaine Lochnagar	L. Doilet	Lochan Dubh	L. Sionascaig	Devoke Water	L. Hir
latitude	55° 05′ N	55° 0′ N	55° 0′ N	56° 13′ N	56° 12′ N	57° 4′ N	56° 44′ N	56° 46′ N	58° 10′ N	54° 20′ N	52° 17′ N
longitude	4° 27′ W	4° 15′ W	4° 10′ W	4° 30′ W	4° 33′ W	3° 40′ W	5° 35′ W	5° 26′ W	4° 75′ W	3° 23′ W	3° 46′ W
altitude/m	295	210	344	420	100	950	10	230	73	233	435
catchment/ha[a]	95	1290	107	112	1570	28	3290	157	4000	305	23
geology	granite	granite	granite	micaschist	micaschist	granite	quartzite schists	quartzite schists	gneiss/ sandstone	volcanics/ granite	mudstones/ shales
land-use/ vegetation	moorland	forest	forest/ moorland	moorland	forest/ moorland	alpine heath	forest/ moorland	moorland	moorland	moorland	moorland
lake area/ha[a]	12.5	114.3	17.3	11.3	100	4.0	53	8.8	517	34	4.9
maximum depth/m	13.5	20.5	19	9.8	25	21	16.8	9	66	14	8.8
pH	4.77	4.6	4.5[b]	6.0	5.2	5.8	5.9	5.6	6.6	6.2	4.8[b]
Ca^{2+}/ (μeq l^{-1})	41	47	39	78	79	69	47	33	73	118	47
SO_4^{2-}/ (μeq l^{-1})	89	110	124	62	85	82	68	40	71	138	120
S deposition/ (g m^{-2} a^{-1})	1.24	1.29	1.29	1.36	1.36	0.84	0.78	0.78	0.5	2.0	1.81

	Norway						Sweden		
	(12)	(13)	(14)	(15)	(16)	(17)	(18)	(19)	(20)
name	Verevatn	Gulspettvann	Holmevatn	Holetjörn	Ljosvatn	Röyrtjörna	Lilla Öresjön	Sjösjön	Lill Målsjön
latitude	58° 23′ N	58° 40′ N	59° 09′ N	58° 28′ N	58° 24′ N	64° 40′ N	57° 33′ N	61° 42′ N	61° 53′ N
longitude	8° 12′ E	9° 05′ E	9° 05′ E	6° 48′ E	6° 42′ E	12° 10′ E	12° 20′ E	16° 53′ E	17° 09′ E
altitude/m	268	56	588	485	385	163	107	79	82
catchment/ha[a]	60	190	2750	5	22	2400	400	230	30
geology	granite	granite/ gneiss	granite/ gneiss	granitic migmatite	granitic migmatite	granite	gneiss	granite/ gneiss	granite/ gneiss
land-use/ vegetation	forest	forest	forest/ heath	forest	forest/ heath	forest	forest	forest	forest
lake area/ha[a]	9	32	100	1.6	11	26	61	32	8
maximum depth/m	13.9	25	> 15	17	25	15.8	17	16	4
pH	4.4	4.8	4.7	4.57	4.47	6.6	4.6	5.7[b]	5.5[b]
$Ca^{2+}/(\mu eq\ l^{-1})$	—	160	22	26	23	70	124	na	na
$SO_4^{2-}/(\mu eq\ l^{-1})$	—	175	—	75	79	28	210	na	na
S deposition/ $(g\ m^{-2}\ a^{-1})$	1.8	1.3[c]	1.3[c]	1.3[c]	1.3[c]	0.15	1.8	0.5	0.5

[a] 1 ha = $10^4\ m^2$. [b] Pre-liming. [c] Estimated from Eliassen *et al.* (1988).

Post-1970 change and modelling

In addition to work within SWAP on long (post-glacial) and medium (post-1800) timescales, Flower *et al.* (this symposium) consider very recent (post-1970) timescales to assess the evidence for lake responses to decreasing acid deposition, liming and other changes in the catchments of acidified lakes. A final paper (Jenkins *et al.*, this symposium) compares the diatom-based pH reconstructions for the main study sites with reconstructions based on the use of the catchment acidification model, MAGIC.

The SWAP project has been funded by a grant from the Central Electricity Generating Board (U.K.) and the National Coal Board (U.K.) to the Royal Society. Most of the work presented here has been financed from this source but additional support has also been received: for U.K. work from the Department of Environment (DoE), the Natural Environment Research Council (NERC) and the Central Electricity Generating Board (CEGB); for Norwegian work from the Norwegian Council for Science and the Humanities (NAVF), and for Swedish sites from the Swedish Natural Science Research Council (NFR) and the Swedish National Environmental Protection Board (SNV).

We thank the SWAP Management Committee, especially Sir John Mason, Hans Martin Seip, Lars Walløe, Sir Richard Southwood, Carl-Olof Tamm, Jack Talling and Tom West for their help and encouragement, Ron Harriman, Ron West, for water chemistry, John Kingston, Sheri Fritz, Keith Camburn for help with diatom taxonomy, John Line for computer programming, Cajo ter Braak for statistical assistance, Karin Olsson for help with ^{210}Pb analyses, Dick Derwent and Jimi Irwin for data on S deposition, and Stuart Phethean, Don Monteith and Paul Raven for help with fieldwork. We are grateful to John Kingston and John Birks for their help with the editing of several papers in this volume.

Reference

Eliassen, A., Hor, Ø., Iversen, T., Saltbones, J. & Simpson, D. 1988 Estimates of airborne transboundary transport of sulphur and nitrogen over Europe. *EMEP/MSC-W report* no. 1/88.

Phil. Trans. R. Soc. Lond. B **327**, 233–238 (1990)
Printed in Great Britain

Radiometric dating of the United Kingdom SWAP sites

By P. G. Appleby[1], N. Richardson[2], P. J. Nolan[3] and F. Oldfield[2]

Departments of [1] Applied Mathematics and Theoretical Physics, [2] Geography and [3] Oliver Lodge Laboratory, Department of Physics, University of Liverpool, P.O. Box 147, *Liverpool L*69 3*BX, U.K.*

Measurements of ^{210}Pb by direct gamma assay have been used to date sediment cores from Surface Water Acidification Project (SWAP) study sites in the U.K. The results were checked against additional dating evidence from the artificial fallout isotopes ^{137}Cs and ^{241}Am. At one of the sites, Devoke Water in Cumbria, the ^{137}Cs and ^{241}Am data were crucial in identifying a recent sediment hiatus. At sites with recently afforested catchments the sediment record indicated substantial increases in accumulation rates.

Introduction

Accurate dating techniques are crucial to the use of sediment records for palaeolimnological reconstructions of recent environmental change. The precision to which this can be accomplished has been greatly enhanced over the past 20 years by the development of a range of radiometric techniques that use radioisotopes both from natural and artificial sources. The successful utilization of these methods depends on a clear understanding of the mechanisms by which the radioisotopes are incorporated into the sediments. The principal isotope for dating on the timescale of the past 100–150 years, the period of greatest relevance to the Surface Water Acidification Project (SWAP) Palaeolimnology Programme, is ^{210}Pb. By using this isotope, determination of lake sediment dates with a precision of five to ten years is often attainable. Artificial radioisotopes such as ^{137}Cs and ^{241}Am have been present in the environment only for the past 35 years and can be used for dating only the most recent sediments. The use of these isotopes does however provide a valuable check on the accuracy of the ^{210}Pb calculations. By using these techniques, our principal objective within the SWAP programme was to provide a reliable sediment chronology at each site. We report here on the results of this project.

Methods

Sediments from each core were measured non-destructively for ^{210}Pb, ^{226}Ra, ^{137}Cs and ^{241}Am by direct gamma assay by using an Ortec HPGe GWL series well-type coaxial low background intrinsic germanium detector (Appleby *et al.* 1986). Background suppression for this detector is achieved by using a 100 mm thick lead castle, a 305 mm diameter × 305 mm long sodium iodide (NaI(Tl)) escape suppression shield and a 3 mm thick copper lining. ^{210}Pb is measured by its gamma emissions at 46.5 keV and ^{226}Ra by the 295 keV and 352 keV γ rays emitted by its daughter isotope, ^{214}Pb; ^{137}Cs and ^{241}Am are measured by their emissions at 662 keV and 59.5 keV, respectively. The absolute efficiency of the detector has been measured by using a series of calibrated sources and sediment samples of known activity. The effect of self absorption of low energy γ rays has been estimated by using sources of different masses. Background counts are done at regular intervals to ensure maintenance of the low background characteristics.

^{210}Pb *dating*

^{210}Pb occurs naturally as one of the radioisotopes in the ^{238}U decay series. Radioactive disequilibrium between ^{210}Pb and its parent isotope, ^{226}Ra (half-life 1600 years), arises through the mobility of the intermediate gaseous isotope ^{222}Rn. A proportion of the ^{222}Rn formed by ^{226}Ra decay in soils diffuses into the atmosphere where it decays to ^{210}Pb. This is precipitated onto the land surface and into lakes where it is adsorbed onto sedimentary particles. Pathways by which ^{210}Pb accumulates in lake sediments are discussed in detail in Oldfield & Appleby (1984). ^{210}Pb activity in sediments in excess of the fraction that derived from decay of the *in situ* ^{226}Ra is called unsupported ^{210}Pb. It declines in accordance with the exponential radioactive-decay law and can be used for age determinations provided there is an appropriate model for estimating the initial activity. The ^{210}Pb half-life of 22.26 years makes it well suited to dating sediments laid down over the past 100–150 years. Unsupported ^{210}Pb is measured by subtraction of ^{210}Pb supported by the parent ^{226}Ra from the total ^{210}Pb activity. In most situations the supported ^{210}Pb can be assumed to be in radioactive equilibrium with the *in situ* ^{226}Ra. Figure 1*a* shows the total and supported ^{210}Pb activity against depth for a sediment core from Loch Chon in the Trossachs, Central Scotland. The unsupported ^{210}Pb activity in this core is shown in figure 1*b*.

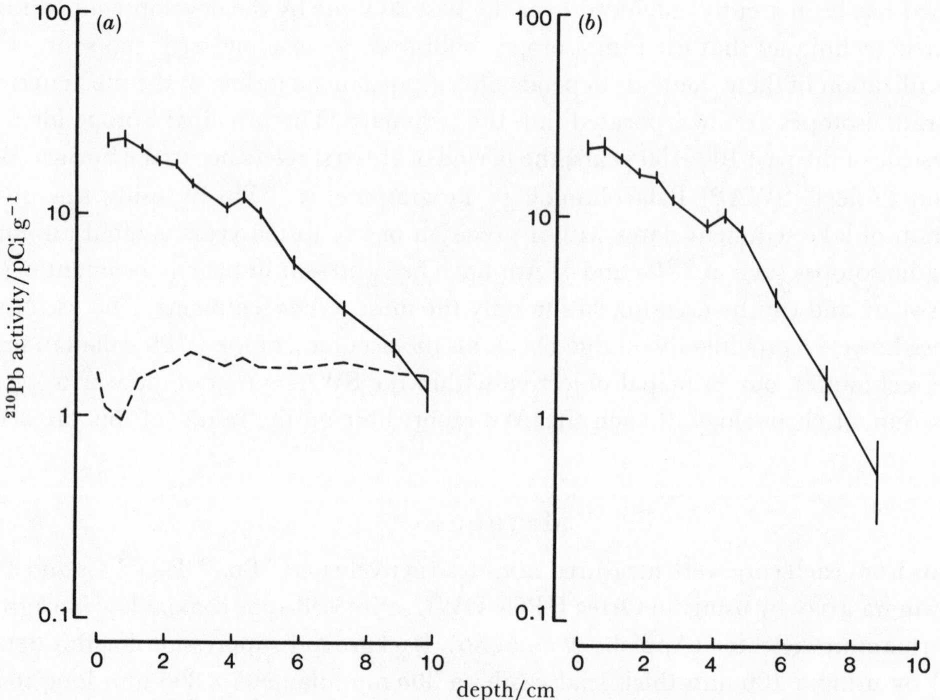

FIGURE 1. ^{210}Pb activity against depth in a core from Loch Chon, Scotland; (*a*) total (——) and supported (----) ^{210}Pb and (*b*) unsupported ^{210}Pb.

There are two principal models for determining the initial activity of a sediment and hence for calculating ^{210}Pb dates, the CRS (constant rate of unsupported ^{210}Pb supply) model and the CIC (constant initial ^{210}Pb concentration) model. Variants of these models have been developed to account for processes such as sediment mixing. The CRS model (Appleby & Oldfield 1978;

Robbins 1978) is perhaps the most widely accepted. It is based on the hypothesis that the ^{210}Pb supply is dominated by a constant direct atmospheric fallout. There is some evidence (Krishnaswamy & Lal 1978) that the atmospheric ^{210}Pb flux may be subject to short-term fluctuations, but as most sediment samples span several years, short-term variations will generally be smoothed out. This model will not be valid where there are alterations or interruptions to the ^{210}Pb supply due to, for example, sediment focusing or a sediment hiatus. In these cases dates are calculated either by the CIC model (where there is evidence for a constant primary accumulation rate) or by using a composite of both models. Factors governing model choice are set out in Appleby & Oldfield (1983) and Oldfield & Appleby (1984). In this study, the CRS model has generally been used, though dates have routinely been calculated by both models and elements of the CIC model incorporated where this has been thought appropriate.

^{131}Cs *and* ^{241}Am *dating*

Although ^{210}Pb is now routinely used for dating, problems frequently arise over the interpretation of data from sites with disturbed sediment records. In these cases, dates given by the artificial isotope ^{137}Cs may be of considerable value. Until the Chernobyl accident in 1986, the most common source of ^{137}Cs was fallout from the atmospheric testing of nuclear weapons. Where this isotope is strongly adsorbed onto sediments, the variation of the ^{137}Cs activity with depth in a core should reflect the fallout history, with the onset of fallout in 1954 and peak fallout in 1963 providing distinct chronological markers. These may be used to confirm ^{210}Pb dates where they are unambiguous, or to resolve ^{210}Pb dates where they are uncertain. In practice the value of ^{137}Cs dating has often been significantly reduced by the evident mobility of this isotope (Davis *et al.* 1984). The problem has recently been exacerbated by the fallout

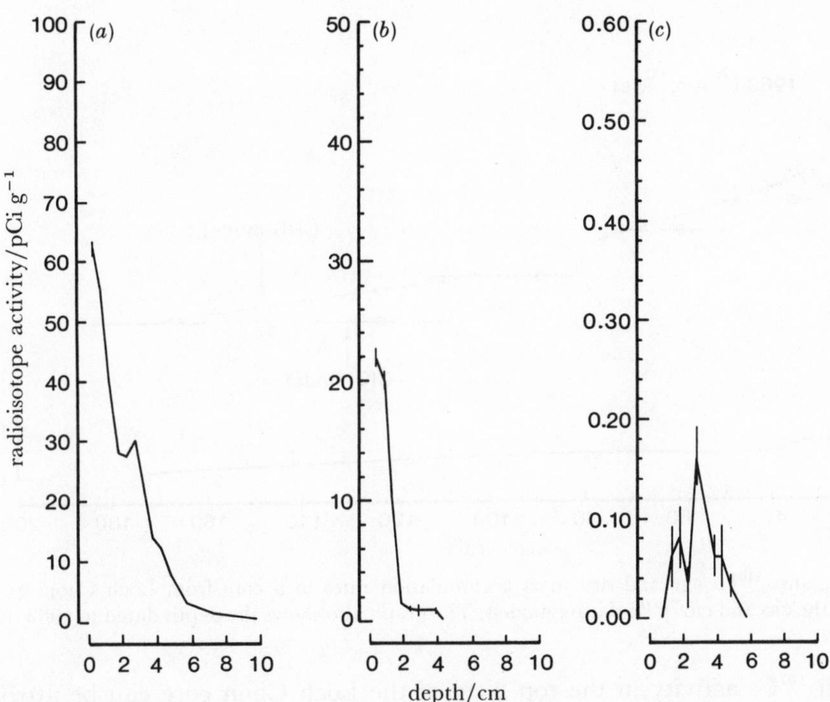

FIGURE 2. Artificial fallout radioisotopes against depth in a core from Loch Chon, Scotland; (*a*) ^{137}Cs, (*b*) ^{134}Cs and (*c*) ^{241}Am.

of ^{137}Cs from the Chernobyl accident. In regions of high fallout, downward diffusion of Chernobyl ^{137}Cs has obliterated the weapons-testing ^{137}Cs profile. In these cases, measurement of ^{241}Am, another fallout product from atmospheric nuclear weapons testing, may provide a useful alternative. The amount of ^{241}Am fallout is very small, only about 0.42% of the ^{137}Cs fallout (Eakins & Cambray 1985). Despite this, ^{241}Am has been detected in cores from many lakes, and evidence from a growing data set suggests that ^{241}Am is significantly less mobile than ^{137}Cs. Graphs of ^{137}Cs, ^{134}Cs and ^{241}Am activity against depth for the Loch Chon sediment core are shown in figure 2.

Results

^{210}Pb chronologies for Loch Chon calculated by using the CRS and CIC ^{210}Pb dating models are illustrated in figure 3. There is good agreement between the two sets of dates for the most recent sediments, both models indicating a reasonably constant accumulation rate since 1954 of 0.013 g cm^{-2} a^{-1}. This is supported by the ^{137}Cs and ^{241}Am data. The ^{137}Cs activity derived from weapons testing fallout (calculated by subtracting Chernobyl ^{137}Cs from the total ^{137}Cs activity) has a well defined peak at 2.75 cm, as does the ^{241}Am activity, and this level is dated to 1966 by the CRS model and 1964 by the CIC model. Both ^{210}Pb models indicate an abrupt transition in the early 1950s from an earlier accumulation rate of 0.0096 g cm^{-2} a^{-1} to the above more recent value. A consequence of this transition (Appleby & Oldfield 1978) is that CIC model dates below 4 cm are about 10 years younger than the CRS model dates. The increase in accumulation rate is presumably associated with the 1950s afforestation programme in the Loch Chon catchment; its onset is indicated by the reduction in unsupported ^{210}Pb activity at a depth of 3.75 cm (dated 1953–1956) shown in figure 1*b*. In view of this direct evidence in support of the CRS model assumptions, the CRS model dates were thought to be the more reliable.

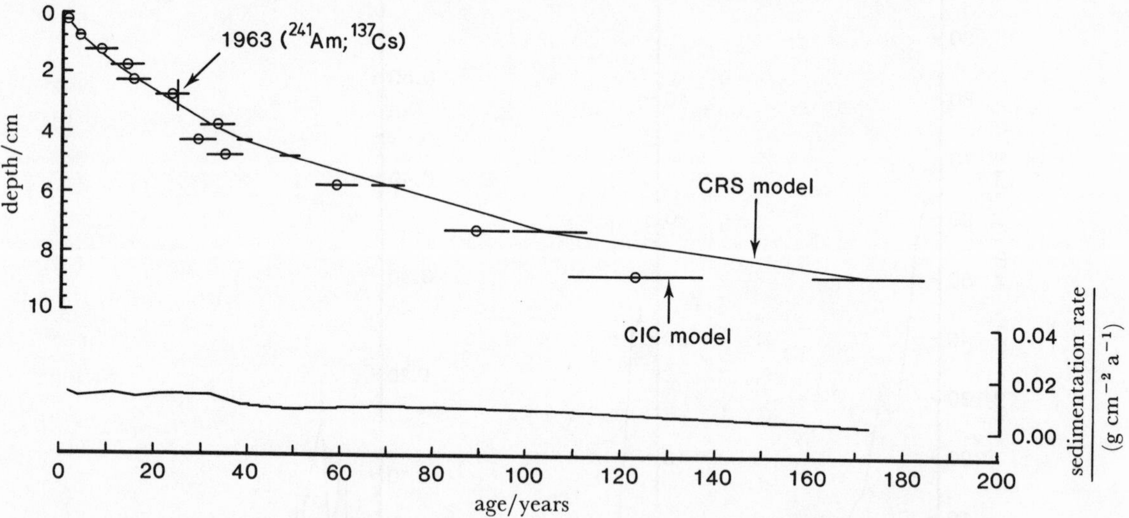

Figure 3. Depth against ^{210}Pb age and dry mass accumulation rates in a core from Loch Chon, Scotland, as determined by the CRS and CIC ^{210}Pb dating models. The graph also shows the depth dated to 1963 by the ^{137}Cs and ^{241}Am data.

The very high ^{137}Cs activity in the top 2 cm of the Loch Chon core can be attributed to fallout from the Chernobyl accident in May 1986. This core was obtained in 1987 and the origin of the ^{137}Cs is confirmed by the associated presence of the short-lived isotope ^{134}Cs (figure

2*b*). Chernobyl fallout was detected in most post-1986 cores and provides evidence of the retrieval of an undisturbed sediment–water interface.

Table 1 gives a summary of the radiometric parameters obtained from SWAP sites in the U.K. Mean accumulation rates are given in table 2. Results from individual sites, summarized below, have been presented in separate reports.

Table 1. Radiometric parameters of SWAP lake-sediment cores

	unsupported ^{210}Pb			^{226}Ra		
	surf. conc.	invent.	flux	mean conc.	^{137}Cs invent.	^{241}Am invent.
site	(pCi g^{-1})	(pCi cm^{-2})	(pCi cm^{-2} a^{-1})	(pCi g^{-1})	(pCi cm^{-2})	(pCi cm^{-2})
Loch Sionascaig	53.5	12.7	0.40	1.03	10.7[a]	0.06
Lochan Dubh	10.3	11.3	0.35	1.65	7.9[a]	0.07
Loch Doilet	6.3	19.3	0.60	1.73	14.4[a]	0.07
Lochan Uaine	78.1	99.7	3.10	23.06	10.1[a]	—
Coire an Lochan	46.6	16.3	0.51	14.10	3.2[a]	—
Loch Chon	21.9	10.4	0.33	1.66	17.8[a]	0.04
Loch Tinker	29.6	20.4	0.64	1.33	23.4	0.10
Round Loch	24.9	10.6	0.33	1.47	6.3	0.06
Devoke Water	24.7	34.6	1.68[b]	0.94	29.3	0.51

[a] Denotes sites cored after May 1986.
[b] ^{210}Pb flux estimated from post-1963 inventory.

Table 2. Comparison of sediment accumulation rates at SWAP sites

	mean accumulation rates					
	(i) (g cm^{-2} a^{-1})			(ii) (mm a^{-1})		
site	(*a*) post-1950	(*b*) 1910–1950	(*b*) pre-1910	(*a*) post-1950	(*b*) 1910–1950	(*b*) pre-1910
Loch Sionascaig	0.0083	0.0086	0.0091	0.75	0.72	0.74
Lochan Dubh	0.0148	0.0104	0.0074	1.56	0.77	0.47
Loch Doilet	0.0540	0.0384	0.0186	4.17	2.30	0.97
Lochan Uaine	0.0223	0.0169	0.0178	0.83	0.52	0.50
Coire an Lochan	0.0096	0.0096	—	0.30	0.30	—
Loch Chon	0.0133	0.0096	0.0096	1.13	0.52	0.44
Loch Tinker	0.0193	0.0223	0.0231	1.61	1.47	1.20
Round Loch	0.0113	0.0120	0.0184	1.51	1.30	1.85
Devoke Water	0.0525	—	—	2.90	—	—

Northwest Scotland

^{210}Pb dates for Loch Sionascaig were unambiguous and gave a constant sediment accumulation rate over the past 150 years of 0.0088 g cm^{-2} a^{-1} or 0.74 mm a^{-1}. The ^{137}Cs results for this core were of no chronological value, even when allowance was made for the contribution from Chernobyl fallout. The ^{137}Cs activity was greatest in the topmost sample, and declined monotonically with depth. A small ^{241}Am peak was detected at a depth consistent with the ^{210}Pb dates.

Loch Doilet and Lochan Dubh both have nonlinear ^{210}Pb profiles, suggesting accelerating sediment accumulation rates. The increase has been very much more pronounced in Loch Doilet, presumably because of the disturbances to its catchment arising from the afforestation programme that began in the 1930s. Both cores have relatively well-defined ^{137}Cs and ^{241}Am peaks at depths reasonably consistent with the ^{210}Pb dates. Traces of Chernobyl fallout were observed at the top of the Loch Doilet core.

The Trossachs

Despite its much smaller catchment, Loch Tinker has experienced significantly higher sediment accumulation rates than Loch Chon. However, whereas the core from Loch Tinker has a linear ^{210}Pb profile suggesting reasonably constant accumulation rates over the past 150 years, the data from Loch Chon indicates accelerated accumulation rates over the past 35 years, presumably due to afforestation in the early 1950s. In both cores the ^{210}Pb dates are supported by ^{137}Cs and ^{241}Am data. The enhanced ^{137}Cs activities at the top of the Loch Chon core derive from Chernobyl fallout and have virtually obliterated the 1963 peak caused by weapons testing fallout.

The Cairngorms

Lochan Uaine and Coire an Lochan are both characterized by very high unsupported ^{210}Pb activities in the topmost sediments. This usually indicates very slow sediment accumulation rates, though at both these sites the very high ^{226}Ra activities may be a contributory factor. In the Lochan Uaine core ^{210}Pb equilibrium (corresponding to *ca.* 150 years of sediment accumulation) is achieved at 8 cm. In Coire an Lochan it appears that equilibrium is achieved at only 2.25 cm. The ^{210}Pb dates for Lochan Uaine suggest a modest increase in sediment accumulation since 1970. This is supported by ^{137}Cs data.

Galloway and Cumbria

The ^{210}Pb data from Round Loch of Glenhead indicates constant sedimentation since *ca.* 1900. There is some suggestion of higher accumulation rates in the 19th century, though this has not been observed in other cores from this lake. The ^{210}Pb dates are consistent with the ^{137}Cs and ^{241}Am data. The data from Devoke Water is contradictory in that ^{210}Pb equilibrium appears to have been achieved at 12.5 cm, though the ^{137}Cs and ^{241}Am data point clearly to an early 1960s date for sediments at a depth of 7 cm. This incompatibility is explained by a sediment hiatus at 9 cm, dated 1954. The high surface concentrations coupled with the high inventories (table 1) suggest that the primary sedimentation rate is quite low but that the core is from a site of intensive sediment focussing. The ^{210}Pb and ^{137}Cs results suggest that the primary sedimentation rate is reasonably constant. On this assumption the ^{210}Pb indicates a loss of *ca.* 50 years from the sediment record.

References

Appleby, P. G. & Oldfield, F. 1978 The calculation of ^{210}Pb dates assuming a constant rate of supply of unsupported ^{210}Pb to the sediment. *Catena* **5**, 1–8.

Appleby, P. G. & Oldfield, F. 1983 The assessment of ^{210}Pb from sites with varying sediment accumulation rates. *Hydrobiologia* **103**, 29–35.

Appleby, P. G., Nolan, P., Gifford, D. W., Godfrey, M. J., Oldfield, F., Anderson, N. J. & Battarbee, R. W. 1986 ^{210}Pb dating by low background gamma counting. *Hydrobiologia* **141**, 21–27.

Davis, R. B., Hess, C. T., Norton, S. A., Hanson, D. W., Hoagland, K. D. & Anderson, D. S. 1984 ^{137}Cs and ^{210}Pb dating of sediments from soft-water lakes in New England (U.S.A.) and Scandinavia, a failure of ^{137}Cs dating. *Chem. Geol.* **44**, 151–185.

Eakins, J. D. & Cambray, R. S. 1985 Studies of environmental radioactivity in Cumbria, part 6. Report AERE-R 11182. Harwell: United Kingdom Atomic Energy Research Authority.

Krishnaswamy, S. & Lal, D. 1978 Radionuclide limnochronology. In *Lakes, chemistry geology & physics* (ed. A. Lerman), pp. 153–177. New York: Springer-Verlag.

Oldfield, F. & Appleby, P. G. 1984 Empirical testing of ^{210}Pb-dating models for lake sediments. In *Lake sediments and environmental history* (ed. E. Y. Haworth & J. W. G. Lund), pp. 93–124. Leicester: University Press.

Robbins, J. A. 1978 Geochemical and geophysical applications of radioactive lead. In *Biogeochemistry of lead in the environment* (ed. J. O. Nriagu), pp. 285–293. Amsterdam: Elsevier Scientific.

Phil. Trans. R. Soc. Lond. B **327**, 239–242 (1990)
Printed in Great Britain

Lead-210 chronology of the Scandinavian SWAP sites

By F. El-Daoushy
Department of Physics, Box 530, S-751 21 Uppsala, Sweden

In the Surface Water Acidification Project (SWAP) sediment profiles from five Scandinavian sites were analysed for ^{210}Pb by using refined isotope dilution alpha spectrometry. The ^{210}Pb parameters of these lakes were very similar to those obtained for protected forest lakes with no land-use activities. These data demonstrated almost exclusive atmospheric inputs and an internal deposition regulated by the organic fractionation and the grain-size distribution in the sediments. Preliminary speciation experiments showed minor losses of ^{210}Pb ($\leqslant 5\%$) through enhanced dissolution of fulvic compounds at acid conditions (pH $\geqslant 4$). The sediment accumulation rates (constant rate of unsupported ^{210}Pb supply (CRS) model) of the lakes gradually increased, by at least a factor of three, over the past century although ^{210}Pb parameters did not show any strong signs of enhanced land-use activities. This is perhaps caused by more efficient preservation of the sediments through humic precipitation under more acid conditions.

Introduction

The most suitable dating method for recent freshwater sediments of the past 150 years or so is to use ^{210}Pb (cf. El-Daoushy 1988). Low accumulation rates typical of acid lakes may make the construction of sediment chronologies difficult (cf. Davis *et al.* 1984; El-Daoushy 1988). Moreover, the poor understanding of the influence of acidification on the accumulation of ^{210}Pb (cf. Gambrell *et al.* 1980; Hanson *et al.* 1982; Nriagu 1984; Simola & Liehu 1984) in such lakes has caused further limitations in evaluating and modelling chronological anomalies. The observed correlation between ^{210}Pb minima and diatom-inferred pH minima (Simola & Liehu 1984) may indicate either major losses of unsupported ^{210}Pb through dissolution of fulvic fractions (lower ^{210}Pb fluxes) or increased sedimentation (lower ^{210}Pb concentrations) by effective precipitation and accumulation of humic compounds. Speciation studies have shown, however, that acidification alone cannot explain the observed variations of the ^{210}Pb fluxes in acidified freshwater lakes (El-Daoushy & Garcia-Tenorio 1988).

Materials and methods

The Scandinavian SWAP sites and lake characteristics are described elsewhere (Battarbee & Renberg, this symposium). The organic content of sediments ranged from 30% to 70% and the average total dry mass in samples analysed was about 0.5 g. Surface sediment layers amounted to $\leqslant 0.1$ g whereas deeper samples contained as much as 1 g dry matter. Calculated dry-matter densities of the sediments by using organic and water contents agreed well with measured values for Lilla Öresjön, Verevatn and Röyrtjörna, thus suggesting that the assumed organic and inorganic dry densities of 1.4 and 2.5 g cm^{-3} were quite reasonable and that the composition of the sediments could be described as simple organo-clay deposits along with diatom minerals. Such comparisons were not possible for Gulspettvann and Holmevatn as the data required were missing. Several sediment layers from Gulspettvann and Holmevatn contained appreciable amounts of other minerals, such as graphite (Gulspettvann) and fine sand (Holmevatn), despite the high organic content in these layers (50 %).

Because of the high organic content of the sediments examined, a chemical extraction was used that provided high-quality alpha sources free from organic and inorganic remnants. Absolute ^{210}Pb measurements of the small samples required further refinements of laboratory routines through careful examination of memory effects arising from adsorption on glassware and long-term background records of the detectors.

Results and discussion

With the exception of Holmevatn, values for the supported ^{210}Pb (0.4–1.0 pCi g^{-1}) could be determined for each core by using the deeper sediments (figure 1*a*). Preliminary speciation experiments demonstrated that ^{210}Pb fractionation in these sediments was similar to that occurring in inland lakes in Sweden (El-Daoushy 1988). Speciation studies in these lakes

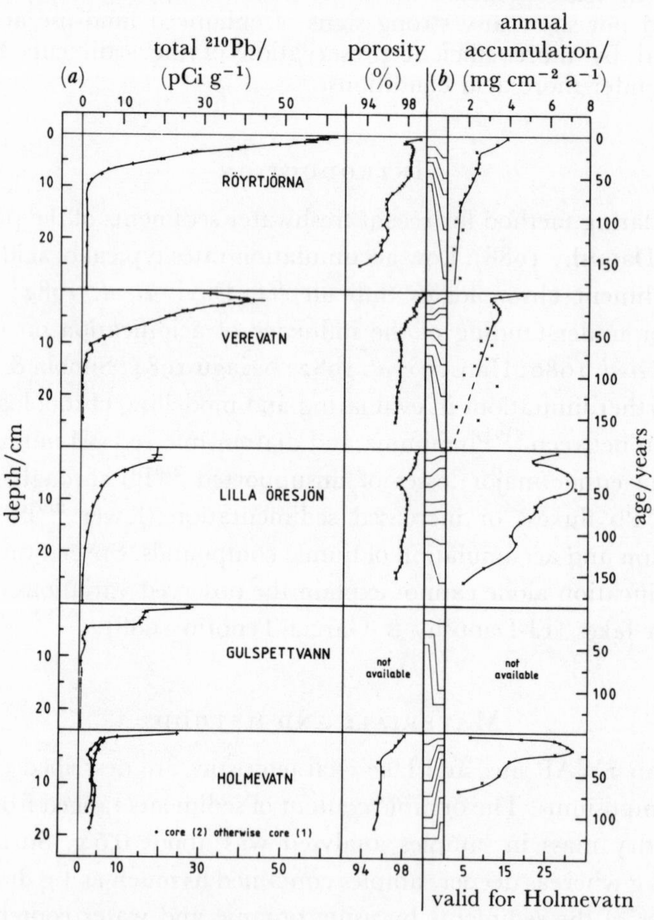

FIGURE 1. Total ^{210}Pb activity and porosity against actual depth (*a*); activities are given with one standard deviation. Annual accumulation against ^{210}Pb ages (*b*). Cores from Holmevatn are probably not long enough to provide supported ^{210}Pb; (*a*) and (*b*) are correlated to show chronological changes in various profiles. Holmevatn has much higher annual accumulation than other lakes and a special scale is used for it. The scatter of sediment accumulation in the deeper part of Verevatn may be due to age uncertainties rather than to real changes.

showed that the unsupported ^{210}Pb was controlled by organic fulvic and humic compounds whereas the supported ^{210}Pb was limited to organo-clay complexes. According to these experiments the estimated levels of the supported ^{210}Pb (figure 1*a*) are close to expectations. The general features of the ^{210}Pb against depth profiles are similar to profiles obtained for Swedish inland lakes, which demonstrated secular equilibrium between ^{226}Ra and ^{210}Pb (El-Daoushy 1988) and constant levels of supported ^{210}Pb in most cases. Speciation results gave an indication that the two cores from Holmevatn were probably not long enough to allow for a complete decay of the unsupported ^{210}Pb. In these cores the supported ^{210}Pb found in the organo-clay complexes of the deeper sediments was much lower than the values shown in figure 1*a* and supported ^{210}Pb was assumed for this lake. Apart from Holmevatn, the stable and low levels of ^{210}Pb in the deeper sediments (figure 1*a*) suggest minor chronological variations in the origin and composition of the lake sediments. Calculated dry matter densities of Lilla Öresjön, Verevatn and Röyrtjörna showed that these lakes have a sediment composition similar to Swedish inland lakes. The course of sediment accumulation in these inland lakes was mainly governed by grain-size distribution. However, chemical speciation is also important (El-Daoushy & Garcia-Tenorio 1988) and at the neutral pH values of inland lakes, these processes

TABLE 1. AGES OF SEDIMENT LAYERS DATED ACCORDING TO THE CONSTANT RATE OF UNSUPPORTED ^{210}Pb SUPPLY (CRS) MODEL

(Ages of sediment layers at Gulspettvann are dated by using the constant initial ^{210}Pb concentration (CIC) model.)

	ages/(^{210}Pb years)				
actual depth/cm	Gulspettvann	Holmevatn	Lilla Öresjön	Verevatn	Röyrtjörna
0.5	—	—	—	—	3±1
1.0	—	4.5±2	3±1	2±1	10±1
1.5	17.5±1	—	—	4±1	19.5±1
2.0	—	7±2	7±1	6.5±1	25.5±1
2.5	18±1	—	—	9.5±1	31.5±1
3.0	—	8.5±2	12±1	12.5±1	38±1
3.5	20±1	—	—	15.5±1	44±1
4.0	—	10.5±2	16.5±1.5	18±1	50±1
4.5	92±7	—	—	21±1	59±1
5.0	—	12.5±2	22±1.5	24.5±1	69±1.5
5.5	105±7	—	—	—	78±2
6.0	—	15.5±2	29±1.5	34.5±1	89±2
6.5	128±12	—	—	41.5±1	101±2.5
7.0	—	—	38.5±1.5	48±1	111±3
7.5	103±12	—	—	56±1	121±5
8.0	—	20±2.5	46.5±2	62±1.5	135±8
8.5	—	—	—	71±1.5	154±10
9.0	—	22.5±2.5	54±2	78±1.5	170±20
9.5	—	—	—	86±2	185±25
10.0	—	25±2.5	61±2	98±2	—
11.0	—	29±2.5	67±2	111±3	—
12.0	—	33±3	73±3	136±4	—
13.0	—	37.5±3.5	79±3	153±5	—
14.0	—	43.5±4	86±4	186±15	—
15.0	—	51±4	—	—	—
16.0	—	59±5	103±4	—	—
17.0	—	70±7	112±6	—	—
18.0	—	83±9	—	—	—
19.0	—	105±11	141±8	—	—
20.0	—	—	159±10	—	—

may have caused losses of fine particulates because of inefficient flocculation. The ^{210}Pb fluxes in the lakes studied under SWAP were independent of the sediment accumulation rates and similar to those obtained for the inland lakes. The flux values were about 0.16 pCi cm^{-2} a^{-1} for Holmevatn and Verevatn, 0.12 and 0.24 pCi cm^{-2} a^{-1} for Lilla Öresjön and Röyrtjörna, respectively. As for inland lakes, the initial ^{210}Pb concentrations were lower at sites with higher accumulation rates because of dilution (figure 1*b*). This suggests that the progressive decceleration of ^{210}Pb concentrations towards the surface (figure 1*a*) is due to an accelerating sediment accumulation (figure 1*b*) during the past century (table 1), possibly because of the enhanced preservation of the humic sediments as a consequence of a continuous lowering of pH in the lakes. However, the influence of land-use activities may have contributed to the increase of sediment accumulation in Röyrtjörna as its ^{210}Pb flux was slightly higher than the atmospheric flux (El-Daoushy 1988). The porosity characteristics (figure 1*a*) show that accumulation of the sediments (figure 1*b*) occurs through chemical precipitation and flocculation followed by physical sedimentation and compaction. The chemical deposition in these lakes is more important than the physical sedimentation in freshwater lakes with low organic content.

References

Davis, R., Hess, C., Norton, S., Hanson, D., Hoagland, K. & Anderson, D. 1984 ^{137}Cs and ^{210}Pb dating of sediments from softwater lakes in New England (USA) and Scandinavia, a failure of ^{137}Cs dating. *Chem. Geol.* **44**, 151–185.

El-Daoushy, F. 1988 A summary on the lead-210 cycle in nature and related applications in Scandinavia. *Environ. Inter.* **14**, 305–319.

El-Daoushy, F. & Garcia-Tenorio, R. 1988 Speciation of Pb-210/Po-210 in aquatic systems and their deposits. *Sci. tot. Environ.* **69**, 191–209.

Gambrell, R. P., Khalid, R. A. & Patrick, W. H. 1980 Chemical availability of mercury, lead and zinc in mobile bay sediment suspensions as affected by pH and redox. *Environ. Sci. Technol.* **14**, 431–436.

Hanson, D. W., Norton, S. A. & Williams, J. S. 1982 Modern and paleolimnological evidence for accelerated leaching and metal accumulation in soils in New England caused by atmospheric deposition. *Wat. Air Soil Pollut.* **18**, 227–239.

Nriagu, J. 1984 Dynamics of particulate metals in lakes of northern Ontario. In *Proceedings of a workshop on paleolimnological studies of the history and effects of acid precipitation* (ed. S. Norton), pp. 106–127. U.S.A. Environmental Protection Agency, Corvallis, Oregon.

Simola, H. & Liehu, A. 1984 Coincidence of anomalous lead-210 minima with diatom-inferred pH minima in lake sediments: implications on dating acceptability. *Aqua Fenn.* **15**, 257–262.

Phil. Trans. R. Soc. Lond. B **327**, 243–249 (1990)
Printed in Great Britain

Diatom communities – their response to changes in acidity

By F. E. Round

Department of Botany, University of Bristol, Woodland Road, Bristol BS8 1UG, U.K.

The non-planktonic habitats of some Welsh lakes were studied to determine the composition of the diatom component in each, the seasonality of the diatoms, discreteness or otherwise of each community, and the relation of each community to the mean pH of the water of the lakes. A discussion on the diatom plankton of acid waters is also presented in this symposium.

Introduction

Interpretation of diatom data obtained from lake cores depends entirely on information derived from the ecology of extant species. That individual diatom communities respond to changes in acidity is not in doubt. There is, however, little definitive data in the literature on diatom habitats, and extracting habitat information from core material (which is a mixture of at least five discrete communities) is hampered by confusion over the exact composition of the communities, apart from that of the plankton. This arises from the complexity of the micro-habitats present in the benthos and the inevitability of some natural contamination from one habitat to another, added to which is the likelihood of unnatural contamination during sampling.

In this study of lakes in Wales, only the epipelon, the epipsammon, the epilithon and the epiphyton were sampled. The plankton community was relatively unimportant so this is considered separately and more generally.

Methods

Epipelic samples were obtained without contaminants by using appropriate sampling techniques that remove only the live (raphid and hence motile) cells, that is, by harvesting live cells off cover glasses placed on sediment surfaces (see Round (1981) for further details on all community structure and sampling). The sand was freed of all other silt, plant detritus, etc., before the discrete epipsammon was removed by heating in sulphuric acid. The epilithon was the most difficult to remove as material from other communities settles on to stone surfaces and this has to be separated by washing the stone surface before scraping off the diatoms. The epiphyton was usually fairly clean and could be scraped off the plant surfaces. It is never possible to remove all contaminant cells during sampling and laboratory processing so at the counting stage these were discounted. A minimum number of 100 valves was counted for community analysis. Counting excessive numbers is counter productive when determining dominance in communities as contaminants can confuse the data.

The location of the lakes is given together with the mean pH values of the water in figure 1. A few lakes were sampled monthly for three years but the majority were visited only once or twice during that period.

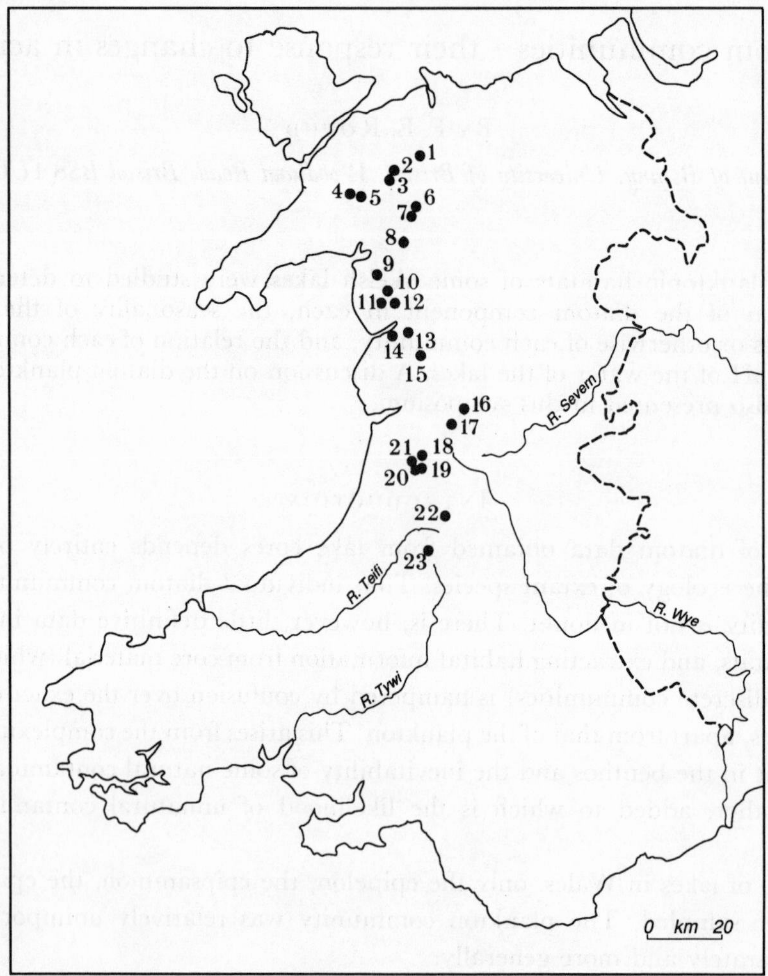

FIGURE 1. Map of Wales showing location of sites mentioned in the text (pH values are given in parenthese). 1, Llyn Geirionydd (6.6); 2, Llyn Ogwen (4.9); 3, Llyn Idwal (5.6); 4, Llyn Nantlle (6.6); 5, Llyn y Gadair (6.1); 6, Llyn Newydd (4.5); 7, Llyn y Manod (5.0); 8, Llyn Mair (5.4); 9, Llyn cwm Bychan (5.6); 10, Llyn Dulyn (4.9); 11, Llyn Bodlyn (5.4); 12, Llyn cwm Mynach (5.6); 13, Llyn Gwernan (6.2); 14, Llyn Cregennen (6.8); 15, Tal-y-Llyn (6.5); 16, Glaslyn (4.9); 17, Bugeilyn (4.4); 18, Llyn Syfydrin (4.7); 19, Llyn Blaenmelindwr (4.9); 20, Llyn Rhosgoch (5.4); 21, Llyn Pendam (5.1); 22, Llyn Hir (4.8); 23, Llyn Berwyn (4.4).

RESULTS

To use diatom associations based on discrete communities, so as to extend the analysis of diatom data from cores, several aspects required investigation. First, is there a seasonal succession of diatoms in the benthic associations? As there is a very pronounced seasonal succession in the plankton in both acid and alkaline lakes, necessitating frequent sampling through the year, this feature was checked. For the epiphytic and epilithic communities, no or only slight seasonal variation occurred. For example, in Llyn Syfydrin, *Frustulia rhomboides* was dominant in over 90% of the sampling times over three years. This is a raphid diatom, but in this habitat is immobilized in mucilage. *Eunotia incisa* was subdominant and on one occasion the next most abundant species, *Tabellaria flocculosa*, was dominant. On all sampling dates these three species formed the only conspicuous elements. In the epipelon of this lake, *Pinnularia subcapitata* was dominant on all sampling dates. An epiphytic example of species on *Isoetes* from Llyn Rhosgoch shows dominance of *Eunotia incisa* and subdominance of *Tabellaria flocculosa* and *T. quadriseptata* through three years' sampling. Such data answer a second question: how many samples are needed for defining any benthic association? At least in the acid lakes this study suggests that one will suffice, though more are preferable. A third question is, how many species are needed to characterize an association and can the dominant one alone be used? In this study only a few species at each site were needed, as the associations were dominated by only between one and three species.

Epilithon

The lakes sampled fell into two discrete groups when the epilithic diatom populations were tabulated: the ones with *Eunotia incisa–Tabellaria flocculosa sensu lato* dominant and those with *Achnanthes minutissima* dominant. The distinction is clearly related to pH–Ca^{2+}–conductivity levels: low in the former and higher in the latter. This feature agrees well with the effect of liming on some of these lakes (for example, Hir and Pendam) where, after liming, *A. minutissima* became the dominant species. This is also in agreement with data from Galloway (Flower *et al.* 1986) where *A. minutissima* does not become an important component of the flora until the alkalinity (calcium carbonate) reaches around 2.0 mg l^{-1}. At > 3.4 mg l^{-1} it is usually the dominant in the surface sediment diatom assemblage. Also associated with the higher pH lakes are *Brachysira vitrea*, *Cymbella minuta*, *Fragilaria capucina* and *Peronia fibula*. In the low pH group there are scattered occurrences of *Eunotia praerupta*, *E. denticulata*, *Cymbella aequalis*, *Eunotia curvata* and *Pinnularia subcapitata*. *Oxyneis* (*Tabellaria*) *binalis* is also common in a few of the acid lakes, but more common in the epipsammon (see below). It is significant that *E. incisa* does not extend into the less acid lakes, though *Achnanthes austriaca* and *Tabellaria flocculosa* do. *Brachysira vitrea*, *Denticula tenuis*, *Cymbella minuta*, *Peronia fibula*, *Tabellaria flocculosa*, *Oxyneis binalis*, is a possible sequence in relation to increasing acidity.

Other distinctive sub-groupings can be picked out, for example, the very high percentage of *Achnanthes austriaca* in Llynnau Dulyn, Pendam and Mair, and of *Frustulia rhomboides* in Llynnau cwm Bychan, Berwyn and Syfydrin. The count of *Brachysira vitrea* in Llyn Rhosgoch may show high metal content, as it is correlated with this in Llyn Geirionydd. *Tabellaria flocculosa* is abundant in Glaslyn, Bodlyn and Llyn y Gadir, and *Oxyneis binalis* in Llyn cwm Mynach together with *Tabellaria quadriseptata* and *Eunotia faba*. These latter three species can be used to subdivide the low-pH group lakes.

The less acidic group has *Peronia fibula* in one subset and *Cymbella minuta* in another. The occurrence of *Stenopterobia delicatissima–Denticula tenuis–Cymbella microcephala* seems to distinguish Llynnau Gwernan and Cregennen and *Gomphonema gracile* divides Llynnau Nantle, Tal-y-Llyn, Ogwen and Idwal from the remainder.

The species from the most acidic group, which are also found in the less acidic sites are *Achnanthes austriaca*, *Tabellaria flocculosa* and *Frustulia rhomboides* but in none of these lakes do they achieve any degree of dominance.

A species that occurs as isolated valves in samples is *Fragilaria virescens* v. *exigua* and this is recorded in quantity in some lakes (R. J. Flower, personal communication) but I have never encountered it in quantity in any micro-habitat. Jones & Flower (1986) also found that this taxon was present in the deep-water sediment but not in the epipsammon or epilithon of Round Loch of Glenhead.

There do not appear to be any good minor species to characterize the epilithon. The dominants *Eunotia incisa*, *Tabellaria flocculosa* and *Achnanthes minutissima* are, as might be expected, attached non-motile diatoms. The less abundant *Frustulia rhomboides* and *Brachysira vitrea* are raphid, and to some extent motile, but they both tend to live in mucilage masses (tubes?) and are only motile when released from the mass.

Epiphyton

The host flora varies from lake to lake and the following have been sampled when present at the collecting site: *Isoetes lacustris* L., *Littorella uniflora* (L.) Aschers, *Lobelia dortmanna* L., *Equisetum fluviatile* L., *Juncus bulbosus* L., *Nuphar lutea* (L.) Sn, *Glyceria fluitans* (L.) R. Br. and *Sparganium* spp. The data show clearly the overwhelming abundance of *Eunotia incisa* with *Tabellaria flocculosa* subdominant and *T. quadriseptata* and *Peronia fibula* frequently present and occasionally becoming dominant.

Tabellaria flocculosa achieved high percentage cover on *Isoetes* in three lakes, in one lake on *Equisetum* and in one lake on *Glyceria*. In the case of its occurrence on *Glyceria* this was in Llyn Bodlyn and in this lake it is also the dominant on *Isoetes*. In the case of three different hosts (*Juncus*, *Equisetum* and *Nuphar* in Bugeilyn and *Isoetes*, *Juncus*, *Lobelia* in Dulyn), all were overwhelmingly colonized by *Eunotia incisa* (the same species dominated in the epilithon of these lakes), suggesting that when water chemistry is the major stress many species will be prevented from competing and a single species is often favoured; this then tends to colonize all the available substrata. The only exception seemed to be *Equisetum* in Dulyn, which had *Tabellaria* dominant rather than *Eunotia*. However, resampling of this *Equisetum* revealed an outer layer of *Tabellaria* and an adnate layer of *Eunotia incisa* that could be removed from the stem only by scraping with a razor blade. With the *Tabellaria* removed the flora would appear just as on the other hosts.

Disappointingly, there seems to be little or no specificity in the colonization of the different aquatic macrophytes. The epiphytic flora is, however, slightly less diverse than the epilithic. More sites have an epiphytic flora that is dominated by a single species (more than 75% in the counts). Contamination of the epiphyton by species from stones or sediments is surprisingly slight, for example, *Achnanthes austriaca*, *Brachysira vitrea* and *Frustulia rhomboides* are only rarely present. In the case of plants from Llyn Berwyn there is a *Gomphonema* species, which I can only place in *G. parvulum*, which is abundant in the epiphytic flora but absent from the epilithon. This species requires detailed study (see comments in Krammer & Lange-Bertalot (1986) as it is frequently recorded as a dominant species in polluted rivers and different ecotypes must be involved).

Epipelon

The sediment was not easily sampled in many of these upland lakes and hence the data for this habitat are sparse. The lake margins were stony and as sampling was by wading, the deeper, probably more productive sites, could not be reached. Hence the large species of *Pinnularia*, *Neidium*, *Surirella* are possibly under-recorded. However, these genera are well known as true epipelic inhabitants and their occurrence in quantity in cores would show a rich epipelic community. The near-shore sediments do differ somewhat in composition from the deeper sediments and this survey has extended knowledge only of the near-shore segment of the epipelon.

The dominant species vary greatly from lake to lake, for example, *Pinnularia subcapitata* in Llyn Syfydrin, *Cymbella aequalis* (usually accompanied by *C. hebridica*) in Llyn Blaenmelindwr and Llyn cwm Bychan, *Neidium hercynicum* in Llyn Manod and Llyn Newydd. *Stenopterobia delicatissima* and *Navicula leptostriata* are often present but never in quantity.

Plankton

This community was not sampled in the Welsh lakes visited and this section is a discussion based on previous experience and data from the literature.

The majority of species occurring in the plankton have never been recorded live for any period of time in the benthic associations. One must write 'for any period of time', since immediately after rapid declines in planktonic populations, live planktonic species can be quite common, especially in the epipelon and epilithon, but they rarely remain as live cells for more than a few days and are usually undetectable after a week or so. Diatoms are not common in the plankton of highly acidic lakes (Davis 1987) and in these Welsh lakes the only taxa that might commonly occur and contaminate the benthos are species of *Cyclotella* and *Aulacoseira* (particularly the *Aulacoseira* (*Melosira*) *distans* group, see Haworth (1988). However, *Cyclotella* has not been found in any of the benthic samples investigated and *Aulacoseira* (*distans* type) are rather rare and either form only a small component of the plankton, or perhaps occur in some unsampled microhabitats. In my samples from Llyn Hir it is hard to find a single cell of *Aulacoseira*, yet in the core, four different forms occur and the percentage occurrence of the genus is 15 %, which is, in fact, the highest percentage figure for any genus (S. C. Fritz, personal communication). Similar results were obtained for *Melosira* (*Aulacoseira*) *perglabra* in a north American lake, where its centre of distribution was the epipelon (De Nicola 1986) though not ever recorded in any quantity. There are still many diatoms recorded in material from lake cores that cannot be attributed to any of the benthic communities; some may be contaminants from the watershed but years of intensive work will be required before the distribution of many species can be satisfactorily determined. Some planktonic diatoms, for example, *Rhizosolenia* and *Attheya* are so delicate that they may not survive to contaminate the benthos, they have to occur in considerable quantity to be detected in cores.

Most planktonic diatoms (for example, *Aulacoseira italica*, *A. granulata*, *Cyclotella* spp., *Stephanodiscus* spp., *Rhizosolenia longiseta*, *R. eriensis*, *Attheya zachariasi*, *Diatoma elongatum*, *Centronella reicheltii*, *Fragilaria crotonensis*, *Asterionella formosa* and *Synedra acus* are almost never found actively growing or even as contaminants in benthic communities and when found in core material can be regarded as certain indicators of planktonic phases. In a few Welsh lakes, *Asterionella ralfsii* valves have been found in the benthos; these are presumably contaminants from planktonic populations of this rare (in the U.K.) diatom. It is abundant in some low pH Finnish lakes (Ronkko & Simola 1986). Although not encountered in this study, the author has found small *Cyclotella* species live and constantly present in the mucilage secreted by some epiphytic communities. This is, however, very rare though reported elsewhere, for example, Jenkerson & Hickman (1986) who found *Cyclotella* but not *Stephanodiscus*, though both were present in quantity in the plankton. In another study, Moss (1981) found that *Synedra* and *Diatoma* species occurred in both the epiphytic and planktonic habitats; they multiplied in both so were not casual in either habitat. However, this was a study in eutrophic waters and these do seem to have somewhat different habitat characteristics compared with oligotrophic acid lakes. A problem genus is *Tabellaria*. First, it is a very confused genus (see Flower & Battarbee 1985; Lange-Bertalot 1988); secondly, some species are planktonic and others benthic; and thirdly, there are reports that populations multiply in the benthos and then migrate into the plankton, an aspect that needs a careful modern study. One species, *T. binalis* (now transferred to the new genus *Oxyneis*, Round *et al.* 1990) is quite clearly benthic–epipsammic. *T. flocculosa* in its commonest form (Type III of Koppen) and *T. quadriseptata* are attached, occurring in the epilithon and epiphyton. There are, however, planktonic forms of *T. flocculosa* (for example, it is in the plankton that this species achieves overall dominance in one of the ponds sampled by DeNicola (1986), while *T. fenestrata* is said to be totally planktonic. It is extremely difficult to identify some of the variants. The morphological colony variants in the plankton of the English Lake District (Knudsen 1955) are not easily distinguished in core material. There is evidence that variants are stable entities in lakes as similar forms were found in Irish loughs (Round & Brook 1959) and records from the turn of the century had the same forms in the same loughs (West & West 1906), a rare opportunity to study populations over a 60-year period.

In some waters there are substantial interactions between planktonic populations and macrophytes. Certain macrophytes have an adverse effect on planktonic diatoms, and conversely, excessive phytoplankton may reduce macrophytes (and hence diatom epiphytes), though in some instances excessive growth of epiphytes can reduce the host plants, which has repercussions on the diatom content of cores (Phillips *et al.* 1978). It has also been shown (Reynolds *et al.* 1982) that the flux of planktonic diatoms to the sediments is an important transport path of the trace metals zinc and lead, and hence perturbations of the phytoplankton populations may influence the contents of these in sediments.

Conclusions

Diatom-community changes associated with acidification, which are detectable from core studies are usually confined to demonstration of the loss of the planktonic community (Davis 1987), though a shift from an epipelic to an epiphytic flora has been shown in a Finnish lake (Simola *et al.* 1985). The low representation of attached or motile diatom species in counts of diatoms from most core material from acid lakes makes it most difficult to reconstruct community changes, although the sediments are sometimes dominated by species from these communities (for example, the 34 Galloway lochs investigated by Flower *et al.* (1986)).

There are distinct epipelic, epipsammic, epiphytic and epilithic communities in acid lakes, but there is considerable overlap between the latter two, and there are no real indicator species to separate them. In addition, the epiphyton developed on the aquatic angiosperms tends to be similar on each host genus.

References

Davis, R. B. 1987 Paleolimnological diatom studies of acidification of lakes by acid rain: an application of quaternary science. *Q. Sci. Rev.* **6**, 147–163.

DeNicola, D. M. 1986 The representation of living diatom-communities in deep water sedimentary diatom assemblages in two Maine (U.S.A.) lakes. In *Diatoms & lake acidity* (ed. J. P. Smol, R. W. Battarbee, R. B. Davis & J. Meriläinen), pp. 73–85.

Flower, R. J. & Battarbee, R. W. 1985 The morphology and biostratigraphy of *Tabellaria quadriseptata* in acid waters and lake sediments in Galloway, south west Scotland. *Br. Phycol. J.* **20**, 69–70.

Flower, R. J., Rippey, B. & Tervet, D. J. 1986 Thirty-four Galloway lochs: bathymetry, water quality & surface sediment diatom assemblages. Working Paper No. 14, Palaeoecology Research Unit, Dept. of Geography, University College London.

Haworth, E. Y. 1988 Distribution of diatom taxa of the old genus *Melosira* (now mainly *Aulacoseira*) in Cumbrian waters. In *Algae and the aquatic environment* (ed. F. E. Round), pp. 138–167. Bristol: Biopress.

Jenkerson, C. G. & Hickman, M. 1986 Inter-relationships among the epipelon, epiphyton & phytoplankton in a eutrophic lake. *Int. Revue ges. Hydrobiol.* **71**, 557–579.

Jones, V. J. & Flower, R. J. 1986 Spatial & temporal variability in periphytic communities: palaeoecological significance in an acidified lake. In *Diatoms & lake acidity* (ed. J. P. Smol, R. W. Battarbee, R. B. Davis & J. Meriläinen), pp. 87–94.

Krammer, K. & Lange-Bertalot, H. 1986 Bacillariophyceae. I. Teil: Naviculaceae. In *Süsswasserflora von Mitteleuropa* (ed. H. Ettl, J. Gerloff, H. Heynig & D. Mollenhauer), p. 876. Stuttgart: Fischer.

Lange-Bertalot, H. 1988 Die Gattung *Tabellaria* unter besonderer Berücksichtigung von *Tabellaria ventricosa* Kützing (Bacillariophyceae). *Nova Hedwigia* **46**, 413–431.

Moss, B. 1981 The composition and ecology of periphyton communities in freshwaters. II. Inter-relationships between water chemistry, phytoplankton populations and periphyton populations in a shallow lake and associated experimental reservoirs (Lund tubes). *Br. Phycol. J.* **16**, 59–76.

Phillips, G. L., Eminson, D. & Moss, B. 1978 A mechanism to account for macrophyte decline in progressively eutrophicated waters. *Aquat. Bot.* **4**, 103–126.

Reynolds, C. S., Morison, H. R. & Butterwick, C. 1982 The sedimentary flux of phytoplankton in the south basin of Windermere. *Limnol. Oceanogr.* **27**, 1162–1175.

Ronkko, J. & Simola, H. 1986 Geological control upon the floral manifestation of eutrophication in two headwater lakes. *Proceedings of the Finnish–Soviet symposium on methods in palaeoecology* (ed. H. Simola), pp. 89–96.

Round, F. E. 1981 *The ecology of algae* (653 pages). Cambridge University Press.

Round, F. E. & Brook, A. J. 1959 The phytoplankton of some Irish loughs and an assessment of their trophic status. *Proc. R. Irish Acad.* **60**, 168–191.

Round, F. E., Crawford, R. M. & Mann, D. G. 1990 *The diatoms. Biology and morphology of the genera* (719 pp.). Cambridge University Press.

Simola, H., Kenttamies, K. J. & Sandman, O. 1985 The recent pH-history of some Finnish headwater and seepage lakes, studied by means of diatom analysis of ^{210}Pb dated sediment cores. *Aqua Fenn.* **15**, 245–255.

West, W. & West, G. S. 1906 A comparative study of the plankton of some Irish loughs. *Proc. R. Irish Acad.* B **32**, 77–116.

Phil. Trans. R. Soc. Lond. B **327**, 251–256 (1990)
Printed in Great Britain

The ecophysiology of epilithic diatom communities of acid lakes in Galloway, southwest Scotland

M. A. Smith

Division of Environmental and Earth Sciences, Hatfield Polytechnic, College Lane, Hatfield, Hertfordshire AL10 9AB, U.K.

Lake-water chemistry in Galloway, southwest Scotland is characterized by strong correlations between low calcium and high aluminium concentrations and low pH. Nitrate and silicate levels were sufficient for diatom growth but phosphate was limiting. N:P and Si:P ratios indicated severe phosphate limitation according to the Redfield ratio. Chlorophyll-*a* specific epilithic phosphatase activity expressed as a ratio of acid to alkaline phosphatase activity showed a clear relation to pH with acid phosphatase predominating at pH 5.5 and below. Acid phosphatase activity in epilithon from low pH lakes was inducible as phosphate levels decreased, and inhibited by the addition of phosphate. Inducible acid phosphatase activity clearly confers a selective advantage to epilithic diatom communities growing in oligotrophic lakes of low pH.

Introduction

Although it is widely accepted that there is a relation between lake-water pH and diatoms, and that diatom records in sediments can be used to infer past pH (Renberg & Hellberg 1982; Flower & Battarbee 1983; Charles 1985), very little is known of the physiological bases for the changes observed in the diatom communities. Possible causes for changes in the abundance of some species of diatom in lakes that have undergone surface water acidification include changes in nutrient chemistry (Dickson 1978; Nalewajko & O'Mahony 1988), and increases in the concentration of some metals, in particular, aluminium (Schindler 1988; Dillon *et al.* 1988). Increased dissolved aluminium concentrations may result in the precipitation of phosphorus reducing biologically available orthophosphate to very low levels (Hsu & Rennie 1962). Phosphorus starvation and aluminium toxicity have been suggested as factors involved in decreased algal biomass and productivity in acid lakes (Nalewajko & Paul 1985; Patterson *et al.* 1988) and phosphatase production has been used as an indicator of phosphorus limitation (Healey 1973).

Alkaline phosphatase is produced on the external surface of the plasma membrane (Doonan & Jensen 1980) and hydrolyses a wide variety of organic phosphorus compounds to orthophosphate, which is transported into the cell. Inducible alkaline phosphatase activity is widespread among the major algal groups (Owens & Esias 1976). Some species of algae may have up to five different phosphatases including acid phosphatases (Matagne *et al.* 1976; Boavida & Heath 1986). Some are synthesized in response to low external phosphate concentrations (inducible), others remain constant regardless of the external environment (constitutive). Alkaline phosphatase is not efficient below pH 5.5 and this may provide an explanation for the absence of some diatoms from low pH lakes.

Lake survey: environmental and algal characteristics

A survey of 32 lakes of varying water chemistry (Flower 1986) was undertaken during April and September 1988; four sites were monitored on a monthly basis for one year. Water chemistry and measurements of epilithon physiology were used to test the hypothesis that the success of algal communities at low pH and low inorganic nutrient levels is related to their ability to metabolize organic phosphorus via the induction of acid phosphatase activity.

Sampling and analytical methods for a full range of chemical variables (table 1) are given in Smith & Carroll (1988). Epilithic communities from each lake were assayed for acid- (pH 5.0), alkaline- (pH 9.0) and ambient- (at the pH of the lake) phosphatase activity by using *p*-nitrophenyl phosphate as substrate. Phosphatase activity and organic phosphorus concentrations were expressed as a function of the chlorophyll-*a* content of the epilithon (specific epilithic phosphatase activity, SEPA; specific epilithic organic phosphorus, SEOP).

The epilithic communities comprised bacteria and algae but were dominated by diatoms. The composition of diatom assemblages from each site is given in Flower (1986).

In the survey of the 32 lakes soluble reactive phosphate (SRP) levels were rarely above 0.3 $\mu mol\ l^{-1}$ and the N:P ratios (as NO_3-N and PO_4-P) were often much higher than 35:1 (up to 5000:1), which would indicate severe phosphorus limitation according to the Redfield ratio (Redfield 1958). With decreasing pH the lakes typically had decreasing calcium levels (figure 1*a*) and increasing aluminium concentrations (figure 1*b*).

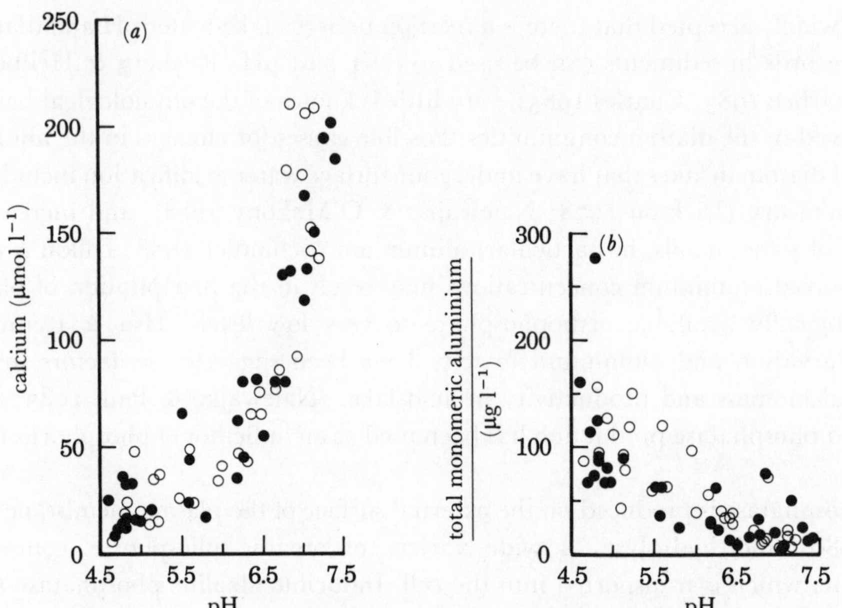

FIGURE 1. (*a*) Calcium and (*b*) total monomeric aluminium for the 32 lakes plotted as a function of pH; (●), April; (○), September.

Water chemistry and physiological results for the four main sites are summarized in table 1. Nitrate and silicate levels were generally higher than 4 $\mu mol\ l^{-1}$ whereas SRP levels were below 0.1 $\mu mol\ l^{-1}$ for up to six months in three of the lakes. Seasonal variations in SRP reflect the spring and autumn growth in planktonic and epilithic communities.

Table 1. Characteristics of water chemistry and epilithon physiology in four Galloway lakes (mean values 1988–1989)

(Abbreviations: n, number of samples; TAl, total aluminium; TMAl, total monomeric aluminium; N-LMAl, non-labile monomeric aluminium; SOP, sestonic organic phosphorus; SEOP, specific epilithic organic phosphorus; SEPA, specific epilithic phosphatase activity.)

	Loch Whinyeon	Loch Fleet	Loch Howie	Loch Grannoch
n	12	12	12	12
colour (absorbance at 250 nm)	0.217	0.268	0.062	0.232
pH	6.96	6.29	5.82	4.68
conductivity/(μS (25 °C) cm^{-1})	71.0	47.3	59.0	51.2
alkalinity/(μeq l^{-1})	303	62.8	28.8	−24.4
NO_3-N/(μmol l^{-1})	13.5	25.7	32.5	19.4
PO_4-P/(μmol l^{-1})	0.07	0.10	0.07	0.16
Si/(μmol l^{-1})	21.0	16.8	51.3	28.1
Ca/(μmol l^{-1})	139	79.7	65.6	23.5
Mg/(μmol l^{-1})	48.6	22.2	44.8	24.3
K/(μmol l^{-1})	9.06	7.63	7.76	6.03
Na/(μmol l^{-1})	213	145	201	170
Cl/(μmol l^{-1})	309	238	329	248
SO_4/(μmol l^{-1})	54.3	42.1	75.6	43.5
TAl/(μg l^{-1})	38.3	105	130	291
TMAl/(μg l^{-1})	14.3	38.4	58.0	198
N-LMAl/(μg l^{-1})	10.7	31.4	32.3	87.1
SOP/(mmol l^{-1})	0.450	0.494	0.513	0.605
SEOP/(mmol P μg Chla^{-1})	0.021	0.011	0.044	0.049
SEPA-acid/(nmol PO_4 (μg Chl$a$)$^{-1}$ min^{-1})	1.65	2.03	7.17	3.94
SEPA-alkaline/(nmol PO_4 (μg Chl$a$)$^{-1}$ min^{-1})	6.25	2.17	4.69	1.87
SEPA-ambient/(nmol PO_4 (μg Chl$a$)$^{-1}$ min^{-1})	2.79	2.06	8.36	3.40

Phosphatase activity

At all 32 sites studied there was a clear relation with pH for both planktonic and epilithic communities when acid- to alkaline-phosphatase activity was expressed as a ratio (figure 2). In lakes with low pH and high aluminium concentrations (> 100 μg l^{-1}), phosphatase activity was low but the ratio of acid- to alkaline-phosphatase activity remained greater than 1 (Carroll

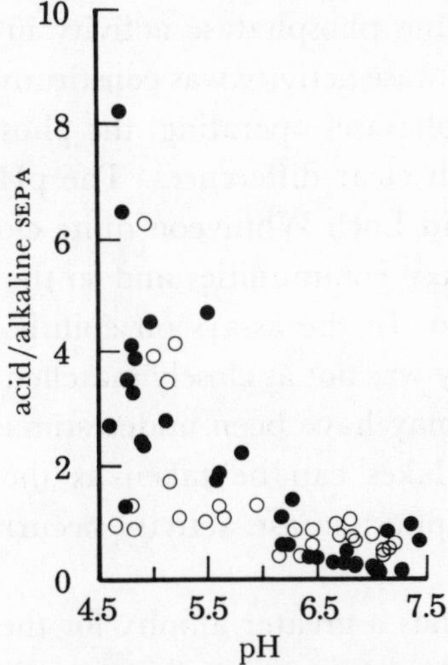

Figure 2. Acid:alkaline phosphatase activity (SEPA) for the 32 lakes plotted as a function of pH; (●), April; (○), September.

& Smith 1989). This differs from the report by Jansson (1981) that phosphatase activity was stimulated by aluminium in an acidified lake, but is consistent with the finding of Mulholland *et al.* (1986) that some of the least acidic sites with lower aluminium levels were the most phosphate limited.

Maximum phosphatase production occurred at the time of lowest SRP levels (figure 3). Phosphatase activity was high (1–5000 times) compared with other published field measurements similarly normalized for chlorophyll-*a* (Pick 1987). Healey & Hendzel (1979) showed that maximum alkaline phosphatase activities for algal cultures were dependent on external calcium concentrations of 100 μmol l^{-1} or more. Loch Whinyeon was the only lake where calcium concentrations exceeded 100 μmol l^{-1} and in Loch Grannoch the mean calcium level was 24.3 μmol l^{-1}, one quarter of that required to maximize alkaline phosphatase activity in cultures.

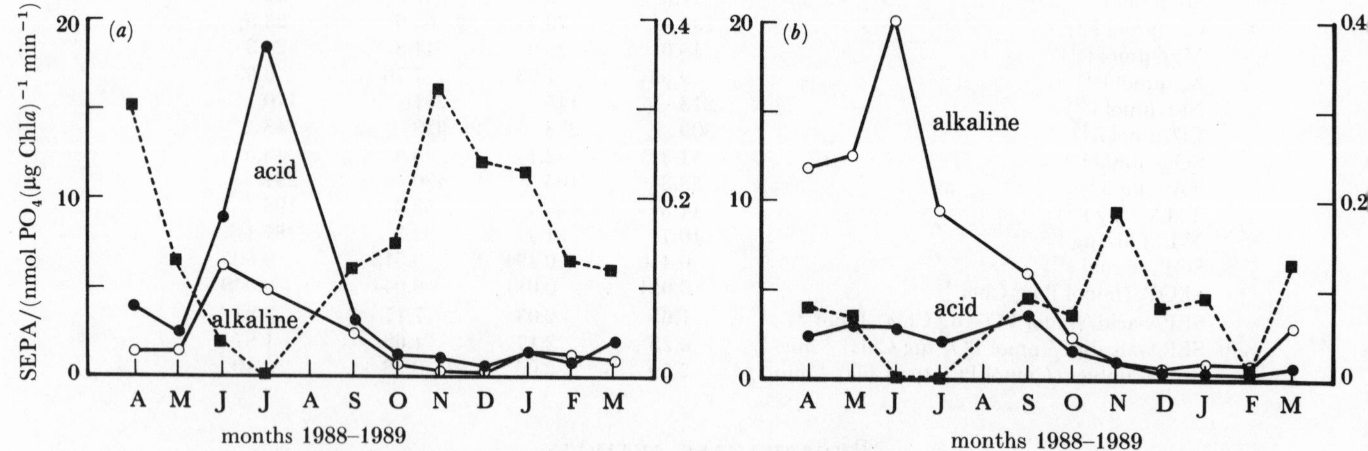

FIGURE 3. Seasonal variation in acid- and alkaline-chlorophyll-*a* specific epilithic phosphatase activity, and in soluble reactive phosphate (SRP) levels (----) for (*a*) Loch Grannoch (mean pH 4.68) and (*b*) Loch Whinyeon (mean pH 6.96); (■), SRP; (●), acid-SEPA; (○), alkaline-SEPA.

The acid phosphatase activity in Loch Grannoch epilithon increased (inducible) as SRP decreased whereas the alkaline phosphatase activity increased only slightly (constitutive) (figure 3*a*). Conversely, the alkaline phosphatase activity in Loch Whinyeon epilithon was inducible whereas the acid phosphatase activity was constitutive (figure 3*b*). Probably because there were several inducible phosphatases operating, the phosphatase data from Loch Howie and Loch Fleet did not show such clear differences. The pH for the phosphatase assays on epilithon from Loch Grannoch and Loch Whinyeon quite closely matched the optimum pH for phosphatase production by those communities and so the assays gave a good estimate of maximum phosphatase production. In the assays on epilithon from Loch Howie and Loch Fleet, for which the pH of the assay was not as closely matched to the pH of the lake, acid- and alkaline-phosphatase production may have been underestimated. The inherent- or ambient-phosphatase activity for all the lakes can be taken as the best estimate of phosphatase production. Maximum inducible phosphatase activity occurred during the summer months May to August, in all four lakes.

Inducible phosphatase activity has a greater affinity for the substrate and is inhibited to a greater extent with increasing SRP concentrations than constitutive phosphatase activity. The epilithon from Loch Grannoch showed inducible acid phosphatase activity (figure 4*a*) and the epilithon from Loch Whinyeon showed inducible alkaline phosphatase activity (figure 4*b*) with orthophosphate inhibition.

The phosphatase enzyme kinetics were examined in more detail at the peak of phosphatase production. Measurements of phosphatase activity with increasing substrate concentration and increasing SRP levels (figure 5) were analysed graphically, according to the methods of Lineweaver & Burk (1934) and Dixon & Webb (1979). At comparable SRP levels the ambient phosphatase activity for epilithon from Loch Whinyeon and Loch Grannoch had similar values. However, the major contribution to ambient phosphatase activity for Loch Grannoch epilithon was acid phosphatase, and for Loch Whinyeon epilithon it was alkaline phosphatase.

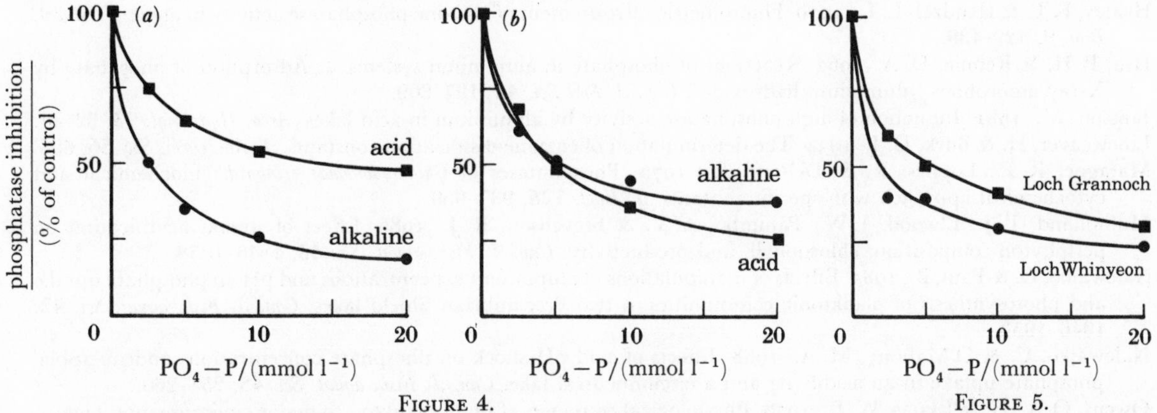

FIGURE 4.　　　　FIGURE 5.

FIGURE 4. The inhibitory effect of increasing inorganic phosphate concentration on acid- and alkaline-SEPA expressed as a fraction of the enzyme activity in the sample containing no added phosphate. The data are means of duplicates; (*a*) Loch Whinyeon, (*b*) Loch Grannoch.

FIGURE 5. Comparison of phosphatase inhibition of ambient SEPA from Loch Whinyeon and Loch Grannoch July samples at the time of maximum phosphatase activity in the lakes. The data are means of duplicates.

It would appear that as lakes become acidified, those epilithic species that depend upon alkaline phosphatase induction to utilize organic phosphorus under conditions of decreasing SRP will be at selective disadvantage. This may well lead to the loss of these particular species from the community through phosphate starvation. Epilithic algae remaining in lakes with pH 5.5 and below have inducible acid phosphatase and are able to hydrolyse organic phosphorus during periods of SRP deficiency. Inducible acid phosphatase may vary in aluminium tolerance from species to species; this is the subject of further investigation.

This work has been supported through SWAP and CEGB (Central Electricity Generating Board) Contract RK:4329.1. Sue Lynam (CEGB) did the ICP and DIONEX analyses; Andrew Carroll the alkalinity, aluminium and organic phosphorus analyses. I am grateful to Matthew Ma and Monica Kanwar for essential support during field-work, and to Rick Battarbee for initiating ideas and continuing encouragement and advice.

REFERENCES

Boavida, M. J. & Heath, R. T. 1986 Phosphatase activity of *Chlamydomonas acidophila* Negoro (Volvocales, Chlorophyceae). *Phycologia* **25**, 400–404.

Carroll, A. D. & Smith, M. A. 1989 Observations on the ecophysiology of diatom populations from lakes in the Galloway region of southwest Scotland. *Proceedings of the 10th international symposium on living and fossil diatoms*, Joensuu, Finland (ed. H. Simola). (In the press.)

Charles, D. F. 1985 Relationships between surface diatom assemblages and lakewater characteristics in Adirondack lakes. *Ecology* **66**, 994–1011.
Dickson, W. 1978 Some effects of the acidification of Swedish lakes. *Verth. Int. Ver. Limnol.* **20**, 851–856.
Dillon, P. J., Evans, H. E. & Scholer, P. J. 1988 The effects of acidification on metal budgets of lakes and catchments. *Biogeochemistry* **5**, 201–220.
Dixon, M. & Webb, E. C. 1979 *Enzymes*, 3rd edn. London: Longman.
Doonan, B. B. & Jensen, T. E. 1980 Ultrastructural localization of alkaline phosphatase in the cyanobacteria *Coccochloris peniocystis* and *Anabaena cylindrica*. *Protoplasma* **102**, 189–197.
Flower, R. J. 1986 The relationship between surface sediment diatom assemblages and pH in 33 Galloway lakes: some regression models for reconstructing pH and their application to sediment cores. *Hydrobiologia* **143**, 93–103.
Flower, R. J. & Battarbee, R. W. 1983 Diatom evidence for recent acidification of two Scottish lochs. *Nature, Lond.* **305**, 130–133.
Healey, F. P. 1973 Characteristics of phosphorus deficiency in *Anabaena*. *J. Phycol.* **9**, 383–394.
Healey, F. P. & Hendzel, L. L. 1979 Fluorometric measurement of alkaline phosphatase activity in algae. *Freshwat. Biol.* **9**, 429–439.
Hsu, P. H. & Rennie, D. A. 1962 Reactions of phosphate in aluminium systems. 1. Adsorption of phosphate by X-ray amorphous 'aluminium hydroxide'. *Can. J. Soil Sci.* **42**, 197–209.
Jansson, M. 1981 Induction of high phosphatase activity by aluminium in acid lakes. *Arch. Hydrobiol.* **93**, 32–44.
Lineweaver, H. & Burk, D. J. 1934 The determination of enzyme dissociation constants. *J. Am. chem. Soc.* **56**, 658.
Matagne, R. F., Loppes, R. & Deltour, R. 1976 Phosphatases of *Chlamydomonas reinhardi*: biochemical and cytochemical approach with specific mutants. *J. Bact.* **126**, 937–950.
Mulholland, P. J., Elwood, J. W., Palumbo, A. V. & Stevenson, R. J. 1986 Effect of stream acidification on periphyton composition, chlorophyll, and productivity. *Can. J. Fish. aquat. Sci.* **43**, 1846–1858.
Nalewajko, C. & Paul, B. 1985 Effects of manipulations of aluminium concentrations and pH on phosphate uptake and photosynthesis of planktonic communities in two Precambrian Shield lakes. *Can. J. Fish. aquat. Sci.* **42**, 1946–1953.
Nalewajko, C. & O'Mahony, M. A. 1988 Effects of acid pH shock on phosphate concentrations and microbial phosphate uptake in an acidifying and a circumneutral lake. *Can. J. Fish. aquat. Sci.* **45**, 254–260.
Owens, O. V. H. & Esaias, W. E. 1976 Physiological responses of phytoplankton to major environmental factors. *A. Rev. Pl. Physiol.* **27**, 461–483.
Pettersson, A., Hallbom, L. & Bergman, B. 1988 Aluminium effects on uptake and metabolism of phosphorus by the cyanobacterium *Anabaena cylindrica*. *Pl. Physiol.* **86**, 112–116.
Pick, F. R. 1987 Interpretations of alkaline phosphatase activity in Lake Ontario. *Can. J. Fish. aquat. Sci.* **44**, 2087–2094.
Redfield, A. C. 1958 The biological control of chemical factors in the environment. *Am J. Sci.* **46**, 205–221.
Renberg, I. & Hellberg, T. 1982 The pH history of lakes in southwestern Sweden, as calculated from the subfossil diatom flora of the sediments. *Ambio* **11**, 30–33.
Schindler, D. W. 1988 Effects of acid rain on freshwater ecosystems. *Science, Wash.* **239**, 149–157.
Smith, M. A. & Carroll, A. D. 1988 Methods for the ecophysiological evaluation of living diatom communities of acid lakes in the Galloway region, southwest Scotland. *Occ. Pap. Environ. Stud.* no. 4, Hatfield Polytechnic.

Phil. Trans. R. Soc. Lond. B **327**, 257–261 (1990)
Printed in Great Britain

Diatom quality control and data handling

By M. A. R. Munro[1], A. M. Kreiser[1], R. W. Battarbee[1], S. Juggins[1], A. C. Stevenson[2], D. S. Anderson[3], N. J. Anderson[4], F. Berge[5], H. J. B. Birks[6], R. B. Davis[3], R. J. Flower[1], S. C. Fritz[7], E. Y. Haworth[8], V. J. Jones[1], J. C. Kingston[9] and I. Renberg[4]

[1] *Palaeoecology Research Unit, University College London, 26 Bedford Way, London WC1H 0AP, U.K.*

[2] *Department of Geography, University of Newcastle upon Tyne, Newcastle NE1 7RU, U.K.*

[3] *Department of Botany, Deering Hall, University of Maine, Orono, Maine 04469, U.S.A.*

[4] *Department of Ecological Botany, University of Umeå, S-901 87 Umeå, Sweden*

[5] *2920 Leira, Valdres, Norway*

[6] *Botanical Institute, University of Bergen, Allégaten 41, N-5007 Bergen, Norway*

[7] *Limnological Research Center, University of Minnesota, Minneapolis, Minnesota 55455, U.S.A.*

[8] *Institute of Freshwater Ecology, Ambleside, Cumbria LA22 0LP, U.K.*

[9] *Department of Biology, Queen's University, Kingston, Ontario, Canada*

The diatom data used for reconstructing pH within the Surface Water Acidification Project (SWAP) came from several different laboratories. The laboratories used agreed nomenclature and standardized identifications by using quality control techniques. A diatom database (DISCO) stored and processed counts and site information.

1. Introduction

The diatom section of the Surface Water Acidification Project (SWAP) Palaeolimnology Programme brought together data from many sources. One of the aims of the project was to construct a single large pH calibration dataset, by combining modern lake pH values with modern surface-sediment diatom assemblages and to use the calibration to reconstruct past lake pH values from the assemblages in sediment cores. However, reconstructions based on small regional subsets of chemical and diatom data from several laboratories must be combined in a way that resolves any differences in taxonomy or analytical technique, and selected extracts from this large combined dataset must be created in a form that can be read by the computer programs performing the calibration and reconstruction.

2. Standardization of diatom taxonomy

Because there is considerable variation in practice between diatomists in different laboratories it is essential in cooperative projects to establish agreed protocols for diatom taxonomy and nomenclature. In the SWAP project, diatomists from Norway, Sweden and the U.K. adopted an approach to diatom harmonization similar to that developed by diatomists involved in the Paleoecological Investigation of Recent Lake Acidification (PIRLA) project in the U.S.A. (Charles *et al.* 1987). This has included the use of taxonomic workshops, diatom slide exchange and the circulation of agreed taxonomic protocols both within SWAP and between the SWAP and PIRLA schemes.

(*a*) *Initial identification of problem areas*

The first SWAP diatom taxonomy workshop was held in March 1987. In preparation for this, each of the four laboratories involved circulated diatom slides and accompanying count sheets for three sediment samples to each of the other laboratories, choosing samples representing the range of soft-water floras encountered within SWAP. Each laboratory provided counts from all 12 slides and the results were compared at the taxonomy workshop. Figure 1*a* summarizes the results of one of these slides (Lingmoor Tarn), demonstrating the three main problems encountered: differences in nomenclature, splitting versus amalgamation of taxa and differing criteria used in the identification of a taxon. Figure 1*b* shows the result after revision at the workshop.

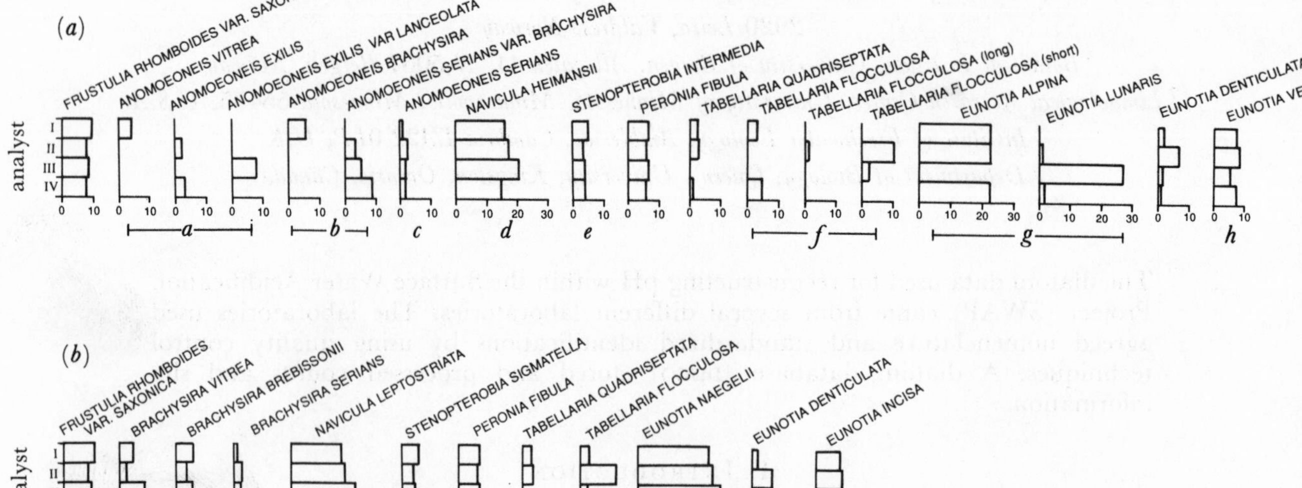

FIGURE 1. (*a*) Dominant taxa in the Lingmoor Tarn slide illustrating problems of nomenclature in groups *a*, *b*, *c*, *d*, *e*, *g*, *h*, problems of splitting versus amalgamation in groups *a*, *f* and the use of differing identification criteria in group *g*; (*b*) dominant taxa in the Lingmoor Tarn slide after full taxonomic and nomenclatural revision. (Horizontal scale is percentage occurrence.)

The agreements from the workshop were circulated to all the workshop participants in a SWAP taxonomic guide. Nomenclature was based on the Checklist of British diatoms (Hartley 1986), which formed the framework for a coded checklist of British diatoms (Williams *et al.* 1988). The SWAP taxonomic guide also included agreements on definitions for boundaries between certain species and their varieties, in some cases following inspection of type material. If possible, published descriptions were referred to. Failing this, the criteria for identification were agreed between the participants.

(*b*) *Applying and refining the SWAP taxonomic guide*

To test the 1987 workshop protocols three slides from lake sediment samples representing the range of pH values encountered within SWAP (one sample from each of the ranges pH < 5, pH 5–6 and pH > 6) were circulated to all SWAP diatomists, who counted the slides without prior access to the countsheets of other diatomists. The results were discussed at a workshop in July 1988.

Many potential problems had been avoided by following the protocols agreed at the previous workshop. However, because of the inclusion of taxa additional to those already encountered, some further problems were raised. Most of these were resolved and a revised edition of the SWAP taxonomic guide was circulated to all diatomists. This workshop also produced a guide for the handling of unknown diatoms.

A major problem encountered at the 1988 workshop was one of identification within the genus *Aulacoseira*. This genus presents particular taxonomic problems because of the difficulties of matching girdle (side) views of the diatom valves with valve (front) views.

(*c*) *Focusing on problems within the genus* Aulacoseira

As a result of the 1988 workshop it was decided to concentrate on the taxonomy of the *Aulacoseira* genus. Three samples containing *Aulacoseira* were selected from SWAP sites and slides were circulated to all SWAP diatomists, who counted 300 valves of *Aulacoseira* from each slide and discussed the results at the diatom workshop in February 1989. There were no problems with the most abundant *Aulacoseira* taxa, such as *A. lirata* and *A. distans* var. *nivalis*. For the less abundant taxa, e.g. *A. lirata* var. *alpigena*, *A. subarctica* and *A. subborealis*, definitions were agreed by using either published definitions or criteria agreed at the workshop. Previously counted surface and core samples containing the problematic *Aulacoseira* taxa were consequently recounted.

This series of workshops and quality control exercises has enabled all diatom data generated within SWAP to be compatible between laboratories and to be suitable for storage and manipulation in a computerized database.

3. The computer database

The diatom database (DISCO) at University College London combines archives of diatom counts, chemical analyses and catchment descriptions for several projects, including SWAP. It uses the commercial program ORACLE and the standard database language SQL. Diatom counts, taxonomic information and chemistry can be entered on or retrieved from the database, by filling out entries on forms that appear on the computer screen. The PIRLA project also required a large computer database (Ahmad & Charles 1988). It also uses a commercial program (SIR) and stores data from many other sources (including chemical analyses and chrysophyte counts). However most of the PIRLA database is hierarchic, with the diatom counts at a lower level in the hierarchy than the site information, whereas DISCO is a relational database, consisting of tables of data with no pre-established structure. The data themselves are used to connect the different tables. Figure 2 shows how common site and sample codes can link different tables to establish a structure similar to the PIRLA database. Many other arrangements are possible.

The database includes the version of the Hartley (1986) diatom checklist coded by Williams *et al.* (1988). Williams' coding scheme allocates a code to each taxon on the list by using a number to represent the original name of the taxon. This does not encode any information about the genus or species name, so the codes are suited to following a taxon through revisions of nomenclature. Some names do not fit this scheme: names of valid taxa that have not been

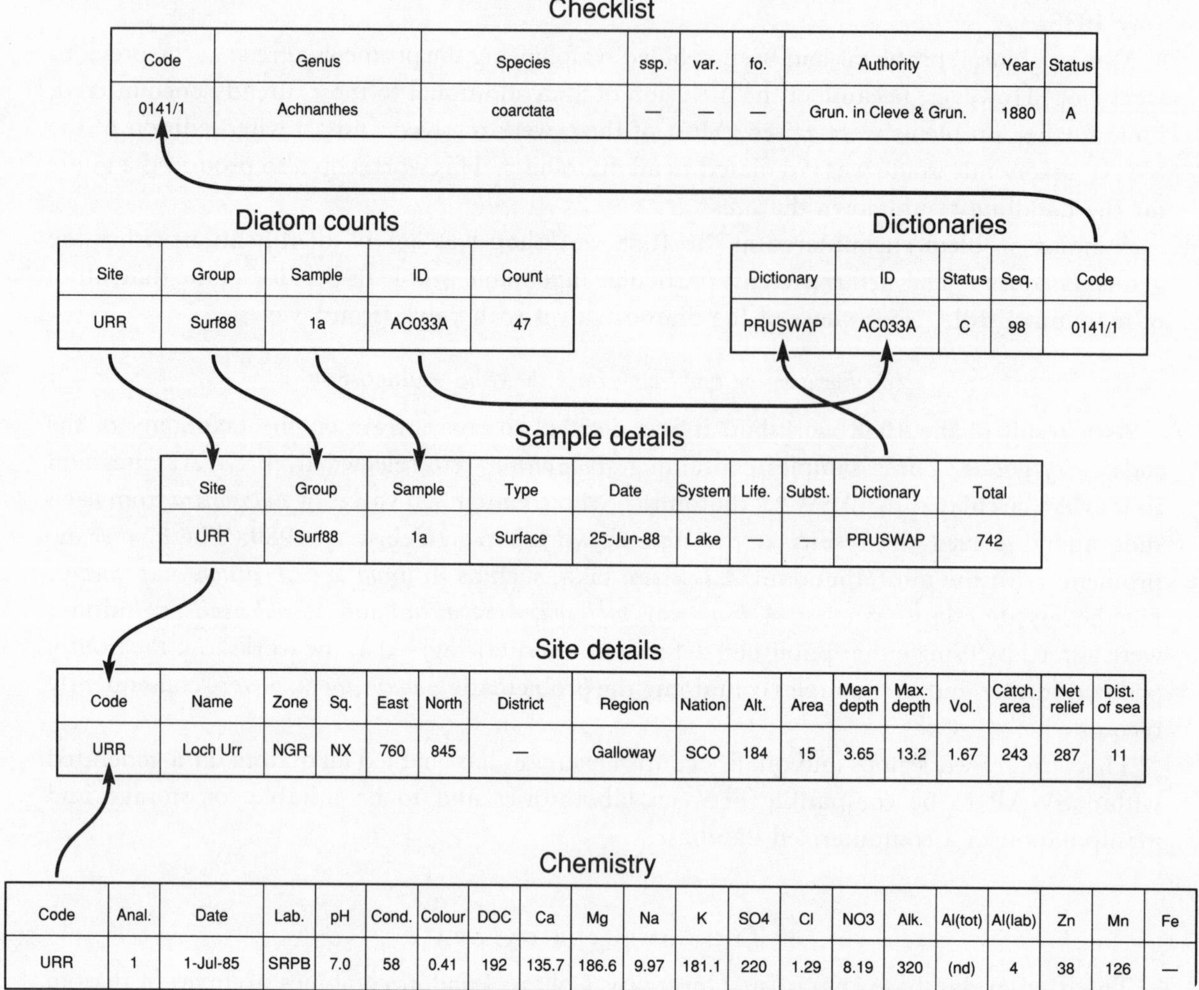

FIGURE 2. The rectangles represent entries in various database tables, the arrows show how common entries can connect the tables. Other connections are possible.

recorded in Britain (so Hartley excluded them), names that refer to aggregate taxonomic categories that do not have any place in a checklist of single taxa (such as *Navicula* spp.) and names needed for newly discovered taxa, or taxa that diatomists can recognize consistently but cannot identify as any checklist entry. It includes these in a supplementary code list. The database also stores tables of chemical analyses for calibration data set values that were used for improving reconstruction methods (Birks *et al.*, this symposium). So far only pH is used, but other data are included, such as: conductivity, colour, dissolved organic carbon, Ca^{2+}, Mg^{2+}, Na^{+}, K^{+}, SO_4^{2-}, Cl^{-}, NO_3^{-}, alkalinity, Al (total), Al (labile), Zn, Mn, Fe, Cu, Pb, dissolved SiO_2 and total P. These will be used for future development of diatom-based reconstruction methods.

4. Data processing

Diatomists submitting counts to the database provided an outline code dictionary for their data. The dictionary was checked to ensure that it contained valid checklist or supplementary list codes, and was compared to previous lists from the same laboratory. The counts were then converted to percentages of the total number of diatoms counted in each sample; any amalgamations and other re-definitions of taxa were performed. The database also provided a list of the more frequently occurring taxa for each group of samples, defined as those present in at least two of the samples and having a frequency of more than 1 % in at least one sample. These lists were compared to help identify unresolved taxonomic problems.

The SWAP calibration data-set was created by merging full sets of surface sediment percentages in this way for the regional datasets from Scotland, Wales, Cumbria, Norway and Sweden. All the aggregates to genus level and above (e.g. *Navicula* spp.) were deleted and the remainder of this list was used to select the taxa to be exported to the calibration programs. The core percentages were then exported to the reconstruction programs as a series of individual site datasets.

The chemical values added to the database were screened in several stages. The program for adding new values included simple checks on the range of the values for various determinands. At least two people checked a complete paper listing of the database values against the original laboratory report. The values were standardized (zero mean, standard deviation = 1), by using both site and regional means, and values outside the range ± 2 were noted. In some cases histograms of the distributions were plotted as a further check, as the values for some determinands were not normally distributed. Values of pH were excluded from the data-set only if they were extremely discordant (such as a value of 3.6 from Llyn Bugeilyn whose other pH values were 5.0, 4.6 and 5.1), or if exceptional conductivity and ionic concentration values suggested that they were influenced by a sea-salt event. Geometric mean pH values were used for calibration (arithmetic means of H^+ concentrations). The groups of analyses used to calculate the means were matched with the calibration dataset to ensure that re-sampled sites (which had two sets of diatom assemblages) had two sets of pH values. The sampling date for the chemistry was normally within three years of the diatom sampling date.

The database will allow further exploration of diatom–water-quality data as samples from a wider range of environmental gradients are included and the full range of chemical data is screened in the same way as the pH values.

References

Ahmad, H. & Charles, D. F. 1988 *PIRLA data base management system user's manual* (2nd ed.). Paleoecological Investigation of Recent Lake Acidification (PIRLA), report no. 32, 266 pp.

Charles, D. F., Whitehead, D. R., Anderson, D. S., Bienert, R., Camburn, K. E., Cook, R. B., Crisman, T. L., Davis, R. B., Ford, J., Fry, B. D., Hites, R. A., Kahl, J. S., Kingston, J. C., Kreis, R. G., Mitchell, M. J., Norton, S. A., Roll, L. A., Smol, J. P., Sweets, P. R., Uutala, A. J., White, J. R., Whiting, M. C. & Wise, R. J. 1987 The PIRLA project (Paleoecological Investigation of Recent Lake Acidification): preliminary results from the Adirondacks, New England, N. Great Lakes and N. Florida. *Wat. Air Soil Pollut.* **31**, 355–366.

Hartley, B. 1986 A check-list of the freshwater, brackish and marine diatoms of the British Isles and adjoining coastal waters. *J. mar. biol. Ass. U.K.* **66**, 531–610.

Williams, D. M., Hartley, B., Ross, R., Munro, M. A. R., Juggins, S. & Battarbee, R. W. 1988 *A coded checklist of British diatoms*. London: ENSIS Publishing.

Phil. Trans. R. Soc. Lond. B **327**, 263–278 (1990)
Printed in Great Britain

Diatoms and pH reconstruction

By H. J. B. Birks[1], J. M. Line[2], S. Juggins[3], A. C. Stevenson[4] and C. J. F. ter Braak[5]

[1] *Botanical Institute, University of Bergen, Allégaten* 41, *N*-5007 *Bergen, Norway*
[2] *University of Cambridge Computer Laboratory, Pembroke Street, Cambridge CB*2 3*QG, U.K.*
[3] *Palaeoecology Research Unit, Department of Geography, University College,* 26 *Bedford Way, London WC*1*H* 0*AP, U.K.*
[4] *Department of Geography, University of Newcastle upon Tyne, Newcastle upon Tyne NE*1 7*RU, U.K.*
[5] *Agricultural Mathematics Group, Wageningen, Box* 100, 6700 *AC Wageningen, The Netherlands, and Research Institute for Nature Management, Box* 46, 3956 *ZR Leersum, The Netherlands*

[Microfiche in pocket]

Palaeolimnological diatom data comprise counts of many species expressed as percentages for each sample. Reconstruction of past lake-water pH from such data involves two steps; (i) regression, where responses of modern diatom abundances to pH are modelled and (ii) calibration where the modelled responses are used to infer pH from diatom assemblages preserved in lake sediments. In view of the highly multivariate nature of diatom data, the strongly nonlinear response of diatoms to pH, and the abundance of zero values in the data, a compromise between ecological realism and computational feasability is essential. The two numerical approaches used are (i) the computationally demanding but formal statistical approach of maximum likelihood (ML) Gaussian logit regression and calibration and (ii) the computationally straightforward but heuristic approach of weighted averaging (WA) regression and calibration.

When the Surface Water Acidification Project (SWAP) modern training set of 178 lakes is reduced by data-screening to 167 lakes, WA gives superior results in terms of lowest root mean squared errors of prediction in cross-validation. Bootstrapping is also used to derive prediction errors, not only for the training set as a whole but also for individual pH reconstructions by WA for stratigraphic samples from Round Loch of Glenhead, southwest Scotland covering the last 10000 years. These reconstructions are evaluated in terms of lack-of-fit to pH and analogue measures and are interpreted in terms of rate of change by using bootstrapping of the reconstructed pH time-series.

Introduction

Diatoms are good ecological indicators of lake-water pH (Battarbee *et al.* 1986). In recent years this feature has been exploited to reconstruct pH from diatom assemblages preserved in lake sediments (Battarbee 1984; Battarbee & Charles 1987) and a variety of numerical procedures have been developed for quantitative inference of pH. Quantitative reconstruction of pH from diatoms is, in practice, a two-step process. First, the responses of modern diatoms to contemporary pH are modelled. This is a regression problem (ter Braak & Looman 1987; ter Braak & Prentice 1988) and involves a modern, training set of diatom assemblages ('response' variables) from surface lake-sediment samples with associated pH data ('predictor' variable).

Second, the modelled responses are used to infer past pH from the composition of fossil diatom assemblages. This is a calibration problem (ter Braak 1987*a*; ter Braak & Prentice 1988).

There are at least five major ecological assumptions in quantitative, palaeoenvironmental reconstructions (Imbrie & Webb 1981).

1. The taxa in the training set are systematically related to the physical environment in which they live.

2. The environmental variable to be reconstructed (in our case pH) is, or is linearly related to, an ecologically important variable in the system of interest.

3. The taxa in the training set are the same as in the fossil data-set and their ecological responses have not changed significantly over the timespan represented by the fossil data. Contemporary patterns of diatom abundance in relation to pH can thus be used to reconstruct pH changes through time.

4. The mathematical methods used in regression and calibration adequately model the biological responses to the environmental variable of interest.

5. Environmental variables other than the one of interest (e.g. pH) have negligible influence, or their joint distribution with the variable of interest in the fossil set is the same as in the training set.

Diatom data contain many taxa (*ca.* 100–300 taxa) and many zero values; values are commonly expressed as percentages of the total valves counted in a sample. They are thus closed, multivariate compositional data and have a constant-sum constraint. Diatom responses to pH are frequently nonlinear. These features confer important statistical properties on the data.

A variety of numerical procedures (reviewed by Battarbee (1984), Charles (1985) and Birks (1987)) have been used to reconstruct pH but none of these are fully satisfactory either theoretically or ecologically (Birks 1987; ter Braak & van Dam 1989). They are nearly all variants of the basic multiple linear regression model and usually involve grouping diatoms into ecological categories (see, for example, Charles (1985); Davis & Anderson (1985); Flower (1986); Charles & Smol (1988)). ter Braak and van Dam (1989) introduced two procedures, maximum likelihood (ML) and weighted averaging (WA) regression and calibration (see also ter Braak (1987*b*)). They are more sound theoretically and perform better than other, more widely used 'ad hoc' pH reconstruction techniques. These two procedures form the basis of this paper; WA regression and calibration are used for pH reconstructions within the Surface Water Acidification Project (SWAP).

The data

(*a*) *The modern data*

The SWAP training set consists of diatom counts of 178 surface samples from lakes in England (five lakes), Norway (51), Scotland (60), Sweden (30) and Wales (32). It includes all taxa (267) that are present in at least two samples with an abundance of 1 % or more in at least one sample and that are identified to species level or below. Abundances are expressed as percentages of the total diatom count (*ca.* 500 valves) for that sample. The sum of the percentages of taxa included range from 65.0 % to 99.1 % (mean = 92.6 %) of the total diatom count per sample.

The pH data for each lake are based on the arithmetic mean of $[H^+]$ (Barth 1975; cf. Middleton & Rovers 1976; Charles 1985), after initial data screening (Munro *et al.*, this symposium). Many lakes have pH data based on three or more readings (131 lakes), though some only have one (32) or two (15) readings. The pH range is 4.33–7.25 ($\bar{x} = 5.59$, median = 5.51, standard deviation (s.d.) = 0.77). Further details of the data and their taxonomic consistency are given by Munro *et al.* (this symposium).

(*b*) *The fossil data*

We use the data of Jones *et al.* (1989) from Round Loch of Glenhead (RLGH), Galloway, southwest Scotland for reconstruction purposes. The 101 samples from 0.3 to 256.5 cm in core RLGH3 cover the last 10000 years. They contain some taxa absent in the training set and vice versa. Only taxa present in both sets are included. These represent 72.8–98.7 % (mean = 88.2 %) of the total diatom count per sample in the core.

Theory and methods

(*a*) *Notation*

We use the following notation throughout; x is the environmental variable to be reconstructed, in our case pH; x_i is the value of x in sample (in our case lake) i; y_{ik} is the abundance of taxon k in sample i ($y_{ik} \geqslant 0$) ($i = 1, \ldots n$ lakes and $k = 1, \ldots m$ diatom taxa); $\hat{x}_i$ is the estimated or inferred value of x for sample i.

(*b*) *Maximum likelihood regression and calibration*

The basic idea (ter Braak & van Dam 1989; ter Braak 1987*a*, *b*; ter Braak & Prentice 1988) is that the relation between the abundance of a diatom taxon and pH can be modelled by an ecological response curve consisting of systematic and random (error) components. Such a curve is fitted to the training set by nonlinear regression. The response curves and their assumed error structure form a statistical model of diatom composition in relation to pH. The curves for all taxa determine jointly what diatom composition is expected at a given pH. This model of responses and their error structure is used to calculate the probability that a particular pH would occur with a given assemblage over the range of possible pH values. The pH that gives the highest probability is the ML estimate.

There are many types of ecological response curves. A compromise is necessary between ecological realism and simplicity (ter Braak & van Dam 1989); the Gaussian unimodal response model with symmetric unimodal curves is a suitable compromise (ter Braak 1987*b*).

The Gaussian logit model is usually applied to presence–absence data (see, for example, ter Braak & Looman (1986)). However, it can be used, as here, as a quasi-likelihood model for proportions and as an approximation to the more complex multinomial logit model (ter Braak & van Dam 1989). The multinomial model can be difficult to fit and its parameters difficult to interpret because of indeterminacies (ter Braak 1988).

Following ter Braak and van Dam (1989), we fitted a Gaussian logit model to all 229 taxa that occurred in six or more lakes in the training set by logit regression (with binomial error structure). (Oksanen *et al.* (1988) fitted the related Gaussian model with Poisson error structure.) From the Gaussian logit regression coefficients, the optimum ($\hat{u}_k$), tolerance ($\hat{t}_k$) and height of the peak ($\hat{c}_k$) of the fitted Gaussian response curve were calculated (ter Braak & Looman 1986, 1987), along with the approximate 95 % confidence intervals for the estimated u_k and the standard error of the estimated t_k (ter Braak & Looman 1986, 1987).

For each taxon, the significance ($\alpha = 0.05$) of the Gaussian logit model was tested against the simpler linear-logit (sigmoidal) model by a residual deviance test. The significance ($\alpha = 0.05$) of the Gaussian logit regression coefficient b_2 against the null hypothesis ($b_2 \geqslant 0$) was also assessed by a one-sided *t*-test (ter Braak & Looman 1986, 1987). If the null hypothesis was rejected in favour of $b_2 < 0$, the taxon's optimum was considered significant. If either the Gaussian unimodal model or the optimum were not significant, the linear logit model and its regression coefficient b_1, were tested against the null model that the taxon showed no relation to pH, by using deviance and two-sided *t*-tests.

For taxa with estimated optima clearly outside the range of sampled pH values, and with a significant linear logit model, the optimum was assumed to be the lowest pH sampled for decreasing linear logit curves and the highest pH sampled for increasing linear logit curves. Some taxa had fitted curves with a minimum ($b_2 > 0$) instead of a maximum. For these taxa a linear logit model was fitted and, for WA calibration (table 3), the optima were taken to be the lowest or highest pH in the training set for decreasing curves and increasing curves, respectively. The tolerances are defined only for taxa with unimodal response curves.

The response curves and their assumed error structure were then used in ML calibration to find the pH with the highest probability of producing the observed diatom assemblages for each sample in both training and fossil data sets. This was done by using an iterative Gauss–Newton numerical optimization procedure with Gallant's (1975) chopping rule for step-shortening. Estimates of WA were used as initial estimates. Some samples failed to converge, however, with this procedure.

Regression and calibration of ML are computer-intensive and liable to find local maxima rather than the overall maximum, especially when the taxon tolerances are very unequal. An alternative approach that is both simpler and computationally easier and has essentially the same aims as ML is WA regression and calibration (ter Braak & van Dam 1989; ter Braak & Prentice 1988).

(*c*) *Weighted averaging regression and calibration*

The idea behind WA (ter Braak 1987*b*) is that in a lake with a certain pH range, diatoms with their pH optima close to the lake's pH will tend to be the most abundant taxa present. A simple and ecologically reasonable estimate of a taxon's pH optimum is thus the average of all the pH values for lakes in which the taxon occurs, weighted by the taxon's relative abundance (WA regression). Conversely, an estimate of the lake's pH is the weighted average of the pH optima of all the taxa present (WA calibration). Taxa with a narrow pH tolerance or amplitude can, if required, be given greater weight in WA than taxa with a wide pH tolerance.

The WA estimate of a taxon's optimum (equivalent to abundance weighted mean (see, for example, Charles (1985); Charles & Smol (1988)), centroid), $\hat{u}_k$, is:

$$\hat{u}_k = \sum_{i=1}^{n} y_{ik}\, x_i \Big/ \sum_{i=1}^{n} y_{ik},$$

and a taxon's tolerance, $\hat{t}_k$, or weighted standard deviation is:

$$\hat{t}_k = \left[\sum_{i=1}^{n} y_{ik}(x_i - \hat{u}_k)^2 \Big/ \sum_{i=1}^{n} y_{ik}\right]^{\frac{1}{2}}.$$

The estimated optima can be used to infer a lake's pH from its diatom assemblage (WA calibration) by:

$$\hat{x}_i = \sum_{k=1}^{m} y_{ik}\,\hat{u}_k \Big/ \sum_{k=1}^{m} y_{ik},$$

whereas a tolerance-weighted estimate would be:

$$\hat{x}_i = \left(\sum_{k=1}^{m} y_{ik}\,\hat{u}_k/\hat{t}_k^2\right) \Big/ \left(\sum_{k=1}^{m} y_{ik}/\hat{t}_k^2\right).$$

The theory of WA and the conditions under which WA approximates ML are fully discussed by ter Braak (1985, 1987*b*), ter Braak & Looman (1986), ter Braak & Barendregt (1986) and ter Braak & Prentice (1988).

In WA reconstructions, averages are taken twice, once in WA regression and once in WA calibration. This results in shrinkage of the range of inferred pH values. To correct for this, a simple linear deshrinking was done by regressing the initial inferred values $\hat{x}_i$ for the training set on the observed values, x_i, by using the linear regression model, so-called 'classical regression':

$$\text{initial } \hat{x}_i = a + bx_i + \epsilon_i,$$

and

$$\text{final } \hat{x}_i = (\text{initial } \hat{x}_i - a)/b,$$

where a is the intercept and b is the slope of the linear regression (ter Braak 1988). ter Braak & van Dam (1989) discuss the importance of deshrinking. They used 'inverse' regression (where x_i is regressed on initial $\hat{x}_i$ values) to 'deshrink', because this minimizes the root mean squared error in the training set. Classical regression deshrinks more than inverse regression (see, for example, Lwin & Maritz (1982)); it takes inferred values further away from the mean. In our case, the mean lies in the pH interval where a lake's pH is very variable, and acidification studies require the reconstructions to be most precise at the lower end of the pH range in the training set. For that, classical regression is preferable (Martinelle 1970; Lwin & Maritz 1982). This deshrinking regression was also done for ML calibration to ensure comparability between results from the two approaches.

(*d*) *Summary statistics*

The root mean square of the error (RMSE) $(x_i - \hat{x}_i)$ was calculated for the training set for comparison of the predictive abilities of ML, WA and weighted averaging with tolerance downweighting (WA(tol)). Wallach & Goffinet (1989) discuss the value of RMSE as a means of evaluating how well a model can be expected to function as a predictive tool. The correlation (r) between x_i and $\hat{x}_i$ was also calculated. As RMSE is invariably under-estimated when based solely on the training set (ter Braak & van Dam 1989; Oksanen *et al.* 1988), split-sampling or cross-validation (Stone 1974; Snee 1977; Picard & Cook 1984) was used to derive a reliable estimate of prediction error and hence to evaluate the predictive abilities of the different methods. This involves randomly splitting the modern data into a training set and a test set, and ensuring that only taxa fulfilling the criteria of two or more occurrences and 1% or more in any one sample in the new training set are included.

(*e*) *Error estimation*

Bootstrapping, a computer-intensive resampling procedure (Efron 1982; Efron & Gong 1983; Diaconis & Efron 1983; Wallach & Goffinet 1989) was used to derive RMSE of prediction for individual pH reconstructions. It also provides another estimate of the overall RMSE of prediction for the training set. The underlying theory is described in Appendix 1.

The idea is that in each of many bootstrap cycles (in our case 1000) a subset of training samples is selected randomly from the original training set to form a bootstrap training set of the same size as the actual training set. This mimics sampling variation in the training set. Sampling is with replacement, so that samples may be selected more than once. Typically some samples will not be selected, and these form a bootstrap test set. In each cycle, WA regression and calibration are used with the bootstrap training set to infer pH for the modern samples in the bootstrap test set. This parallels the use of test sets in cross-validation and provides another estimate of the RMSE of prediction (see Appendix 1). This estimate is less prone to bias (Efron 1982, 1983) because the bootstrap uses the full size of the training set rather than the smaller size used in cross-validation.

In each cycle WA calibration is also used to infer pH for the fossil samples. For each fossil sample, the standard deviation of inferred pH for all bootstrap cycles is calculated. A naive user of the bootstrap might think that this standard deviation, e.g. s_{i1}, is an estimate of prediction error. It is not, because s_{i1} would approach zero if the size of the training set steadily increases. In fact, s_{i1} is that part of the prediction error that is due to the estimation error in the taxon parameters in the calibration formulae $(\hat{u}_k, \hat{t}_k)$. The other, often larger, part of the prediction error is due to variation in taxon abundances at a given value of pH. (In the bootstrap cycles, the taxon abundances of a fossil sample were kept fixed so s_{i1} cannot catch this variation). The latter part, e.g. s_2, is estimated from the training set by the root mean square (across all training samples) of the difference between observed pH and the mean bootstrap pH in all bootstrap cycles when that sample is in the bootstrap test set. Whereas the first part of the error varies from fossil sample to fossil sample, the second part is constant. The estimated RMSE of prediction is the square root of the sum of squares of the two components (see Appendix 1). This procedure can also be applied to each training sample.

(*f*) *Computing*

Gaussian logit and linear logit regressions were done with GLIM (Payne 1986); WA regression and calibration, ML calibration, and associated statistics were implemented by WACALIB 2.1, a special purpose FORTRAN 77 program written by JML. It includes some subroutines from CANOCO (ter Braak 1988) written by CJF ter B. and M. O. Hill and an ML optimization subroutine written by CJF ter B. Detrended correspondence and canonical correspondence analyses were done by means of CANOCO 3.0 (C. J. F. ter Braak (unpublished)). Analogue analysis was implemented by the FORTRAN 77 program ANALOG 1.2 written by JML. Bootstrapping of WA estimates was done by using WACALIB 2.4, an update of WACALIB 2.1 incorporating bootstrapping subroutines written by CJF ter B. Bootstrapping of stratigraphic changes was done with THERRAD (Kitchell *et al.* 1987). All computations were done on an IBM PC/AT or compatible machines.

Results

(*a*) *Comparison of root mean squared error of prediction for different numerical procedures*

When ML, WA and WA(tol) were applied to the full training set, the RMSE (table 1) suggest that there is little to be gained in terms of RMSE by using ML. Moreover 14 of the 178 training samples (pH range 4.79–6.75) failed to converge with ML, i.e. for these samples our numerical procedure was unable to find a single most likely pH value. Cross-validation with a training set of 130 and a test set of 48 lakes produced RMSE for the test set in the order WA < ML < WA(tol).

In a large, heterogeneous data set such as the 178-lake training set, it is possible that some samples are 'rogues' or atypical observations, for example with unusual diatom assemblages weakly related to pH, with poor or unreliable pH data, or with environmental variables other than pH having a major influence on the diatom composition. A data-screening exercise was performed to detect potential 'rogues'.

TABLE 1. ROOT MEAN SQUARED ERROR OF PREDICTION (RMSE) FOR WEIGHTED AVERAGING REGRESSION AND CALIBRATION WITH (WA(tol)) AND WITHOUT (WA) TOLERANCE-DOWNWEIGHTING AND MAXIMUM LIKELIHOOD (ML) REGRESSION AND CALIBRATION AND THE CORRELATION (r) BETWEEN OBSERVED AND PREDICTED pH BY USING DIFFERENT TRAINING SETS

training set		WA	WA(tol)	ML
178 lakes × 267 taxa (229 in ML)	RMSE	0.343	0.324	0.341[a]
	r	0.913	0.921	0.911
130 lakes × 240 taxa	RMSE	0.353	0.338	0.361[b]
	r	0.907	0.914	0.905
Test set 48 lakes × 240 taxa	RMSE	0.331	0.404	0.356
	r	0.915	0.849	0.894
172 lakes × 267 taxa	RMSE	0.323	0.301	—
(6 'rogues' deleted)	r	0.921	0.931	—
167 lakes × 267 taxa	RMSE	0.297	0.278	0.317[c]
(225 taxa in ML)				
(11 'rogues' deleted)	r	0.933	0.941	0.921

[a] Fourteen lakes failed to converge.
[b] Eleven lakes failed to converge.
[c] Ten lakes failed to converge.

In the first screening, a lake was deleted if it (i) formed an extreme outlier on any of the first four axes of a detrended correspondence analysis (Hill 1979) of the diatom data in the full training set; (ii) had a large (extreme 5%) residual distance to the pH-axis in a canonical correspondence analysis (ter Braak 1989) of the diatom data with pH as the only environmental variable; (iii) had a high (> 0.75 pH units) difference between observed and inferred pH in both WA and WA(tol) reconstructions. Six lakes fulfilled all three criteria. The RMSE for WA and WA(tol) for the training set with these six deleted showed some improvement (table 1). In a second screening of the reduced training set (172 lakes), a further five lakes now fulfilled two or three of the above criteria for deletion. When these five were also deleted, the RMSE for WA (0.297), WA(tol) (0.278), and ML (0.317) all showed further improvement (table 1). No lakes appeared to be obvious rogues within the reduced training set of 167 when screened again.

For pH reconstructions at RLGH and all other SWAP sites, this reduced training set of 167 lakes is used. This set has a pH range of 4.33–7.25 ($\bar{x} = 5.56$, median = 5.27, s.d. = 0.77) and 262 taxa.

A series of calibration experiments was done by using this training set to compare different regression and calibration procedures (table 2). Besides WA regression and calibration with and

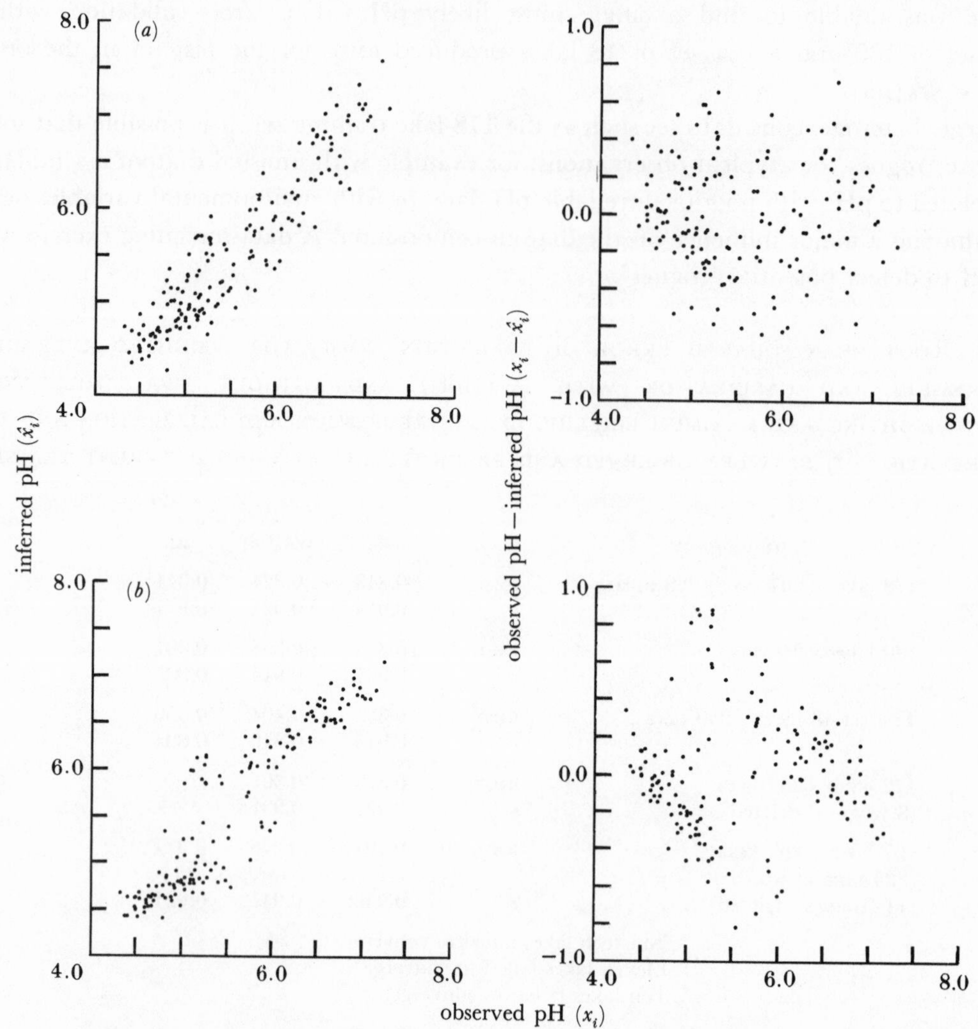

FIGURE 1. Plots of inferred pH ($\hat{x}_i$) against observed pH (x_i) (left hand plots) and of the differences ($x_i - \hat{x}_i$) against observed pH (right-hand plots) for pH inferences derived from (*a*) weighted averaging and (*b*) maximum likelihood regression and calibration.

TABLE 2. ROOT MEAN SQUARED ERROR OF PREDICTION (RMSE) AND CORRELATION (r) BETWEEN OBSERVED AND INFERRED pH WHEN DIFFERENT REGRESSION AND CALIBRATION PROCEDURES ARE USED WITH THE 167 LAKE TRAINING SET

regression procedure	calibration procedure	number of taxa	RMSE	r
WA	WA	274	0.297	0.993
WA	WA(tol)	274	0.278	0.941
ML	WA	224	0.294	0.934
ML	WA(tol)	224	0.282	0.939
ML	WA	168[a]	0.290	0.936
ML	WA(tol)	168[a]	0.292	0.935
ML	ML	225	0.317	0.921

[a] All taxa with statistically significant relation to pH (see table 4).

without tolerance downweighting and ML regression and calibration, 'hybrid' procedures were used with taxon optima and tolerances estimated by ML regression but by using WA (with and without tolerance downweighting) calibration (see, for example, Juggins (1988); Oksanen *et al.* (1988)) and all taxa and only those with a significant relation to pH. The overall conclusion is that ML regression and calibration perform the worst (cf. ter Braak & van Dam 1989), but that all the other procedures perform about equally well, as judged by RMSE. In terms of RMSE there seems little advantage in using ML regression compared with WA regression. Plots of inferred pH ($\hat{x}_i$) against observed pH (x_i) and of the differences ($x_i - \hat{x}_i$) against x_i for WA and ML are shown in figure 1. In WA there is no systematic bias (cf. Oksanen *et al.* 1988) except for a tendency for the differences to be greatest in the pH range 5.3–6.6, and lowest at the extremes. These high differences all occur in poorly buffered lakes where small seasonal changes in alkalinity can cause large variations in pH. In the absence of multiple pH measurements, estimation of a meaningful mean pH is impossible (Flower 1986). In ML two clusters emerge and pH estimates for ten lakes failed to converge, all in the pH range 4.79–5.89.

TABLE 3. ROOT MEAN SQUARED ERROR OF PREDICTION FOR TEN CROSS-VALIDATION EXPERIMENTS USING FOUR RANDOMLY SELECTED TEST SETS OF 50 LAKES, FOUR RANDOMLY SELECTED TEST SETS OF 40 LAKES, ONE RANDOMLY SELECTED TEST SET OF 67 LAKES AND ONE RANDOMLY SELECTED TEST SET OF 47 LAKES

experiment	number of taxa	WA	WA(tol)	WA	WA(tol)
		training set 117 lakes		test set 50 lakes	
1	231	0.310	0.282	0.287	0.339
2	226	0.292	0.276	0.310	0.368
3	228	0.307	0.294	0.309	0.383
4	231	0.313	0.291	0.269	0.305
mean		0.306	0.286	0.294	0.349
		training set 127 lakes		test set 40 lakes	
5	230	0.285	0.271	0.326	0.287
6	229	0.284	0.267	0.313	0.314
7	240	0.298	0.276	0.307	0.303
8	240	0.306	0.281	0.274	0.318
mean		0.299	0.280	0.299	0.327
		training set 100 lakes		test set 67 lakes	
9	248	0.257	0.240	0.338	0.541
		training set 120 lakes		test set 47 lakes	
10	258	0.283	0.267	0.300	0.288

In light of the RMSE results (table 2) and plots of x_i against $\hat{x}_i$ and of ($x_i - \hat{x}_i$) against x_i (not presented here) for these calibration experiments, WA regression and calibration with and without tolerance downweighting were selected for pH reconstructions at RLGH and all other SWAP lakes because of their low RMSE, their computational ease, and their robustness.

Ten cross-validation experiments were done to derive more reliable RMSE for WA and WA(tol), by using four randomly selected test sets of 50 lakes, four test sets of 40 lakes, a single test set of 67 lakes and one test set of 47 lakes (table 3). The RMSE for test sets in these experiments were 0.287–0.338 (mean = 0.308) for WA and 0.287–0.541 (mean = 0.376) for WA(tol). This indicates that WA has a lower prediction error in test sets than WA(tol). This error is, as ter Braak & van Dam (1989) emphasize, the 'appropriate benchmark to compare methods' because all errors are considered (see also Oksanen *et al.* (1988)).

(*b*) *Comparison of the* pH *optima and tolerance estimates*

The basis for these calibration experiments is the estimates of the taxon parameters. The WA and ML estimated optima and tolerances for all taxa in the 167-lake training set are listed in table 4 (see microfiche), along with each taxon's maximum value, number of occurrences, shape of response curve, 95% confidence intervals of the ML-estimated optimum, standard error of the ML-estimated tolerance, curve height, literature pH category, and statistical relation to pH. Ecological discussion of these estimates will be presented in a subsequent SWAP publication. Of the 225 taxa (in six or more lakes) used for ML regression, 88 have unimodal curves with maxima, 78 have sigmoidal curves, 53 show no pattern, five have unimodal curves with minima and one failed to converge. A significant unimodal (88) or sigmoidal (78) response to pH is seen in 166 taxa. Of the 58 taxa with non-significant pH relations, only one has a fitted curve peak ($\hat{c}_k$) > 1% and only 15 have maximum values in the training set > 2.5% (range = 1.03–4.92%). As 74% of the taxa have a significant relation with pH, this provides strong confirmation for the assumption of Davis & Smol (1986) 'that there is a good statistical relation between pH and relative abundance of diatoms.' In the sampled pH range (4.33–7.25) WA estimates of optima are close to the ML estimates, although WA consistently but very slightly underestimates optima compared to ML. This slight bias is, in part, due to the over-representation of acid lakes in the training set, because WA estimates are sensitive to the distribution of x_i (ter Braak & Looman 1986, 1987). Major differences occur, however, at the extreme ends. At low pH, WA overestimates the optimum, whereas at high pH it underestimates it, because of truncation of the taxon response curves at the edges of the pH gradient. As a result of this inevitable truncation, WA compresses estimates of optima towards the centroid of the sampled pH gradient (Oksanen *et al.* 1988).

Estimates of tolerances by WA are almost all underestimated compared with ML, with a range of WA tolerances from *ca.* 0.2 to 0.75 pH units and an ML range of 0.2–1.8 pH units. For taxa with ML tolerances less than 0.75 pH units, WA provides reliable estimates, but at higher values WA systematically underestimates the tolerance (Oksanen *et al.* 1988). Many of the taxa with no significant relation to pH (table 4) have ML estimated tolerances of more than 1 pH unit, suggesting a range of occurrence over at least 4 pH units.

(*c*) *Reconstructions of* pH *for Round Loch of Glenhead*

The WA, WA(tol), and ML pH reconstructions for RLGH are shown in figure 2. The two WA reconstructions are closely parallel; 34 samples failed to converge in ML calibration.

Evaluation of reconstructed pH values

All quantitative palaeoenvironmental reconstruction procedures produce a result, but there is no simple means of evaluating how reliable it is. In addition to overall performance measures like RMSE calculated once from test sets, it is desirable to assess the reliability of individual reconstructed values. Two means towards this end are (i) measures of lack-of-fit of diatom assemblages to pH and (ii) estimated mean squared errors for each inferred pH.

(*a*) *Lack-of-fit to* pH *and analogue measures*

In the screening of the training data we used the squared residual distance of the modern samples to the pH axis in a canonical correspondence analysis of the diatom data as a criterion

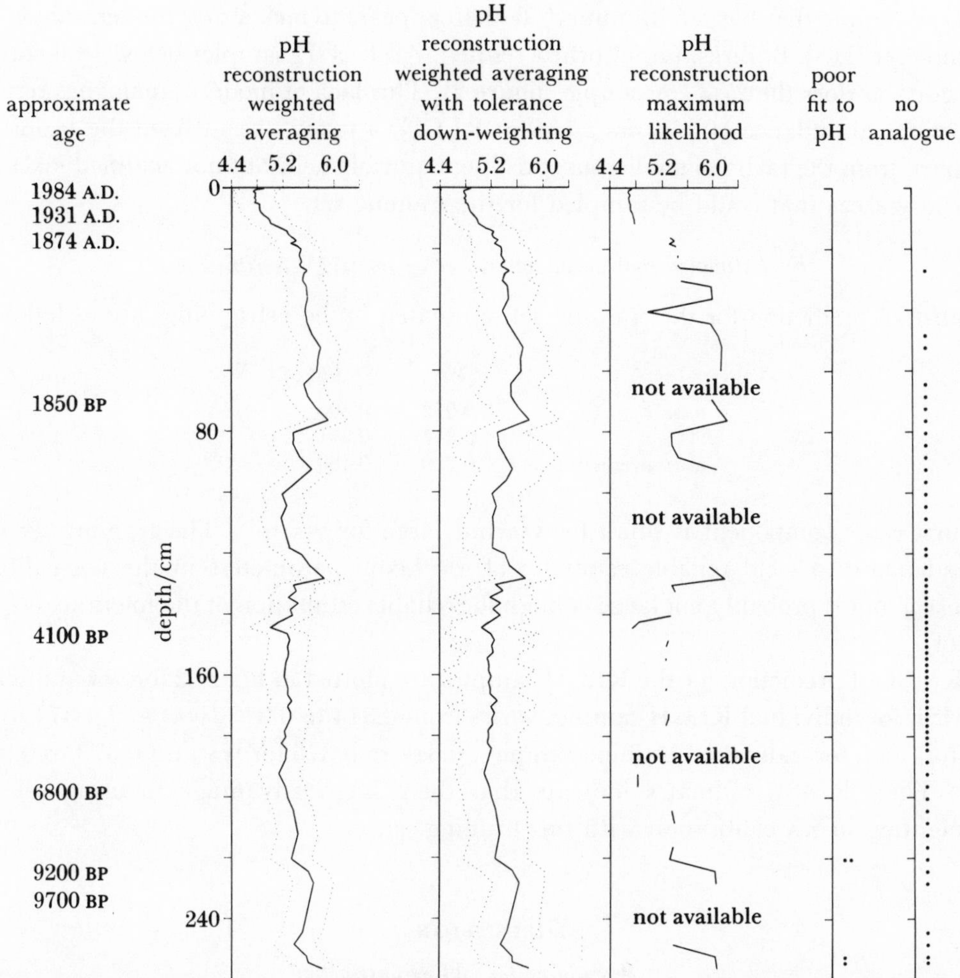

FIGURE 2. Reconstructed pH values for Round Loch of Glenhead plotted against depth (solid lines). The reconstructions are based on weighted averaging, tolerance-downweighted weighted averaging and maximum likelihood procedures. The RMSE of prediction for the weighted averaging estimates are shown as dotted lines. Samples with poor (•) or very poor (••) fit and those lacking close modern analogues in the SWAP training-set (•) are indicated.

of lack-of-fit to pH. Samples with a high residual distance from the pH axis have a poor fit to pH. Fossil, so-called passive, samples can also be positioned on this axis by means of transition formulae (ter Braak 1988). Any fossil sample whose residual distance is equal to or larger than the residual distance of the extreme 5% of the training set is considered to have a 'very poor' fit to pH, and those with values equal to or larger than the extreme 10% are deemed to have a 'poor' fit. One sample at RLGH (220.5 cm) has a very poor fit, and two (252.5, 254.5 cm) have poor fits (figure 2).

A reconstructed pH value is likely to be more reliable if the fossil sample in question has close modern analogues within the training set. Every fossil sample at RLGH was compared with all samples in the training set by using squared X^2 distance as a dissimilarity measure (Prentice 1980). This is:

$$d_{ij}^2 = \sum_{k=1}^{m} [(y_{ik} - y_{jk})^2 / (y_{ik} + y_{jk})],$$

where y_{ik} is the proportion of diatom taxon k in sample i and d_{ij} is the X^2 distance between samples i and j.

Any fossil sample that has a minimum $d_{ij} > 0.45$ appears to lack a *close* modern analogue in the training set (H. J. B. Birks, unpublished results). All RLGH samples below 48.5 cm fall in this category, as does the 27.3 cm sample (figure 2). This lack of modern analogues results, in part, from the abundance of *Melosira arentii* at RLGH, a taxon absent from the training set, and, in part, from the rarity of analogous, pristine, naturally acid but not acidified lakes in the SWAP study areas that could be sampled for the training set.

(*b*) *Estimated root mean squared error for* pH *reconstructions*

The RMSE of prediction for the training set, estimated by bootstrapping, are as follows:

	WA	WA(tol)
RMSE s_{i1}	0.072	0.305
s_2	0.312	0.371
RMSE prediction	0.320	0.480

The first error component is small for WA but large for WA(tol). The training set is thus clearly adequate to yield reliable estimates of the taxon parameters in the WA calibration formula ($\hat{u}_k$), but is probably not large enough for reliable estimation of the tolerances ($\hat{t}_k$) used in WA(tol).

The RMSE of prediction for the RLGH samples are plotted in figure 2 for WA and WA(tol). The RMSE for individual RLGH samples varies from 0.314 to 0.322 (WA) and 0.374 to 0.798 for WA(tol) and, for individual training samples, 0.314 to 0.376 for WA and 0.373 to 0.915 for WA(tol). These RMSE estimates indicate that there is no advantage in using tolerance-downweighting in WA calibration with this training set.

Discussion

(*a*) *Procedures for* pH *reconstruction*

Several conclusions emerge from our analyses (see also ter Braak & van Dam (1989)). Regression and calibration by WA can now replace earlier 'ad hoc' methods for pH reconstruction; WA is ecologically more realistic, statistically more robust, and numerically more accurate than other methods. Although some 'ad hoc' methods may produce lower apparent RMSE, these error estimates are not based on rigorous error-estimation procedures such as cross-validation or bootstrapping, but on regression statistics derived solely for training sets. As ter Braak & van Dam (1989) emphasize, RMSE based on training sets alone give an over-optimistic idea of prediction and performance error. In all our cross-validation experiments, RMSE for test sets is larger than for training sets (see also Juggins (1988); Oksanen *et al.* (1988)). In the SWAP training set the apparent RMSE for WA is 0.297 whereas the more realistic RMSE are 0.308 (cross-validation) and 0.320 (bootstrapping).

Although WA with tolerance-downweighting gives a lower apparent RMSE (0.278) than WA, tolerance-weighting does not improve RMSE in cross-validation (0.376) or bootstrapping (0.480). We therefore recommend simple WA regression and calibration with classical regression deshrinking as the easiest and most reliable pH reconstruction procedure currently available.

The overall RMSE is 0.320 for WA of the 167-lake training set. Standard errors of prediction for individual training samples and fossil samples at RLGH vary from 0.314 to 0.376. As lake pH has inherent seasonal and annual variation and as there are errors in measuring pH, particularly at low ionic-strength water, further reductions in prediction errors seem unlikely. Compared with other pH training sets (reviewed by ter Braak & van Dam (1989)) this RMSE for a large ($n = 167$) training set is lower than is usually found. This is probably because the diatom assemblages are all from surficial sediments collected at or near the deepest part of the lake, many of the lakes have multiple pH determinations, the diatom taxonomy has been carefully harmonized as a result of SWAP taxonomic workshops (Munro *et al.*, this symposium) and the training set was screened by using three different numerical techniques; 11 'rogue' lakes were detected and deleted.

It is surprising that the theoretically more rigorous approach of ML regression and calibration did not perform as well in terms of RMSE as the simpler, approximating approach of WA. This is probably because ML uses more of the data, especially the absences (which WA ignores) and the precise percentage values. The problem of no-analogues and of assemblages containing diatoms of contrasting affinities are therefore more serious in ML than in WA. Although the RLGH samples had about the same amount of lack-of-fit as the modern samples, the lack-of-fit was of a different kind than in the modern samples, as the no-analogue measure showed. It is therefore unsafe to rely on the quantitative aspects of an assemblage as heavily as ML does. By its very nature, ML is more susceptible to 'rogues' than WA. Although we were able to eliminate 11 rogues from the original training set, the computational demands of recomputing taxon optima and tolerances for different screened versions of the training set prevented further screening of the data for samples that are possible 'rogues' in ML regression and calibration. The training set is thus critically screened only for WA.

Regression and calibration by WA have several advantages over more widely used pH inference techniques such as Index B (Renberg & Hellberg 1982) and multiple regression of pH categories (see, for example, Flower (1986); Charles (1985); Charles & Smol (1988)). Besides a lower RMSE (ter Braak & van Dam 1989), the main advantage of WA is that there is no need to assign diatom taxa to pH-preference categories. As Battarbee (1984) discusses and Holmes *et al.* (1989) clearly demonstrate, there are many problems in categorizing taxa, and the particular decision as to which category a taxon is assigned can markedly influence pH inferences by using Index B or multiple regression; WA is free of such problems. It uses the available data on the abundances of individual taxa in relation to pH in the training set. Moreover, because of the simple calculations involved in WA, it is possible to use bootstrapping to derive standard errors of predictions. Bootstrapping is, in theory, possible for ML, but, in practice, is computationally prohibitive. Individual standard errors of prediction for pH reconstructions from fossil assemblages can be valuable in avoiding misinterpretation of inferred pH values.

(*b*) *Reconstructions of* pH *at Round Loch of Glenhead*

The reconstructed pH history at RLGH (figure 2) shows little change from the late-glacial about 10000 years ago to about 4100 years before present (BP) (142 cm). Reconstructed pH varied from 5.4 to 5.8 in the late-glacial and earliest Holocene, but by 9200 BP (224 cm) it stabilized to about 5.2–5.4. Between 4100 and 1850 BP (72 cm) there were short-lived fluctuations, probably associated with inwashing of material from the catchment (Jones *et al.* 1989). Lake acidity changed little (5.3–5.7) until about 1870 A.D. when, between 17.3 cm (1874) and 7.3 cm (1931), pH dropped by over 0.5 units. Reconstructed pH values are never below 5.0 until about 1900 (11 cm). Jones *et al.* (1989) conclude that this marked change in lake acidity resulted from an increase in deposition of strong acids from the atmosphere.

The null hypothesis that the rate of pH change per unit depth between 1874 and 1931 (17.3–7.3 cm) is no different from the rates of pH change in pre acid-deposition times (17.3–256–5 cm) was tested by using bootstrapping of the reconstructed pH time-series to generate empirical probability distributions of pH change with depth. The pH time-series was resampled randomly and with replacement 1000 times to create temporally-ordered data sequences of the same thickness as the interval of interest by using the time-duration or elapsed-time test of Kitchell *et al.* (1987). As the time-series contains unequal depth intervals between pH estimates, it is not possible for each bootstrapped time-series to contain exactly 10 cm. Instead samples are added to the time-series until the depth interval equals or exceeds the specific depth interval being tested. The observed rate of pH change at the time of increased acidic deposition is significantly different ($\alpha = 0.021$) from expectation. The null hypothesis is thus rejected, suggesting that the most rapid pH change per unit depth over the last 10000 years occurred between 1874 and 1931 at RLGH, the very time of increased acid deposition.

This research has been supported in part by SWAP, NAVF, and IBM (Norway). We are grateful to all SWAP diatomists for providing the training set, to Martin Munro for data-base management; to Rick Battarbee, John Boyle, Roger Flower and Viv Jones for valuable discussions; to Hilary Birks and John Kingston for commenting on earlier versions of the manuscript; to Sylvia Peglar and Siv Haugen for technical assistance; to Jennifer Kitchell and Norman MacLeod for providing THERRAD and to H. van der Voet for useful discussions about calibration and bootstrapping.

References

Barth, E. F. 1975 Average pH. *J. Wat. Pollut. Control Fed.* **47**, 2191–2192.

Battarbee, R. W. 1984 Diatom analysis and the acidification of lakes. *Phil. Trans. R. Soc. Lond.* B **305**, 451–477.

Battarbee, R. W. & Charles, D. F. 1987 The use of diatom assemblages in lake sediments as a means of assessing the timing, trends, and causes of lake acidification. *Prog. phys. Geog.* **11**, 552–580.

Battarbee, R. W., Smol, J. P. & Merliäinen, J. 1986 Diatoms as indicators of pH: an historical review. In *Diatoms and lake acidity* (ed. J. P. Smol, R. W. Battarbee, R. B. Davis & J. Meriläinen), pp. 5–14. Dordrecht: Dr W. Junk.

Birks, H. J. B. 1987 Methods for pH-calibration and reconstruction from palaeolimnological data: procedures, problems, potential techniques. Proceedings of the Surface Water Acidification Project (SWAP) mid-term review conference, Bergen 22–26 June 1987, pp. 370–380. London: SWAP.

Charles, D. F. 1985 Relationships between surface sediment diatom assemblages and lake water characteristics in Adirondack lakes. *Ecology* **66**, 994–1011.

Charles, D. F. & Smol, J. P. 1988 New methods for using diatoms and chrysophytes to infer past pH of low-alkalinity lakes. *Limnol. Oceanogr.* **33**, 1451–1462.

Davis, R. B. & Anderson, D. S. 1985 Methods of pH calibration of sedimentary diatom remains for reconstructing history of pH in lakes. *Hydrobiologia* **120**, 69–87.

Davis, R. B. & Smol, J. P. 1986 The use of sedimentary remains of siliceous algae for inferring past chemistry of lake water-problems, potential and research needs. In *Diatoms and lake acidity* (ed. J. P. Smol, R. W. Battarbee, R. B. Davis & J. Meriläinen), pp. 291–300. Dordrecht: Dr W. Junk.

Diaconis, P. & Efron, B. 1983 Computer-intensive methods in statistics. *Scient. Am.* **248**(5), 96–109.

Efron, B. 1982 The jackknife, the bootstrap, and other resampling plans. *SIAM NSF-CBMS Monograph* **38**, 1–92.

Efron, B. 1983 Estimating the error rate of a prediction rule: improvement on cross-validation. *J. Am. statist. Ass.* **78**, 316–331.

Efron, B. & Gong, G. 1983 A leisurely look at the bootstrap, the jackknife, and cross-validation. *Am. Statist.* **37**, 36–48.

Flower, R. J. 1986 The relationship between surface sediment diatom assemblages and pH in 33 Galloway lakes: some regression models for reconstructing pH and their application to sediment cores. *Hydrobiologia* **143**, 93–103.

Gallant, A. R. 1975 Nonlinear regression. *Am. Statist.* **29**, 73–81.
Hill, M. O. 1979 *DECORANA – a FORTRAN program for detrended correspondence analysis and reciprocal averaging.* Cornell University, Ithaca, New York: Section of ecology and systematics.
Holmes, R. W., Whiting, M. C. & Stoddard, J. L. 1989 Changes in diatom-inferred pH and acid neutralizing capacity in a dilute, high elevation, Sierra Nevada lake since A.D. 1825. *Freshwater Biol.* **21**, 295–310.
Imbrie, J. & Webb, T. III 1981 Transfer functions: calibrating micropaleontological data in climatic terms. In *Climatic variations and variability: facts and theories* (ed. A. Berger), pp. 125–134. Dordrecht: D. Reidel.
Jones, V. J., Stevenson, A. C. & Battarbee, R. W. 1989 Acidification of lakes in Galloway, South West Scotland: a diatom and pollen study of the post-glacial history of the Round Loch of Glenhead. *J. Ecol.* **77**, 1–23.
Juggins, S. 1988 A diatom/salinity transfer function for the Thames Estuary and its application to waterfront archaeology. Ph.D. thesis, University of London.
Kitchell, J. A., Estabrook, G. & MacLeod, N. 1987 Testing for equality of rates of evolution. *Paleobiology* **13**, 272–285.
Lwin, T. & Maritz, J. S. 1982 An analysis of the linear-calibration controversy from the perspective of compound estimation. *Technometrics* **24**, 235–242. (Minor correction in *Technometrics* **27**, 445.)
Martinelle, S. 1970 On the choice of regression in linear calibration. Comments on a paper by R. G. Krutchkoff. *Technometrics* **12**, 157–161.
Middleton, A. C. & Rovers, F. A. 1976 Average pH. *J. Wat. Pollut. Control Fed.* **48**, 395–396.
Oksanen, J., Läära, E., Huttunen, P. & Meriläinen, J. 1988 Estimation of pH optima and tolerances of diatoms in lake sediments by the methods of weighted averaging, least squares and maximum likelihood, and their use for the prediction of lake acidity. *J. Paleolimnol.* **1**, 39–49.
Payne, C. D. (ed.) 1986 *The GLIM System Release 3.77*. Oxford: Numerical Algorithms Group.
Picard, R. R. & Cook, R. D. 1984 Cross-validation of regression models. *J. Am. Statist. Ass.* **79**, 575–583.
Prentice, I. C. 1980 Multidimensional scaling as a research tool in Quaternary palynology: a review of theory and methods. *Rev. Palaeobot. Palynol.* **31**, 71–104.
Renberg, I. & Hellberg, T. 1982 The pH history of lakes in southwestern Sweden, as calculated from the subfossil diatom flora of the sediments. *Ambio* **11**, 30–33.
Snee, R. D. 1977 Validation of regression models: methods and examples. *Technometrics* **19**, 415–428.
Stone, M. 1974 Cross-validatory choice and assessment of statistical predictions (with discussion). *Jl R. statist. Soc.* B **36**, 111–147.
ter Braak, C. J. F. 1985 Correspondence analysis of incidence and abundance data: properties in terms of a unimodal response model. *Biometrics* **41**, 859–873.
ter Braak, C. J. F. 1987*a* Calibration. In *Data analysis in community and landscape ecology* (ed. R. H. G. Jongman, C. J. F. ter Braak & O. F. R. van Tongeren), pp. 78–90. Wageningen: Pudoc.
ter Braak, C. J. F. 1987*b* *Unimodal models to relate species to environment.* Doctoral thesis, University of Wageningen.
ter Braak, C. J. F. 1988 CANOCO – a FORTRAN program for canonical community ordination by [partial] [detrended] [canonical] correspondence analysis, principal components analysis and redundancy analysis (version 2.1). Technical Report LWA-88-02, GLW, Wageningen, 95 pp.
ter Braak, C. J. F. & Barendregt, L. G. 1986 Weighted averaging of species indicator values: its efficiency in environmental calibration. *Math. Biosci.* **78**, 57–72.
ter Braak, C. J. F. & Looman, C. W. N. 1986 Weighed averaging logistic regression and the Gaussian response model. *Vegetatio* **65**, 3–11.
ter Braak, C. J. F. & Looman, C. W. N. 1987 Regression. In *Data analysis in community and landscape ecology* (ed. R. H. G. Jongman, C. J. F. ter Braak & O. F. R. van Tongeren), pp. 29–77. Wageningen: Pudoc.
ter Braak, C. J. F. & Prentice, I. C. 1988 A theory of gradient analysis. *Adv. ecol. Res.* **18**, 271–317.
ter Braak, C. J. F. & van Dam, H. 1989 Inferring pH from diatoms: a comparison of old and new calibration methods. *Hydrobiologia* **178**, 209–223.
Wallach, D. & Goffinet, B. 1989 Mean squared error of prediction as a criterion for evaluating and comparing system models. *Ecol. Modelling* **44**, 299–306.

Appendix 1

Bootstrap estimation of sample-specific mean-squared error for pH *reconstructions by weighted averaging*

The notation and bootstrap procedure are described in the main text. In addition, $\text{AVE}(\hat{x}_{i,\text{boot}})$ and $\text{MS}(x_i - \hat{x}_{i,\text{boot}})$ denote the mean and mean square, respectively, of the argument across all the bootstrap cycles where sample i does not belong to the bootstrap training set.

The mean-squared error of the inferred pH of training sample i is estimated by

$\mathrm{MS}(x_i - \hat{x}_{i,\mathrm{boot}})$. This estimator has some importance; (i) it does not suffer from resubstitution bias and (ii) its mean across the training samples yields the bootstrap estimate of overall mean-squared error of prediction. But the corresponding formula cannot be calculated for individual fossil samples, simply because the observed value (x_i) is not available. To obtain a sample-specific error estimator we use the following decomposition:

$$\mathrm{MS}(x_i - \hat{x}_{i,\mathrm{boot}}) = \mathrm{MS}(\hat{x}_{i,\mathrm{boot}} - \mathrm{AVE}(\hat{x}_{i,\mathrm{boot}})) + (x_i - \mathrm{AVE}(\hat{x}_{i,\mathrm{boot}}))^2,$$

which we write in shorthand as:

$$v_i = v_{i1} + v_{i2}.$$

The first part, v_{i1}, can be calculated from the bootstrap cycles for each sample, both fossil and training samples. It represents the effects that the variability of the taxon parameters in the calibration function have on the inferred pH for sample *i*. It reduces in magnitude as the size of the training set increases. But it does so in a sample-specific way. This error component is likely to be relatively small for fossil assemblages consisting of taxa that are frequent and abundant in the training set and to be relatively large for assemblages consisting of taxa that are infrequent and rare in the training set.

The second part, v_{i2}, can be calculated for the training samples only. It includes the error caused by imperfections in the calibration function, even if the parameters are known without error. Diatom assemblages vary even among lakes with the same pH or, conversely, because lakes with the same diatom assemblage may differ in pH. Model specification error also enters v_{i2}. By using multiple regression we investigated whether v_{i2} depends, in a systematic way, on pH, the number of taxa, and the inhomogeneity of an assemblage. For pH we used a second-order polynomial in $\mathrm{AVE}(\hat{x}_{i,\mathrm{boot}})$ and for inhomogeneity the variance ('tolerance') of the optima of the taxa present in the assemblage (Hill 1979). These predictors are suggested from the theory of linear (Martinelle 1970) and WA (ter Braak & Barendregt 1986) calibration. The predictors, however, explained less than 10% of the variance of v_{i2} in the training set. Transformation of the variables (except pH) to logarithms did not improve the fit. Apparently, the second error component is mainly due to other factors. For fossil samples it was therefore taken as a constant, namely the mean v_{i2} across the training set.

The above derivation ignores terms of order $1/n_{\mathrm{boot}}$ with n_{boot} being the number of bootstrap cycles. These terms are negligible with our choice of $n_{\mathrm{boot}} = 1000$.

Phil. Trans. R. Soc. Lond. B **327**, 279–288 (1990)
Printed in Great Britain

Dissolved organic carbon reconstructions from diatom assemblages in PIRLA project lakes, North America

By J. C. Kingston[1] and H. J. B. Birks[2]

[1] *Department of Biology, Queen's University, Kingston, Ontario K7L 3N6, Canada*
[2] *Botanical Institute, University of Bergen, Allégaten 41, N-5007, Bergen, Norway*

[Microfiche in pocket]

Diatom-based palaeolimnological reconstructions of dissolved organic carbon (DOC) are presented for four regional data sets of the North American 'Paleoecological Investigation of Recent Lake Acidification (PIRLA)' project, and for a combined, three-region set. Species optima and tolerances along the DOC gradient were estimated by using maximum likelihood and weighted-averaging regression. Weighted-averaging regression appears to be the most robust and tractable technique for estimating optima, and the apparent error (mean standard error of the relation) was as good for weighted-averaging calibration as for maximum likelihood calibration. Calculated species optima are not entirely consistent among regions and the best 'indicators' for DOC in the PIRLA data-sets are not in good agreement with those found in the literature. Example reconstructions demonstrate that DOC changes are often less than 100 μmol l^{-1}, and that the DOC declines in some recently acidified lakes parallel reconstructed pH declines.

Introduction

Surface-water organic acids (OA) have not received the attention they deserve in recent studies on lake acidification. This is because characterization of this complex of organic compounds is difficult and not standardized; the dynamic interactions between terrestrial and lake pools are poorly known; earlier studies on OA are generally not from 'acidification-sensitive' ecosystems; and long-term records of OA change are rare and anecdotal. Interest in 'natural acidity' has developed recently from various directions: soil scientists and limnologists; laboratory and field researchers; ecosystem manipulators and modellers; and believers and nonbelievers in the effects of SO_4^{2-} deposition on lake-water chemistry.

It is essential to study the limnological gradient of organic matter (OM) from a palaeolimnological perspective, particularly because of the recent debate about the role of 'natural' versus 'anthropogenic' acidification (see, for example, Gorham *et al.* (1986); Kerekes *et al.* (1986); Krug & Frink (1983); Brakke *et al.* (1987)). In water, OM exists as a chemically and physically diverse assemblage, and it may be represented as dissolved organic carbon concentration (DOC), total organic carbon concentration (TOC), 'true colour', 'apparent colour', and noncarbonate alkalinity (Cook *et al.* 1987). Here we consider DOC as a surrogate for OA; OM can also be viewed as a combination of strong and weak acids (average pK values between 3.5 and 4.0 according to Kramer *et al.* (1989)). Between pH values of 4.5–7.0, high amounts of these organic acids (DOC = 750 μmol l^{-1}) can lower pH by up to 2 units, compared with lake-water buffered only by the bicarbonate system (Cook & Jager 1990). Many of the difficulties in understanding OM dynamics stem from the complex assemblage of chemicals being studied. The lack of a standard methodology makes various research approaches difficult to compare. There has been general concern that acidification models are too simple (Marmorek *et al.* 1988; Kramer *et al.* 1989), largely because they have not treated OA as temporally dynamic. Reconstruction of lake-water OA changes is therefore also important for validating acidification models.

The many uncertainties in knowledge of OA in surface waters have been an obvious part of the lake acidification debate. Rosenqvist (1978) proposed that OA from soils, not mineral acid deposition, are the major cause of lake-water acidity, but palaeolimnological studies have not supported this hypothesis (see, for example, Jones *et al.* 1986). Krug & Frink (1983) argued that strong-acid deposition decreased DOC with relatively little effect on lake-water pH. In another example of a debated mechanism, Rosenqvist (1978) and Kramer *et al.* (1989) suggested that surface waters might become acidified as a result of cation exchange during forest growth, but budgets of forest soil chemistry did not support major effects on surface-water acidity (Nilsson *et al.* 1982).

Reconstruction of lakewater OA (as various operational indicators) has been attempted previously by using multiple regression of diatom abundances in cluster analysis groups with respect to total organic carbon (Davis *et al.* 1985) and by using multiple regression of diatom and Cladocera abundances in colour categories versus colour measurements (Huttunen *et al.* 1988). There have been several suggestions in ecological data-sets that indicators of OA may have a major effect on diatom and chrysophyte abundances (Davis *et al.* 1985, Anderson *et al.* 1986, Walker & Paterson 1986, Scruton *et al.* 1987, Taylor *et al.* 1988, Kingston *et al.* 1990). By reconstructing several chemical parameters in PIRLA II, we can provide data for testing hypotheses about chemical interactions during acidification.

Data-sets

The research project 'Paleoecological Investigation of Recent Lake Acidification (PIRLA)' was a multi-university, multi-disciplinary investigation (Charles & Whitehead 1986*a*); all methods were coordinated among regions (Charles & Whitehead 1986*b*); quality assurance (QA) within and among study regions was maintained at a high standard, both for chemical and biological data (Kreis 1990). Diatom methods, including sampling, slide preparation, taxonomy, and QA procedures (Charles & Whitehead 1986*b*, Camburn *et al.* 1984–1986), were coordinated so that the four regions could be directly compared, and that reconstructions could potentially be based on combined data from several regions. Chemical parameters are arithmetic means of several discrete (1 m depth), ice-free water samples. The pH parameter in this paper is measured in samples equilibrated to atmospheric CO_2 (pH_{aer}). It is important to note that PIRLA was designed to study primarily pH and total alkalinity (TAlk), and to avoid high DOC levels that might confound interpretations of lake acidity.

The initial PIRLA study is now designated as 'PIRLA I', whereas the current research (PIRLA II) concentrates on the Adirondack region of New York (Charles & Smol 1990). There are four PIRLA I study regions: Adirondack Park (ADIR), northern New England (NENG), northern Great Lakes states (NGLS), and northern Florida (NFLA). PIRLA II includes a subproject on reconstruction of parameters besides pH, especially DOC.

Regional and three-regions-combined DOC and pH data are summarized in table 1. The northern Florida lakes had very different environmental characteristics and diatom floras, whereas the other three regions were quite similar in terms of environmental gradients and

TABLE 1. SUMMARY OF DOC AND pH DATA FOR THE INDIVIDUAL PIRLA REGIONS AND FOR THE COMBINED NORTHERN DATA SET. DOC IS A COMBINATION OF MEASURED AND CALCULATED VALUES IN ADIR AND NENG. THE pH MEASURE USED HERE IS THE ARITHMETIC MEAN OF SAMPLES EQUILIBRATED WITH ATMOSPHERIC CO_2

(See text for details and abbreviations; med., median; s.d., standard deviation; min., minimum; max., maximum.)

			DOC						pH_{aer}					
region	no. of lakes	no. of taxa	no. of lakes	mean	med.	s.d.	min.	max.	no. of lakes	mean	med.	s.d.	min.	max.
ADIR	47	151	47	315.2	276.0	148.2	197.0	1039.0	47	6.18	6.54	1.09	4.34	7.77
NENG	63	203	63	283.2	271.0	168.6	21.0	833.0	60	6.11	6.46	0.96	4.48	8.14
NGLS	36	134	36	304.6	229.0	173.7	62.0	899.0	36	6.21	6.56	0.83	4.41	7.32
NFLA	32	125	32	956.4	687.0	810.5	125.0	3497.0	32	5.37	5.01	0.94	4.24	7.79
3REG	146	117	146	298.8	269.0	164.3	21.0	1039.0	143	6.16	6.26	0.98	4.34	8.14

diatom floras. Therefore, we compare the DOC predictive powers of the individual PIRLA I regions and use the combined data from the three northern regions (ADIR+NENG+NGLS = 3REG; 146 of 178 lakes) to investigate whether a larger data set is superior for DOC reconstruction.

In 37 out of 47 PIRLA I ADIR lakes, true colour was measured and DOC was not. This was also the case for three NENG lakes. To use DOC as a surrogate for OA, and because it is significantly more interesting to chemists than colour, we calculated 'DOCNEW' values for the lakes that did not have measured values. This was done by using linear models of colour and DOC for Eastern Lake Survey lakes from the same regions (D. J. Blick, U.S.E.P.A. Corvallis, personal communication).

For 3REG reconstructions, we selected all taxa that occurred at 1% or more in three lakes, and that were also present in at least 13 of the surface sediment samples; this gave us 117 taxa. In each regional reconstruction, we used all taxa that occurred at 1% or more in one lake.

The two lakes used for example reconstructions are known to have recently acidified. Big Moose Lake (ADIR; 43° 49′ 02″ N, 74° 51′ 23″W) is a drainage lake with reconstructed declines in pH and TAlk and modelled increases in aluminium (Charles 1984; Charles *et al.* 1988) that correspond well with known fisheries decline. Brown Lake (NGLS; 45° 46′ 50″ N, 89° 29′ 30″ W) is a seepage lake that has reconstructed pH declines similar to historical water chemistry records (Kingston *et al.* 1990; Eilers *et al.* 1989).

NUMERICAL METHODS AND RESULTS

Weighted-averaging regression (ter Braak & Looman 1987) was used to estimate DOC weighted averages (abundance weighted means) and weighted standard deviations ('tolerances') for the diatom taxa in each individual region data-set and for the combined 3REG data-set (table 2, on microfiche in pocket). Optima and tolerances for all taxa in the 3REG data were estimated by fitting a Gaussian logit model (GLM) by using logit regression, as implemented by GLIM (Baker & Nelder 1978). A Gaussian logit model is a special case of the generalized linear model with logit link function and binormal error distribution and is a quasi-likelihood model when used with proportional data (ter Braak & van Dam 1989). For each taxon the GLM was tested at $\alpha = 0.05$ by using deviance and one-sided t-tests against the simpler linear logit model (LLM) to ascertain if the optimum or the GLM, or both, were significant. If they were not significant, the LLM was tested against the null model of the taxon having no relationship with DOC ($\alpha = 0.05$). The simplest significant model was evaluated for each taxon (ter Braak & van Dam 1989).

Several taxa have no significant unimodal (GLM) or sigmoidal (LLM) relationship with DOC (table 3); others have fitted curves with a minimum rather than a maximum, and some have poorly defined optima with estimates beyond the sampled range of DOC (21–1039 μmol l^{-1}). The latter problem arises inevitably in any modern data set because some taxa occur at or near the edge of their ecological ranges (ter Braak & Prentice 1988). In these cases, taxa that have a significant fit to an LLM and have a decreasing linear logit curve are assumed to have an optimum of < 21 μmol l^{-1}, whereas those with increasing linear logit curves are assigned an optimum of > 1039 μmol l^{-1}. In these cases the tolerances are undefined. Tables 2 and 3 show that 54 taxa have no significant modelled relationship with DOC, and only 35 show a significant Gaussian unimodal relationship.

TABLE 3. RESULTS OF FITTING GAUSSIAN LOGIT, LINEAR LOGIT AND NULL MODELS TO THE THREE-REGION DATA IN RELATION TO DOC

characteristic shown by taxon	number of taxa
Gaussian unimodal curves with maxima	67
unimodal curves with minima	14
a significant fit to Gaussian logit model	35
a significant fit to a decreasing linear logit model	26
a significant fit to an increasing linear logit model	2
no significant fit to a Gaussian or linear logit model	54
total number of taxa	117

Weighted-averaging calibration (ter Braak 1987) with (WA(tol)) and without (WA) weighting taxa inversely by their squared tolerance, was used to infer DOC both for the modern data and for the fossil samples in the individual regions and for the 3REG data. A simple inverse linear rescaling was used to de-shrink the initial weighted-average estimates (ter Braak & van Dam 1989). Maximum-likelihood (ML) calibration using the GLM parameters was also used for the 3REG data (ter Braak & van Dam 1989). The standard error (SE) of (observed DOC-inferred DOC) for the modern training sets was used as a mean squared error (MSE) to compare the predictive performance of the different methods (table 4).

TABLE 4. STANDARD ERROR (OBSERVED DOC–INFERRED DOC) FOR RECONSTRUCTION METHODS WITH AN INVERSE REGRESSION DE-SHRINKING

data-set	number of lakes	number of taxa	WA	WA (tol)	ML
ADIR	47	151	98.4	88.2	—
NENG	63	203	123.3	123.6	—
NGLS	36	134	80.1	92.9	—
NFLA	32	125	448.8	360.9	—
3REG	146	117	146.1	146.3	157.9
3REG	146	63[a]	145.3	145.7	145.3

[a] All taxa with a significant fit to a Gaussian or linear logit model (see tables 2 and 3).

Although WA(tol) produces slightly lower MSE than WA (table 4), it produces consistently larger MSE when bootstrapping or cross-validation are used to derive more reliable and more robust SE (Birks *et al.*, this symposium; H. J. B. Birks unpublished results). Maximum-likelihood calibration and logit regression are both extremely demanding computationally, and yet produce results (table 4) slightly inferior to WA; this is so for pH in SWAP (Birks *et al.*, this symposium). Moreover, problems arise in ML calibration because the numerical optimization procedure that was used fails to converge for 33 (22%) modern samples containing 117 taxa and for 42 (29%) modern samples containing 63 taxa. Of the 545 fossil samples, 132 (24%) similarly fail to converge, probably because their diatom assemblages contain taxa of markedly contrasting DOC optima.

ter Braak & van Dam (1989) and Birks *et al.* (this symposium) have shown that, for pH inference, simple WA regression and calibration not only provide a good approximation to ML, but also are often superior to ML; WA is a reliable, robust, and rapid pH-inference procedure. For DOC inference, WA appears to have similar advantages over ML. We only present DOC inferences derived by WA regression and calibration.

Regression and calibration by WA, but with classical linear regression for de-shrinking the initial estimates, were used with the same data-sets to infer pH. This methodology follows exactly Birks *et al.* (this symposium).

All computations (except logit regression) were implemented by the FORTRAN 77 program WACALIB 2.1 (Birks *et al.*, this symposium).

Discussion of DOC optima

Regional optima for the same common taxon (table 2) can be broadly similar (e.g. *Cymbella perpusilla* + sp. 1 + sp. 2, *Navicula tenuicephala*) or quite different (e.g. *Asterionella ralfsii* var. *americana* < 45 μm). All taxonomic authorities are given in table 2. Constrained canonical correspondence analysis (CCA) ordinations were used to evaluate 'indicator organisms'. By using diagnostics within CANOCO version 3 (C. J. F. ter Braak, unpublished results), the cumulative fit per taxon as a fraction of the taxon's total variance reveals a few organisms that are very consistent in terms of their explanation of the DOC gradient from region to region. The ten taxa with the strongest DOC response in the 3REG data set are: *Melosira distans* var. *tenella*, *Fragilaria construens* var. *binodis*, *Navicula mediocris*, *Frustulia* cf. *magaliesmontana*, *Pinnularia biceps* var. 1, *Navicula subatomoides*, *Neidium bisulcatum*, *Neidium affine*, *Cymbella perpusilla* + sp. 1 + sp. 2, and *Achnanthes linearis*. Examination of the size of the first axis contrained to DOC and the first unconstrained axis shows that DOC explains a small but significant amount of taxon variance in NGLS, ADIR, and NFLA, but the signal is much weaker in the NENG and 3REG data; CCA of the NENG data reveals that DOCNEW contributes very little to the first two axes.

Several taxa have been proposed as 'indicators' for various humic acid surrogates in studies from Norway and Canada, including *Frustulia rhomboides* var. *saxonica*, *Anomoeneis serians* var. *brachysira*, *Navicula subtilissima*, *Navicula heimansii*, *Frustulia rhomboides*, *Achnanthes marginulata*, *Achnanthes austriaca* var. *helvetica*. *Navicula krasskei*, *Achnanthes levanderi*, *Melosira ambigua*, *Tabellaria flocculosa* strain 3p, *Asterionella ralfsii* var. *americana*, *Cyclotella stelligera*, and *Cyclotella kuetzingiana* (Davis *et al.* 1985, Anderson *et al.* 1986; Taylor *et al.* 1988). The PIRLA data do not consistently support these findings, and we caution that indicators from one region may show different and conflicting relationships elsewhere. For example, *A. serians* var. *brachysira* and

F. rhomboides var. *saxonica* have optima near the measured DOC means for the PIRLA data, but more importantly, they do not have high fits to DOC in terms of taxon variance explained.

Furthermore, good 'indicators' of DOC are not consistent from region to region within PIRLA. Therefore, individual regional DOC weighted-average means and reconstructions are probably the most reliable for the PIRLA data, subject to further research on error estimation.

Reconstructions

Example reconstructions of DOC are presented in figure 1, along with reconstructions of pH, TAlk, and total Al (J. C. Kingston & H. J. B. Birks, unpublished data). The magnitude of DOC change is small relative to the MSE of the relation in each region (table 4), but in each case DOC declines coincidentally with lakewater pH. In Big Moose Lake, total Al increases dramatically as pH, TAlk, and DOC decline from the 1940s. In Brown Lake, total Al has an opposite trend to DOC until the topmost sediment interval, where they increase together.

In the ADIR PIRLA I cores, two lakes have DOC increases greater than the MSE for the relation, five lakes have decreases less than the MSE, and five lakes show no change. In the

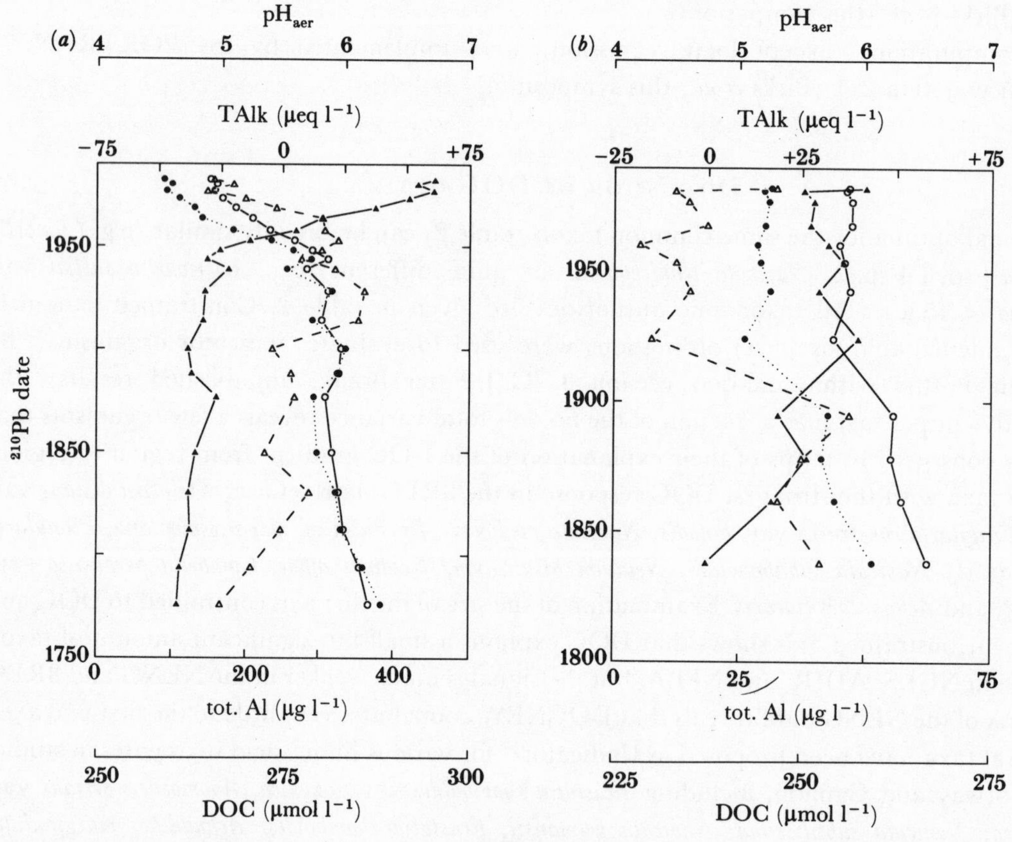

FIGURE 1. Example weighted-averaging (WA) reconstructions of four parameters in two PIRLA I sediment cores, based on data from individual regions. DOC methods are explained in the text, whereas reconstructions of pH_{aer}, total alkalinity, and total aluminium are included to provide a more complete picture of limnological changes during lake acidification (J. C. Kingston & H. J. B. Birks, unpublished data). Mean standard errors of the DOC relationships are given in table 4; (*a*) Big Moose Lake, New York, core 2 (ADIR); (*b*) Brown Lake, Wisconsin, core 2*a* (NGLS); (○——○), pH_{aer}; (●······●), TAlk; (▲——▲), total aluminium; (△——△), DOC.

NGLS PIRLA I cores, one lake has an increase greater than the MSE of the relation, one lake has an increase less than the MSE, one lake has a decrease greater than the MSE, two lakes have decreases less than the MSE, three lakes show essentially no change, and one lake has large fluctuations.

Discussion of reconstructions

Our reconstructions of pH and TAlk for Big Moose Lake match those previously published (Charles 1984; Charles *et al.* 1988; Charles & Smol 1988) and correspond well with measured water chemistry. The DOC reconstruction indicates a lower magnitude of decline than might be expected from hypotheses on the effects of mineral acid deposition (T. J. Sullivan, personal communication) but the direction of the trend meets expectations of recent loss of DOC. The reconstructed total Al increase is similar to previous modelling efforts (Charles 1984), but the reconstructed concentration overestimates the measured concentration and the modelled 1982 concentration by a factor of two. This is caused by a 'no analogue' situation at the top of the core, with high abundances of species such as *Fragilaria acidobiontica* and *Navicula tenuicephala*.

Brown Lake is part of the 50-year water-chemistry comparison between the Birge and Juday surveys of the late 1920s and EPA surveys of the late 1970s and early 1980s (Eilers *et al.* 1989; detailed data in the Depository of Unpublished Data, CISTI, National Research Council of Canada, Ottawa K1A 0S2). The historical and recent values of pH (6.47, 5.94), alkalinity (56.5, 10.7 μeq l^{-1}) and apparent colour (25, 12) each match our reconstructions very well.

The three PIRLA I lakes with large reconstructed increases in DOC are each naturally acidic; Barnes Lake and Little Echo Pond (ADIR) have also acidified recently (Charles *et al.* 1990; D. F. Charles, personal communication), whereas Otto Mielke Lake (NGLS) has become slightly less acidic (Kingston *et al.* 1990). Processes leading to these DOC increases are unknown, but may relate to land clearance, forest regrowth, or wetland expansion.

Conclusions

Diatom response to environmental gradients in the PIRLA regional calibrations shows that pH consistently explains more of the species variance than DOC, that pH and DOC are generally unrelated to each other, and that DOC can usually be reconstructed to show the timing, magnitude and direction of trends. We suspect that improved DOC reconstructions could result from a more even sampling of the natural DOC gradient in lakes, which, as we mentioned earlier, was not a priority in PIRLA I. Some PIRLA reconstructions support hypotheses that surface-water DOC declines are caused by deposition of mineral acids (figure 1). In general, DOC declines coincidentally with lakewater pH in recently-acidified PIRLA study lakes. Although the magnitude of these DOC declines seems small, the acid–base character of the DOC (charge density and dissociation constants) might also be changing.

This paper is contribution 4-II of the Paleoecological Investigation of Recent Lake Acidification (PIRLA) II project; PIRLA I was funded primarily by the Electric Power Research Institute (RP-2174-10) and PIRLA II was funded by the U.S. Environment Protection Agency (Co-operative Agreement CR-815360 with Queen's University). The research described herein has not been subjected to U.S. Environmental Protection Agency review and therefore does not necessarily reflect the views of the Agency, and no official endorsement should be inferred.

Thanks to A. J. Uutala and P. R. Sweets for database retrievals; to C. J. F. ter Braak for providing CANOCO version 3.0; and to J. M. Line for WACALIB programming. Thanks to all PIRLA investigators, especially R. B. Cook, D. F. Charles, P. R. Sweets, J. P. Smol, S. S. Dixit, B. F. Cumming, R. B. Davis and D. S. Anderson for data sharing and discussions; to T. J. Sullivan for helpful comments; and to K. E. Duff for formatting and computing.

References

Anderson, D. S., Davis, R. B. & Berge, F. 1986 Relationships between diatom assemblages in lake surface sediments and limnological characteristics in southern Norway. In *Diatoms and lake acidity* (ed. J. P. Smol, R. W. Battarbee, R. B. Davis, & J. Meriläinen), p. 97. Dordrecht: Dr W. Junk.

Baker, R. J. & Nelder, J. A. 1978 *The GLIM system, release* 3. Numerical Algorithms Group, University of Oxford.

Baker, L. A., Eilers, J. M., Cook, R. B., Kaufmann, P. R., & Herlihy, A. T. 1990 Current water chemistry and biological processes in case study regions: intercomparison and synthesis in Regional Case Studies. In *Acid deposition and aquatic ecosystems: regional case studies* (ed. D. F. Charles). New York: Springer-Verlag.

Brakke, D. F., Henriksen, A. & Norton, S. A. 1987 The relative importance of acidity sources of humic lakes in Norway. *Nature, Lond.* **329**, 432–434.

Camburn, K. E., Kingston, J. C. & Charles, D. F. 1984–86 *PIRLA diatom iconograph*, report number 3, PIRLA Unpublished Report Series. Bloomington: Indiana University.

Charles, D. F. 1984 Recent pH history of Big Moose Lake (Adirondack Mountains, New York, U.S.A.) inferred from sediment diatom assemblages. *Verh. internat. Verein. Limnol.* **22**, 559–566.

Charles, D. F. & Smol, J. P. 1988 New methods for using diatoms and chrysophytes to infer past pH of low-alkalinity lakes. *Limnol. Oceanogr.* **33**, 1451–1462.

Charles, D. F. & Smol, J. P. 1990 The PIRLA II project: regional assessment of lake acidification trends. *Verh. internat. Verein. Limnol.* (In the press.)

Charles, D. F. & Whitehead, D. R. 1986*a* The PIRLA project: paleoecological investigations of recent lake acidification. *Hydrobiologia* **143**, 13–20.

Charles, D. F. & Whitehead, D. R. 1986*b* *Methods and project description.* Palo Alto, California: Electric Power Research Institute.

Charles, D. F., Whitehead, D. R., Engstrom, D. R., Fry, B. D., Hites, R. A., Norton, S. A., Owen, J. S., Roll, L. A., Schindler, S. C., Smol, J. P., Uutala, A. J., White, J. R. & Wise, R. J. 1987 Paleolimnological evidence for recent acidification of Big Moose Lake, Adirondack Mountains, N.Y. (USA). *Biogeochemistry* **3**, 267–296.

Charles, D. F., Binford, M. W., Furlong, E. T., Hites, R. A., Mitchell, M. J., Norton, S. A., Oldfield, F., Paterson, M. J., Smol, J. P., Uutala, A. J., White, J. R., Whitehead, D. R. & Wise, R. J. 1990 Paleoecological investigation of recent lake acidification in the Adirondack Mountains, N.Y. *J. Palaeolimnol.* (In the press.)

Cook, R. B., Kelley, C. A., Kingston, J. C. & Kreis, R. G., Jr. 1987 Chemical limnology of soft water lakes in the Upper Midwest. *Biogeochemistry* **4**, 97–117.

Cook, R. B. & Jager, H. I. 1990 Upper Midwest: the effects of hydrologic lake type and acidic deposition on lakewater chemistry. In *Acid deposition and aquatic ecosystems: regional case studies* (ed. D. F. Charles). New York: Springer-Verlag. (In the press.)

Davis, R. B., Anderson, D. S. & Berge, F. 1985 Palaeolimnological evidence that lake acidification is accompanied by loss of organic matter. *Nature, Lond.* **316**, 436–438.

Driscoll, C. T., Yatsko, C. P. & Unangst, F. J. 1987 Longitudinal and temporal trends in the water chemistry of the North Branch of the Moose River. *Biogeochemistry* **3**, 37–62.

Eilers, J. M., Glass, G. E., Pollack, A. K. & Sorensen, J. A. 1989 Changes in conductivity, alkalinity, calcium, and pH during a 50-year period in selected northern Wisconsin lakes. *Can. J. Fish. Aquat. Sci.* **46**, 1929–1944.

Gorham, E., Underwood, J. K., Martin, F. B. & Ogden, J. G., III 1986 Natural and anthropogenic causes of lake acidification in Nova Scotia. *Nature, Lond.* **324**, 451–453.

Huttunen, P., Meriläinen, J., Cotten, C., & Rönkkö, J. 1988 Attempts to reconstruct lake water pH and colour from sedimentary diatoms and Cladocera. *Verh. internat. Verein. Limnol.* **23**, 870–873.

Jones, V. J., Stevenson, A. C. & Battarbee, R. W. 1986 Lake acidification the land-use hypothesis: a mid-post-glacial analogue. *Nature, Lond.* **322**, 157–158.

Kerekes, J., Beauchamp, S., Tordon, R., Tremblay, C. & Pollock, T. 1986 Organic versus anthropogenic acidity in tributaries of the Kejimkujik watersheds in Western Nova Scotia. *Wat. Air Soil Pollut.* **31**, 165–173.

Kingston, J. C., Cook, R. B., Kreis, R. G., Jr, Camburn, K. E., Norton, S. A., Sweets, P. R., Binford, M. W., Mitchell, M. J., Schindler, S. C., Shane, L. & King, G. 1990 Paleoecological investigation of recent lake acidification in the Northern Great Lakes States. *J. Palaeolimnol.* (In the press.)

Kramer, J. R., Cronan, C. S., DePinto, J. V., Hemond, H. F., Perdue, E. M. & Visser, S. 1989 *Organic acids and acidification of surface waters.* Washington, D.C.: Utility Air Regulatory Group.

Kreis, R. G., Jr. 1989 Variability study – interim results. In *Palaeoecological investigation of recent late acidification* (PIRLA): 1983–1985, (ed. D. F. Charles & D. R. Whitehead), pp. (4-1)–(4-48). Palo Alto, California: Electric Power Research Institute.

Krug, E. C. & Frink, C. R. 1983 Acid rain on acid soil: a new perspective. *Science, Wash.* **221**, 520–525.

Lawrence, G. B., Fuller, R. D. & Driscoll, C. T. 1986 Spatial relationships of aluminium chemistry in the streams of the Hubbard Brook Experimental Forest, New Hampshire. *Biogeochemistry* **2**, 115–135.

Marmorek, D. R., Bernard, D. R., Jones, M. L., Rattie, L. R. & Sullivan, T. J. 1988 *The effects of mineral acid deposition on concentrations of dissolved organic acids in surface waters.* Vancouver, British Columbia: Environmental and Social Systems Analysts, Ltd.

McDowell, W. H. & Likens, G. E. 1988 Origin, composition, and flux of dissolved organic carbon in the Hubbard Brook Valley. *Ecol. Monogr.* **58**, 177–195.

Nilsson, S. I., Miller, H. G. & Miller, J. D. 1982 Forest growth as a possible cause of soil and water acidification: an examination of the concepts. *Oikos* **39**, 40–49.

Rosenqvist, I. T. 1978 Alternative sources for acidification of river water in Norway. *Sci. total Envir.* **10**, 39–49.

Scruton, D. A., Elner, J. K. & Rybak, M. 1987 Regional calibration of fossil diatom – contemporary pH relationships for insular Newfoundland, Canada, including historical pH reconstruction for five lakes and assessment of paleo-inferred productivity changes in one lake. In *Acid rain: scientific and technical advances* (ed. R. Perry, R. M. Harrison, J. B. N. Bell & J. N. Lester), p. 457. London: Selper Ltd.

Taylor, M. C., Duthie, H. C. & Smith, S. M. 1988 Errors associated with diatom-inferred indices for predicting pH in Canadian Shield lakes. In *Proceedings of the 9th international diatom symposium* (ed. F. E. Round), p. 273. Koenigstein: Otto Koeltz.

ter Braak, C. J. F. 1987 *Calibration.* In *Data analysis in community and landscape ecology* (ed. R. H. G. Jongman, C. J. F. ter Braak & O. F. R. van Tongeren), pp. 78–90. Wageningen: Pudoc.

ter Braak, C. J. F. & Looman, C. W. N. 1987 *Regression.* In *Data analysis in community and landscape ecology* (ed. R. H. G. Jongman, C. J. F. ter Braak & O. F. R. van Tongeren), pp. 29–77. Wageningen: Pudoc.

ter Braak, C. J. F. & Prentice, I. C. 1988 A theory of gradient analysis. *Adv. ecol. Res.* **18**, 271–317.

ter Braak, C. J. F. & van Dam, H. 1989 Inferring pH from diatoms: a comparison of old and new calibration methods. *Hydrobiologia* **178**, 209–223.

Walker, I. R. & Paterson, C. G. 1986 Associations of diatoms in the surficial sediments of lakes and peat pools in Atlantic Canada. *Hydrobiologia* **134**, 265–272.

Discussion

R. A. SKEFFINGTON (*National Power Technology and Environmental Centre, Leatherhead, Surrey, KT22 7SE, U.K.*) Is there any evidence from controlled experimental studies that diatoms respond to DOC, alkalinity or Al *per se*? In particular a response to alkalinity seems unlikely as it is a measurement that essentially records the results of a titration, and humans are the only organisms that perform titrations. Diatoms must be responding to something that correlates with alkalinity, such as pH. How confident can Dr Kingston be that the apparent statistical relation between diatom abundance and DOC, alkalinity and Al are not simply reflections of the correlation of these variables with pH?

J. C. KINGSTON. There is an algal physiology literature of potential mechanisms of carbon species influence over phytoplankton, with implications for acidification effects (see, for example, Williams & Turpin (1987)). There is a larger literature on toxic metal effects on phytoplankton, mainly from point-source effects of factories or mine drainage. Some detailed physiological research (A. Smith, personal communication), as well as controlled enclosure experiments (Pillsbury & Kingston 1990) does show toxic effects of Al on the very phytoplankton species that are known to decline in recently acidified lakes.

The program CANOCO provides excellent diagnostic tools for determining colinearity of measured environmental parameters, and we avoid reconstructions by WACALIB of highly colinear variables. Each data set must be critically examined, but we are usually able to reconstruct the four parameters. Each of these parameters can be shown to explain new, significant amounts of variance in the total species data.

To say that only humans can perform titration misses the point. Although we do not know the exact physiological mechanisms of action in most cases, we can evaluate with great confidence whether measured environmental variables do explain variance in the species data, and we can prevent misleading interpretation of colinear variables.

R. B. Davis (*Department of Botany and Plant Pathology, University of Maine, U.S.A.*). Could some of the regional differences in diatom response to DOC be the result of different sources of the DOC?

J. C. KINGSTON. Yes, it is suspected, but not investigated very thoroughly at present, that the acid-base characteristics of DOC from different sources can be very different. Therefore, a certain concentration of DOC from upland soils may be quite different from the same concentration of DOC from a sedge fen, or from a *Sphagnum* bog. Regional differences in vegetation and soils exist across eastern North America, and an operational environmental parameter such as DOC does not account for this. We are most interested in acid–base characteristics, which are rarely measured (Wright *et al.* 1988).

References

Pillsbury, R. W. & Kingston, J. C. 1990 The pH-independent effect of aluminum on cultures of phytoplankton from an acidic Wisconsin lake. *Hydrobiologia* (In the press.)

Williams, T. G. & Turpin, D. H. 1987 Photosynthetic kinetics determine the outcome of competition for dissolved inorganic carbon by freshwater microalgae: implications for acidified lakes. *Oecologia (Berlin)* **73**, 307–311.

Wright, R. F., Lotse, E. & Semb, A. 1988 Reversibility of acidification shown by whole-catchment experiments. *Nature, Lond.* **334**, 670–675.

Phil. Trans. R. Soc. Lond. B **327**, 289–293 (1990)
Printed in Great Britain

Recent acidification and changes in the subfossil chrysophyte flora of lakes in Sweden, Norway and Scotland

By G. Cronberg

Institute of Ecology/Limnology, University of Lund, P.O. Box 65, S-221 00 Lund, Sweden

The subfossil chrysophyte flora was investigated in sediment cores from eight lakes in Scotland and Scandinavia. In the Scottish lakes, scales were rare or absent. However, Scandinavian lakes contained numerous different chrysophyte scales. In Lilla Öresjön (Sweden) and Verevatn (Norway) the changes in the subfossil chrysophyte community reflect the recent acidification of these lakes.

Introduction

During the last decade, chrysophyte remains in sediments have been used for the interpretation of lake history (Battarbee *et al.* 1980; Munch 1980) and more recently the study of subfossil chrysophyte scales has been shown to be a useful tool in demonstrating lake acidification (Smol *et al.* 1984). As most chrysophytes have a planktonic life form, they are dependent on water quality and nutrient concentration for their survival. The various species have well-defined habitats and nutrient demands and have their optimum growth in different types of water. Therefore they can be used as good indicators of lake-water pH.

The scaled chrysophytes studied belong mainly to the genera *Mallomonas* and *Synura*. These organisms are free-swimming, unicellular or colonial, golden-brown flagellates with the cell surface covered by silica scales and bristles. Most chrysophytes also produce silicified resting stages called stomatocysts (previously called cysts or statospores) endogenously in the cell. When the organisms die, the silica scales and stomatocysts are deposited in the lake sediment and are often preserved. The morphology of scales and stomatocysts is taxon-specific. However, to make a correct identification of these organisms, their ultrastructure has to be studied by using electron microscopy.

Study sites and methods

The lakes studied in this investigation were Lochan Uaine, Lochan Dubh, Loch Doilet, Loch Tinker and Loch Chon in Scotland, Röyrtjörna and Verevatn in Norway and Lilla Öresjön in Sweden. For more information see Battarbee & Renberg (this symposium).

The Scottish sediment cores were taken with a Mackereth mini-corer and the Scandinavian ones with a freeze corer. The sediment cores were sectioned into 0.5 cm or 1 cm slices. For chrysophyte analyses, weighed subsamples were digested in 30% H_2O_2 at room temperature for one to two weeks. The samples were then carefully rinsed with distilled water and diluted to a known volume. For the investigation of chrysophyte scales a defined volume of the sample was dropped onto a cover glass, air dried and mounted with naphrax. The scales were identified and counted with a Zeiss standard phase-contrast microscope at magnification 1250 times. Normally 200 scales were counted per subsample, or at least 100 when scales were very scarce.

The scaled chrysophytes were divided into pH categories according to Siver & Hamer (1989). These pH categories are constructed in the same manner as those of the system devised by Hustedt (1939) for diatoms: ACB, acidobiontic; ACF, acidophilous; IND, indifferent (= circumneutral); ALKF, alkaliphilous; ALKB, alkalibiontic (table 1).

Results and discussion

The Scottish sediments contained no, or very few, chrysophyte scales. However, the Scandinavian sediments, especially Lilla Öresjön and Verevatn, contained many different scales (table 1). The investigation of the subfossil scales shows an obvious change in the chrysophyte flora during recent years in these two sites.

Table 1. Weighted mean pH, pH categories and abundance of chrysophyte scales in sediments from Röyrtjörna, Verevatn and Lilla Öresjön

(*Mallomonas*, *M*; *Synura*, *S*; numerous scales, +++; several scales, ++; single scales, +; no scales found, –; see text for details of pH categories; weighted mean pH values from Siver & Hamer (1989).

Taxon	weighted mean pH	pH categories	Röyrtjörna	Verevatn	Öresjön
M. canina	4.9	ACB	+	+++	+++
S. sphagnicola	5.3	ACB	+	+++	+++
M. allorgei	5.8[a]	ACB	–	+	+++
M. lychenensis	5.9[a]	ACB	–	+++	+
S. echinulata	5.9	ACB–ACF	–	+++	+++
M. punctifera	5.9	ACF	+	+++	+++
M. hamata	6.0	ACB–ACF	+	+++	+++
S. spinosa	6.1	ACF	–	+++	+
M. caudata	6.7	IND	++	+++	+++
M. crassisquama	6.9	IND	++	+++	+++
M. teilingii	7.2[a]	ALKF	+	–	–
M. tonsurata	7.6	ALKF–ALKB	–	–	+++
M. acaroides	8.1	ALKB	+	–	–

[a] Mean pH values from Swedish localities.

Sediments from all the lakes investigated here also contained many chrysophyte stomatocysts of various sizes and appearances. A study of these will be presented in future papers.

Röyrtjörna

In this lake few subfossil scales of chrysophytes were found (table 1). The most common species recorded were *Mallomonas crassisquama*, *M. caudata*, and *M. acaroides*. The relative abundance of these species changed little throughout the core with mean values of about 55%, 30% and 15%, respectively, indicating relatively high pH conditions and no evidence for recent acidification.

Lilla Öresjön

See figure 1. In the 25 cm long sediment core, the chrysophyte community changed considerably. Scales of 7 *Mallomonas* and 2 *Synura* species (table 1) were found in large quantities. Below a depth of 7.5 cm–10 cm, stable conditions prevailed and *Mallomonas crassisquama*, *M. caudata* and *M. tonsurata* were most abundant. Between 2.5 cm and 7.5 cm, there was a transitional zone in which *M. caudata* reached a maximum, *M. crassisquama* decreased and acidophilous–acidobiontic species including *M. canina*, and *M. allorgei*,

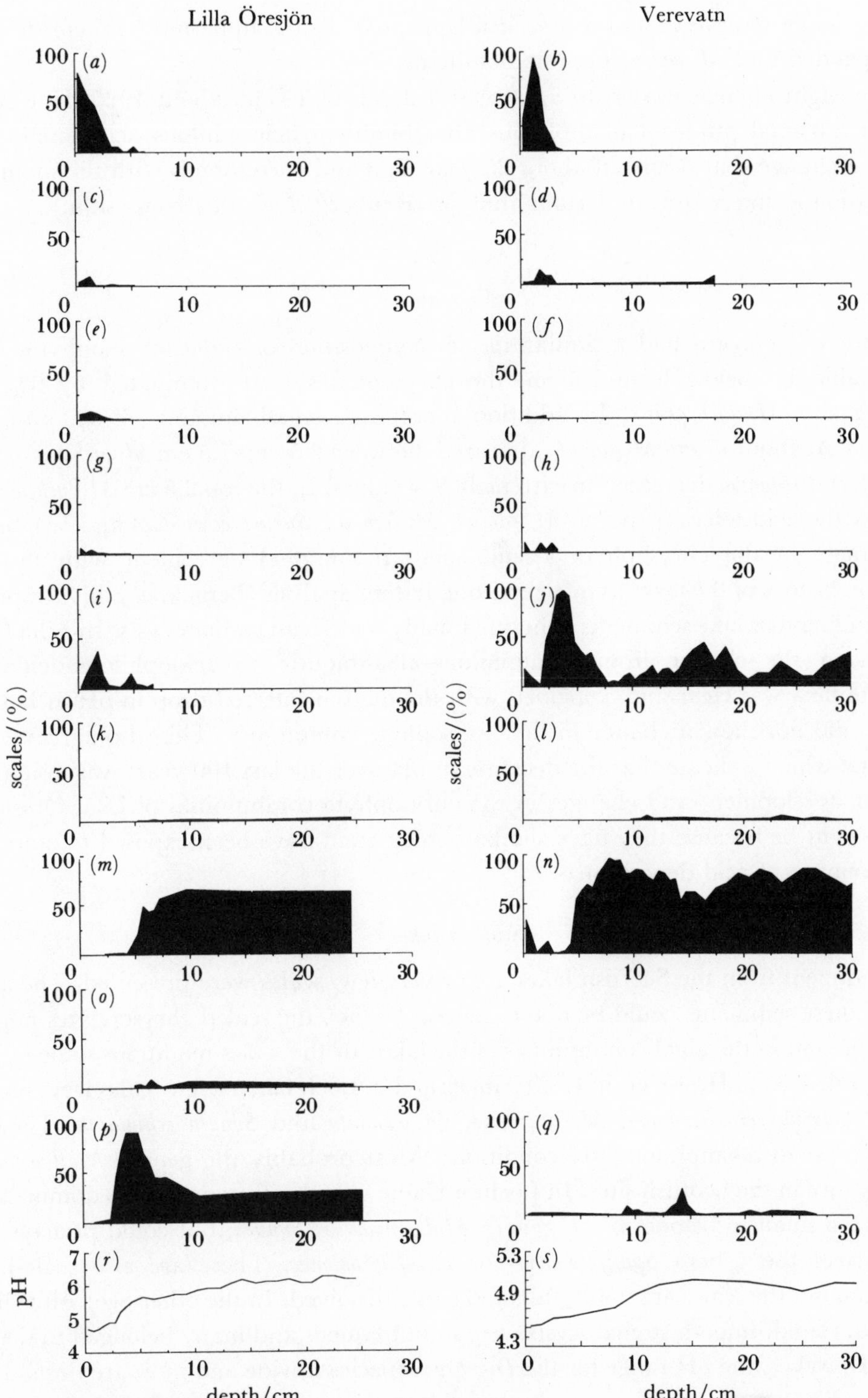

FIGURE 1. The distribution of *Mallomonas* and *Synura* scales, and the variation in diatom-inferred pH in sediment cores from Lilla Öresjön, Sweden and Verevatn, Norway (Berge *et al.* and Renberg *et al.*, this symposium). (Levels analysed for scales: Öresjön, 0 cm–5 cm every 0.5 cm, 5 cm–10 cm every 1.0 cm and 10 cm–25 cm every 5.0 cm; Verevatn, 0 cm–15 cm every 0.5 cm and 15 cm–30 cm every 1.0 cm.) (*a*, *b*) *M. canina* (ACB), (*c*, *d*) *M. hamata* (ACB/ACF), (*e*, *f*) *S. sphagnicola* (ACB), (*g*, *h*) *S. echinulata* (ACB/ACF), (*i*) *M. allorgei* (ACB), (*j*) *M. lychenensis* (ACB), (*k*, *l*) *M. punctifera* (ACF), (*m*, *n*) *M. crassiquama* (IND), (*o*) *M. tonsurata* (ALKF/ALKB), (*p*, *q*) *M. caudata* (IND), (*r*, *s*) pH (diatoms).

M. hamata, *Synura sphagnicola* and *S. echinulata* appeared. In the uppermost 2.5 cm these latter species expanded and *M. canina* became dominant.

The first slight change started to appear at a depth of 10 cm, about 1925. However, the major shift at 5 cm depth from alkaliphilous–alkalibiontic to acidophilous–acidobiontic species represents a change that occurred about 25 years ago and corresponds with the main period of acidification as inferred from diatom analysis (Renberg *et al.*, this symposium).

Verevatn

See figure 1. Verevatn had a similar species composition of scaled chrysophytes to Lilla Öresjön (table 1). Below 5 cm–7.5 cm, the chrysophytes were dominated by *Mallomonas crassisquama* and *M. lychenensis*. In addition there were small amounts of *M. caudata* and *M. punctifera*. At about 17 cm *M. hamata* appeared. Between 2.5 cm–7.5 cm *M. lychenensis* peaked whereas *M. crassisquama* decreased to extremely low values. In the top 2.5 cm *M. lychenensis* was replaced by the acid tolerant species *M. canina*, *M. hamata*, *Synura echinulata* and *S. sphagnicola*. These changes in the chrysophyte assemblages are in good agreement with the recent acidification history of the lakes as inferred from diatom analysis (Berge *et al.*, this symposium).

The Scandinavian lake sediments contained many scales and stomatocysts. In Lilla Öresjön and Verevatn the change from alkaliphilous–alkalibiontic to acidophilous–acidobiontic chrysophyte taxa was clear and coincided with the diatom-inferred drop in pH at both sites. Röyrtjörna did not show a change in the chrysophyte community. This also agrees with the diatom data, which indicate that the decrease in pH over the last 100 years was insignificant. The similar development and changes in the chrysophyte communities of Lilla Öresjön and Verevatn might be because they have similar geology and have been exposed to more or less the same amount of acid deposition.

Scottish lakes

In the sediment from the Scottish lakes no, or very few, scales were preserved. The absence of scales in these sediments could be due to several factors, the scaled chrysophytes might not have been present in the algal communities of the lakes, or the scales might, for some unknown reason, have dissolved. However, in Loch Tinker and in Loch Chon a few scales were recorded, namely *Mallomonas crassisquama*, *M. acaroides*, *M. caudata* and *Synura echinulata*. These taxa indicate neutral to alkaliphilous pH conditions. Most probably the genera *Mallomonas* and *Synura* were rare in the Scottish sites. In Lochan Uaine very small stomatocysts dominated and these were too small to belong to the genera *Mallomonas* or *Synura*, but could perhaps be the stomatocysts of the genera *Spiniferomonas* or *Paraphysomonas*. These are also scale-bearing chrysophytes, but the scales are small, thin and easily dissolved. In the other Scottish sediments investigated, round, smooth stomatocysts were most frequent and many belonged to the genus *Dinobryon*. However, the pH range for the *Dinobryon* species is wide and most are unsuitable for use as pH-indicators.

References

Battarbee, R. W., Cronberg, G. & Lowry, S. 1980 Observations on the occurrence of scales and bristles of *Mallomonas* spp. (Chrysophyceae) in the micro-laminated sediment of a small lake in Finnish north Karelia. *Hydrobiologia* **71**, 225–232.

Hustedt, F. 1939 Systematische und ökologische Untersuchungen über die Diatomeen-Flora von Java, Bali und

Sumatra nach dem Material der deutschen limnologischen Sunda-Expedition. 3. Die ökologische Faktoren und ihr Einfluss auf die Diatomeen-Flora. *Arch. Hydrobiol.* (Suppl.) no. **16**.

Munch, C. S. 1980 Fossil diatoms and scales of Chrysophyceae in the recent history of Hall Lake, Washington. *Freshwat. Biol.* **10**, 61–66.

Siver, P. A. & Hamer, S. 1989 Multivariate statistical analysis of the factors controlling the distribution of scaled chrysophytes. *Limnol. Oceanogr.* **34**, 368–381.

Smol, J. P., Charles, D. F. & Whitehead, D. R. 1984 Mallomonadacean microfossils provide evidence of recent acidification. *Nature, Lond.* **307**, 628–630.

Stevenson, A. C., Patrick, S. T., Kreiser, A., Battarbee, R. W. 1987 Palaeoecological evaluation of the recent acidification of susceptible lakes. Methods utilized under DoE contract PECD 7/7/139 and the Royal Society SWAP Project, Palaeoecology Research Unit, University College London. Research Paper no. 26, pp. 1–36.

Phil. Trans. R. Soc. Lond. B **327**, 295–298 (1990)
Printed in Great Britain

Midge fauna development in acidified lakes in northern Europe

By Y.-W. Brodin

National Swedish Environmental Protection Board, Box 1302, *Solna, S*-171 25, *Sweden*

Analyses of stratigraphical sedimentary remains of aquatic midges (Chironomidae, Chaoboridae and Ceratopogonidae) revealed pronounced faunal changes attributable to acidification in north European lakes from about 1850 and onwards. Increased lake acidification during this century generally caused a reduction of midge fauna stability, diversity, productivity and survival rate. The similarity of chironomid species composition between lakes increased. Changes in chironomid species composition also revealed that oligotrophication is a typical feature of acidified lakes.

Introduction

The recent acidification of lakes has exerted profound effects on aquatic fauna, the most obvious consequences being decreased animal diversity and elimination of several species, especially among fish, snails, mussels, crustaceans and mayflies (Oekland & Oekland 1986). Only a few groups of insects seem to be increasing in numbers in greatly acidified lakes, for example, water beetles (Coleoptera), water boatmen (Corixidae) and damselflies (Agrionidae) (Oekland & Oekland 1986).

The main objective of this paper is to outline important effects of acidification on aquatic midges in north European lakes, with special emphasis on chironomids.

The present study is based on analyses of remains of midge larvae (Chironomidae, Chaoboridae and Ceratopogonidae) in sediment cores from three strongly acidified lakes in Scotland (Round Loch of Glenhead), Norway (Verevatn) and Sweden (Lilla Öresjön), and two moderately acidified lakes in Scotland (Loch Tinker and Loch Chon). Locations, site characteristics and chemical data for these lakes are described by Battarbee & Renberg (this symposium).

Methods

Laboratory and taxonomic methods employed for analyses of aquatic midges are described by Brodin (1990). The Shannon Wiener index was used to calculate temporal changes in species diversity (Southwood 1971). Temporal changes in faunal stability were calculated by using the ps index described by Whittaker (1972).

Midge productivity was calculated by using the number of fourth instar larvae per cubic centimetre and the sediment accumulation rate. Calculations of survival rate were based on the relative proportion of fourth larval instars. Calculations of lake trophic conditions were based on the trophic preference and dominance of different chironomid species (Brodin 1990).

Core chronologies used were derived from ^{210}Pb dates for each site (Appleby *et al.*, this symposium; El-Daoushy, this symposium).

Results

Despite differences in catchment characteristics of the sites studied, a close agreement in the trends of the different midge fauna parameters was observed (figure 1 and table 1). Consequently, the midge faunal development was divided into four phases defined by major differences in the character of the midge fauna.

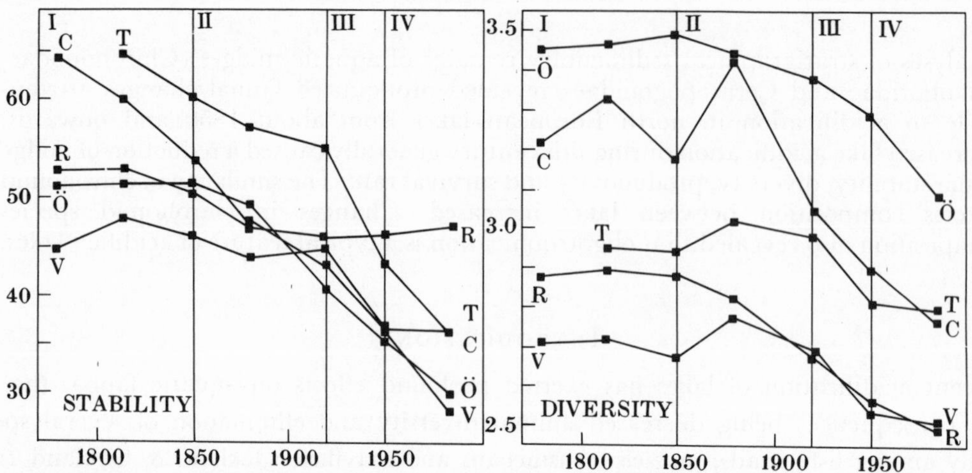

Figure 1. Temporal development of midge fauna stability and diversity in Loch Chon (C), Lilla Öresjön (Ö), Round Loch of Glenhead (R), Loch Tinker (T) and Verevatn (V). Midge faunal phases (I–IV), showing varying degrees of lake acidification are outlined (cf. text).

Table 1. Midge productivity, survival rate and lake trophic level during different midge faunal phases (cf. text). Phase I, *ca.* 1780–1850: phase II, *ca.* 1850–1920; phase III, *ca.* 1920–1950; phase IV, *ca.* 1950–1985. Diatom inferred pH for midge faunal phases is given in parentheses. Diatom data were obtained from Kreiser *et al.* (this symposium), Jones *et al.* (this symposium), Berge *et al.* (this symposium) and Renberg *et al.* (this symposium).

	productivity (ind. × 10^{-3}, m^{-2} a^{-1})				survival rate (%)				lake trophic level (> 3.5 = oligotrophic) (< 3.5 = ultraoligotrophic)			
	I	II	III	IV	I	II	III	IV	I	II	III	IV
Loch Chon	11.9 (6.2)	9.7 (6.2)	8.6 (6.0)	6.4 (5.7)	37.4	47.2	33.9	19.2	3.7	4.2	3.1	3.1
Lilla Öresjön	8.4 (6.0)	7.7 (6.0)	6.3 (5.7)	3.8 (4.6)	44.4	45.3	40.2	32.5	3.8	3.7	4.0	3.6
Round Loch of Glenhead	10.6 (5.5)	9.8 (5.0)	5.2 (4.7)	4.1 (4.7)	50.1	47.2	42.4	43.6	4.2	3.8	3.5	3.4
Loch Tinker	12.4 (6.2)	12.9 (6.0)	7.8 (5.7)	4.6 (5.7)	40.9	42.1	39.9	31.1	3.8	4.3	3.8	3.5
Verevatn	2.7 (5.0)	3.9 (4.7)	3.6 (4.7)	1.6 (4.5)	39.7	40.7	34.6	17.6	4.1	4.2	3.6	3.5

Faunal stability decreased distinctly in Loch Chon during phase I (*ca.* 1780–1850). Otherwise no major changes in midge fauna of the lakes studied occurred. Diversity and productivity was comparatively high, as was the survival rate. During phase II (*ca.* 1850–1920) all the lakes experienced decreases in stability and diversity decreased in Loch Chon, Round Loch of Glenhead and Lilla Öresjön.

Apart from stability in Round Loch of Glenhead, all lakes experienced decreases in midge fauna stability, diversity, productivity and survival rate during phase III (*ca.* 1920–1950). Changes in chironomid species' composition during this period also show oligotrophication. During phase IV, from about 1950 and onwards, the midge fauna of the lakes experienced a further decline in stability, diversity, productivity and survival rate, and continued lake oligotrophication. An increased in similarity of species composition between lakes also occurred (Brodin 1990).

Ceratopogonids decreased in relative numbers during phase IV and were not found in any of the lakes after 1975. Otherwise, ceratopogonids, chaoborids and chironomids occurred in largely unchanged relative numbers throughout the phases. The chironomids comprised 78–100% of the midge fauna in the lakes. Chaoborids and ceratopogonids each comprised 0–8%.

Discussion

The sites studied represent a range of acidified lakes in northern Europe. The similarity in trends of midge fauna parameters between sites allows the generalization to be made that acidified northwest European lakes have experienced gradual but continuous decreases in midge diversity, productivity and survival potential.

The main changes in the midge faunas show a close temporal correlation with periods of decreasing pH in the studied lakes, as inferred from diatoms. It is also clear that the most dramatic changes in the midge faunas occurred when pH was estimated to have dropped to levels below 5.0–5.5, at least during certain seasons of the year (Brodin 1990). These changes may be explained by decreased environmental stability as well as increased pH fluctuations (Dickson 1983), increased concentrations of toxic aluminium (Baker & Schofield 1982) and profound changes in the composition of microorganisms and algae that serve as important food items for aquatic midges (Anderson 1987).

Some authors have suggested that oligotrophication is a typical feature of acidified lakes (see, for example, Persson & Broberg (1985)). This view is supported by the changes in the chironomid species composition of the lakes in this study. However, it could be argued that the increased oligotrophic character of the chironomid fauna was mainly an effect of the harsh environmental conditions in the lakes rather than the trophic level. Yet the chironomid fauna of these lakes is very similar to that of non-acidified lakes with low trophic levels (Thienemann 1954; Saether 1979). Thus lake trophic level seems to be a more decisive factor governing chironomid species composition in acidified lakes than is lake pH.

Of the midge families studied, only ceratopogonids have experienced distinct decreases in relative numbers in inverse proportion to increasing lake acidification, a decline that may be attributed to oligotrophication (Thienemann 1954).

Chaoborids have generally been reported to be favoured in acidified lakes, in both absolute and relative numbers (Oekland & Oekland 1986). This is not confirmed by the present study where chaoborids as a whole showed no marked changes in relative numbers and a definite decrease in absolute numbers.

References

Andersson, G. 1987 Effects of acidification on aquatic organisms. *Nordic Council of Ministers, Envir. Rep.* **1987:5**, 94–123.

Baker, J. P. & Schofield, C. P. 1982 Aluminium toxicity to fish in acidic waters. *Wat. Air Soil Pollut.* **31**, 289–309.

Brodin, Y.-W. 1990 Non-biting midges (Diptera, Chironomidae) as indicators of past and present trends in lake acidification in Northern Europe. *Nat. Swedish Environ. Prot. Board Rep.* (In the press.)
Dickson, W. 1983 Water acidification – effects and counter measures: summary document. *Nat. Swedish Environ. Prot. Board Rep.* **1636**, 267–273.
Oekland, J. & Oekland, K. A. 1986 The effects of acid deposition on benthic animals in lakes and streams. *Experientia* **42**, 471–486.
Persson, O. & Broberg, O. 1985 Nutrient concentrations in the acidified lake Gårdsjön: the role of transport and retension of phosphorous, nitrogen and DOC in watershed and lake. *Ecol. bull.* **37**, 176–192.
Saether, O. A. 1979 Chironomid communities as water quality indicators. *Holarctic Ecol.* **2**, 65–74.
Southwood, T. R. E. 1971 *Ecological methods with particular reference to the study of insect populations*, pp. 1–391. London: Methuen & Co.
Thienemann, A. 1954 *Chironomus. Die Binnengew.* **20**, 1–834. Stuttgart: Schweizerbart'sche Verlag.
Whittaker, R. H. 1972 Evolution and measurement of species diversity. *Taxon* **21**, 213–251.

Phil. Trans. R. Soc. Lond. B **327**, 299–309 (1990)
Printed in Great Britain

Recent lake acidification and cladoceran dynamics: surface sediment and core analyses from lakes in Norway, Scotland and Sweden

By J. P. Nilssen† and S. Sandøy‡

Biological Institute, Zoological Division, P.O. Box 1050, *Blindern, N*-0316 *Oslo* 3, *Norway*

To interpret the remains of Cladocera in lake sediments in relation to pH history, fish abundance, vegetation change, trophic level change and other historic events, it is necessary to understand the balance of abiotic and biotic forces responsible for their present distribution, population dynamics and morphological types. Once these factors are understood, we can reverse the arguments to infer past lake conditions. Many cladoceran species are influenced by fish and invertebrate predation. Some species, especially in the plankton, also show a clear physiological relation to pH and aluminium levels in lakes. Moreover, several littoral–benthic species have a habitat distribution restricted to rock, sand, mud, vegetation, or a combination of some of these.

Remains of littoral and planktonic cladocerans were analysed in surface sediments of 18 Norwegian lakes with pH ranging from 4.5–7.5. In addition, sediment cores from four sites in Norway, four in Scotland and one in Sweden were analysed. The majority of sites showed evidence of recent acidification. In lakes with non-planktivorous fish, analyses of cladoceran remains gave no information on past fish populations, but indicated the pH history of the lakes. In lakes with present or past populations of planktivorous fish, the cladoceran record could be used to assess past fish status as well as past pH. In some lakes changes in the cladoceran communities could be related to changes in macrophyte distribution.

Introduction

Cladocera recovered from lake sediments in palaeolimnological studies are usually restricted to the primarily littoral–benthic dwelling family Chydoridae, whereas representation of planktonic species is usually restricted to *Bosmina* spp. (see, for example, Alhonen (1970)). Complex aquatic interactions are therefore impossible to reconstruct, especially as many species (e.g. copepods) are not preserved in the sediments.

Until recently, Cladocera remains have been mainly used to show development from oligo- to eutrophy in lakes. Species replacement within the Chydoridae and the genus *Bosmina* is very marked and easily assessed where there have been clear changes in lake trophy and fish predation (Whiteside 1970; Kerfoot 1974; Hofmann 1978; Boucherle & Züllig 1983).

The use of cladoceran remains to reconstruct acidification is a more difficult task. The changes in species abundance and composition over small pH ranges can be difficult to detect and demand a thorough knowledge of the ecology of the animals involved in the change (Nilssen 1978; Nilssen & Sandøy 1986). In addition, there are very few quantitative studies of crustaceans over a gradient of pH below 5.5.

Changes in cladoceran composition have been associated with acidification, but many, if not

† Present address: P.O. Box 198, N-4951 Risør, Norway.
‡ Present address: Directorate for Nature Management, Tungasletta 2, N-7004 Trondheim, Norway.

the majority, of these are related to predation and vegetation changes and thus only indirectly related to varying pH.

This study aimed to explore the use of cladoceran analysis in detecting changes in predation, pH, vegetation and other historic events in acid and acidified lakes (see Frey (1960)). We focus on the planktonic communities that are better pH indicators than the littoral communities and present results from a study of surface sediment samples for 18 lakes and of cores from nine lakes.

Sites, materials and methods

The cores were from Norway (Verevatn, Gulspettvann, Holmevatn, Röyrtjörna), Scotland (Loch Chon, Loch Tinker, Lochan Dubh, Lochan Uaine) and Sweden (Lilla Öresjön) (see Battarbee & Renberg, this symposium).

Sampling for surface sediments was done in 1985 and 1986 with a gravity corer, the Skogheim sampler (Skogheim 1979), usually at the deepest part of each lake. The sediment cores were extruded immediately on the shore of the lake, or within two days in the laboratory.

Samples of wet sediments were heated and stirred with a magnetic stirrer in 100 g l^{-1} KOH for about 1 h to deflocculate the sediment. The samples were then sieved through 90 μm and 20 μm mesh sizes, to retain small shell parts. Subsamples of a known volume were transferred with a pipette to a heated slide and mounted in glycerine jelly, then covered with a cover slip. Identification, counting and measurements were made under a microscope at times 80 magnification. For each sediment sample, the most abundant body part was chosen for each species to represent the number of individuals, weighted by the number potentially contributed by one individual in one mount. Except for a few samples with very low numbers of cladoceran remains, at least 200 individuals were counted.

In addition, we measured total shell length, rostrum and mucro on *Bosmina* spp., length of postabdomen on *Daphnia* spp., shell or postabdomen, or both, on the large-sized Chydoridae: *Alona affinis*, *Acroperus elongatus*, *A. harpae* and *Eurycercus lamellatus* to detect effects of fish predation in the littoral–benthic zone.

To identify unknown body parts, remains collected from the sediment surface were compared with animals sampled with a 90 μm plankton net. Two methods were used: cladoceran remains were digested with hydrochloric acid and the remaining parts studied under a microscope, or animals were mounted in polyvinyl lactophenol on a slide covered with a cover-slip. After two days they became transparent. Most of this work concentrated on planktonic animals, but non-chydorid littoral animals were also studied.

This method enabled all planktonic Cladocera and most non-chydorids in the littoral–benthic region (species not commonly included in palaeolimnological studies) to be counted. These analyses greatly increased processing time and led to difficult taxonomic problems. However, our simultaneous ecological studies in lake enclosures, pH-manipulated lakes and natural lakes over a wide pH gradient have made the analyses and interpretations easier.

Cluster analyses were done on a DEC VAX 8600 at the University of Oslo with the programme SPSS-X.

Results and discussion

(a) *Acidification of lakes and changes involving Cladocera*

The major processes that affect animals in acidified lakes change physiological, competitive and predatory interactions. Major pelagic taxa, like fish and daphnids, are physiologically vulnerable to acidic environments, whereas other species like the important invertebrate predators: copepods, corixids and *Chaoborus* can withstand considerable acidity (Nilssen *et al.* 1984). The changing species composition with decreasing pH seems in most cases to have only an indirect relation to pH. The most important factor for the species composition of zooplankton was found to be high aluminium concentrations and low food supply (Hörnström & Ekström 1983). During acidification below pH 5.2–5.5, fish have problems with reproduction and population densities decrease strongly. The invertebrate predators, both in the littoral and in the pelagic zones, increase with acidification (Nilssen 1980; Stenson 1985).

The benthic community becomes different from that in non-acidified lakes. The increase in the periphyton growth and the expansion of *Sphagnum* spp. and *Juncus bulbosus* f. *fluitans* imply an increase of the total plant biomass and a change in the physical structure of the habitat. Simultaneously, some macrophytes may decrease with acidification, e.g. isoëtids (Eriksson *et al.* 1983; Wallin & Renberg 1985).

There are problems in assessing cause–effect relations with changes in species composition and abundance in acidified lakes. Furthermore, it is evident that the alternations observed in the acidified systems have a multi-causal background. The effect of the many stresses produced by biotic and abiotic factors will vary between different organisms.

(b) *Habitat relations of the species recorded in this study*

The habitat relations of the littoral–benthic species recorded in this study are shown in figure 1. The expansion of *Sphagnum*, *Juncus bulbosus* f. *fluitans* and the increase of filamentous algae (reported in Nilssen (1980); Eriksson *et al.* (1983); Stenson (1985)) have created new habitats, microhabitats and new feeding niches, which may have contributed to the faunal development of Cladocera in the littoral and profundal parts of the lakes. Even if other macrophyte species have decreased due to low pH and competition from the new plants, the new habitats created by the colonizing plants may have allowed larger populations of littoral–benthic species of Cladocera to develop. If, conversely, the decreasing macrophytes are not replaced by new plant species, there will be fewer habitats available for the littoral–benthic species and the total diversity may decrease. If the macrophytes die out, the composite habitat of plants and soft mud will be replaced by a habitat of coarser mud, resulting in a change in littoral–benthic species composition (cf. figure 1.).

(c) *Predation and cladoceran remains*

Table 1 shows the general relations between fish predation and cladoceran abundances and communities. As the genus *Bosmina* is an important prey species both for fish (the larger specimens) and invertebrate predators (the smaller specimens), its morphology was investigated in detail. Large Chydoridae were also measured, but so far no clear relation with fish predation has been found (S. Sandøy & J. P. Nilssen, unpublished data).

Figure 2 shows the distribution of shell length and mucro length of small and large specimens of *Bosmina longispina*, respectively, comparing lakes with planktivorous fish (13, 15) and lakes

species | open littoral | profundal | planktonic | sheltered littoral | on vegetation

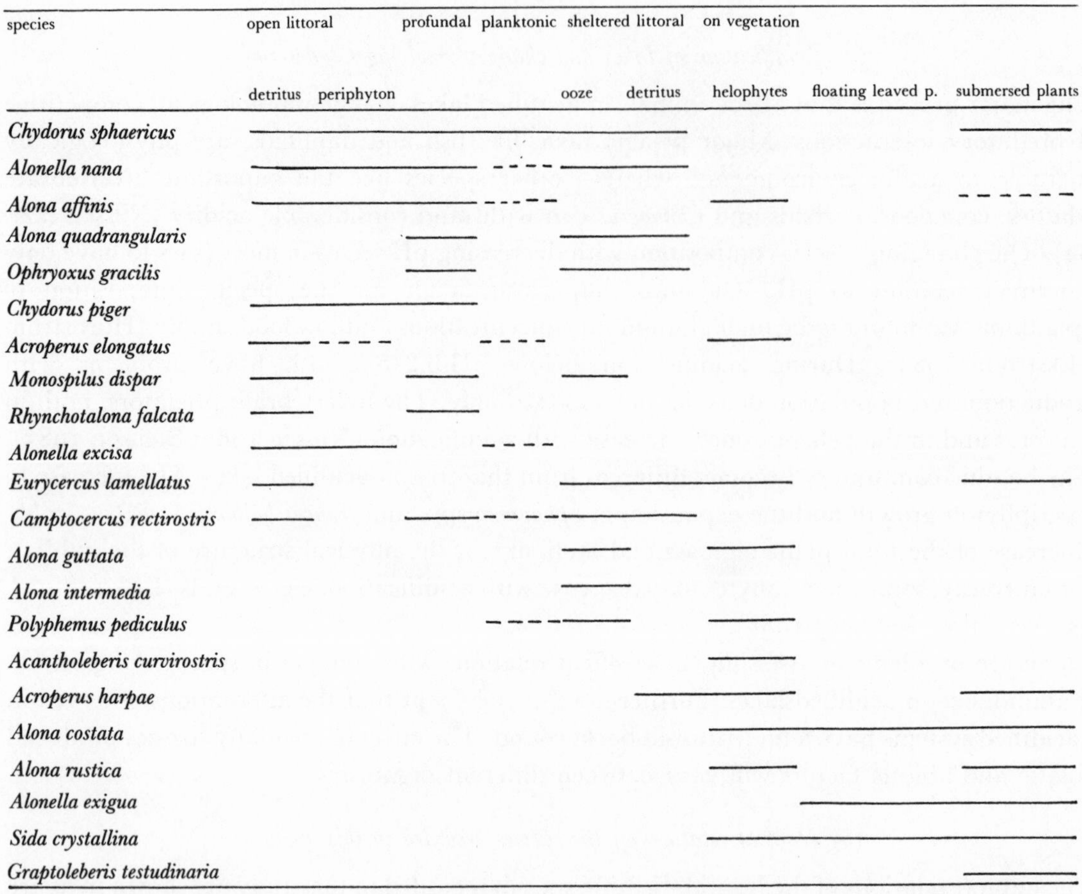

detritus | periphyton | ooze | detritus | helophytes | floating leaved p. | submersed plants

Chydorus sphaericus
Alonella nana
Alona affinis
Alona quadrangularis
Ophryoxus gracilis
Chydorus piger
Acroperus elongatus
Monospilus dispar
Rhynchotalona falcata
Alonella excisa
Eurycercus lamellatus
Camptocercus rectirostris
Alona guttata
Alona intermedia
Polyphemus pediculus
Acantholeberis curvirostris
Acroperus harpae
Alona costata
Alona rustica
Alonella exigua
Sida crystallina
Graptoleberis testudinaria

FIGURE 1. Habitat ecology of the littoral–benthic species recorded in this study (based on Fryer 1968; Whiteside 1970; Whiteside & Swindoll 1988; Flössner 1972; S. Sandøy & J. P. Nilssen, unpublished data). Most important habitats marked with continuous line, and occasional occurrence with dotted line. Comments on separate species: *E. lamellatus*, *C. rectirostris*, *A. affinis*, *A. harpae*, *A. quandrangularis*, *A. elongatus* (larger species, potentially subject to fish predation); species common in and between *Spagnum* spp.: *A. curvirostris*, *A. rustica*, *A. excisa*, *A. nana*, *C. piger*, *C. sphaericus*; sand: *M. dispar*; rock–sand: *A. elongatus*, *R. falcata*; mud: *C. piger*, *A. quadrangularis*, *A. intermedia*; vegetation: *G. testudinaria*, *S. crystallina*, *C. rectirostris*, *A. harpae*, *A. affinis*, *A. nana* (the last two species are less strongly associated with vegetation).

TABLE 1. OCCURRENCE OF CLADOCERA AS RELATED TO FISH ABUNDANCE AND LAKE pH

(Degree of planktivory among fish species depends upon lake size, share of littoral region and fish species competition. With pH below 5.0, fish and *Daphnia* spp. are usually not present if humic levels are low and aluminium is above 200 μg l^{-1}. Fish abundance and lake pH are based on literature and unpublished data (J. P. Nilssen & S. Sandøy).)

	planktivorous fish absent	planktivorous fish present
low pH	few or no *Daphnia*, no *Leptodora*, no *Bythotrephes* large-sized Chydoridae and Macrothricidae	uncommon combination in Scandinavia
high pH	large-sized *Daphnia* few small-sized plankton species	small *Daphnia*, small-sized species adaptation to invertebrate predators

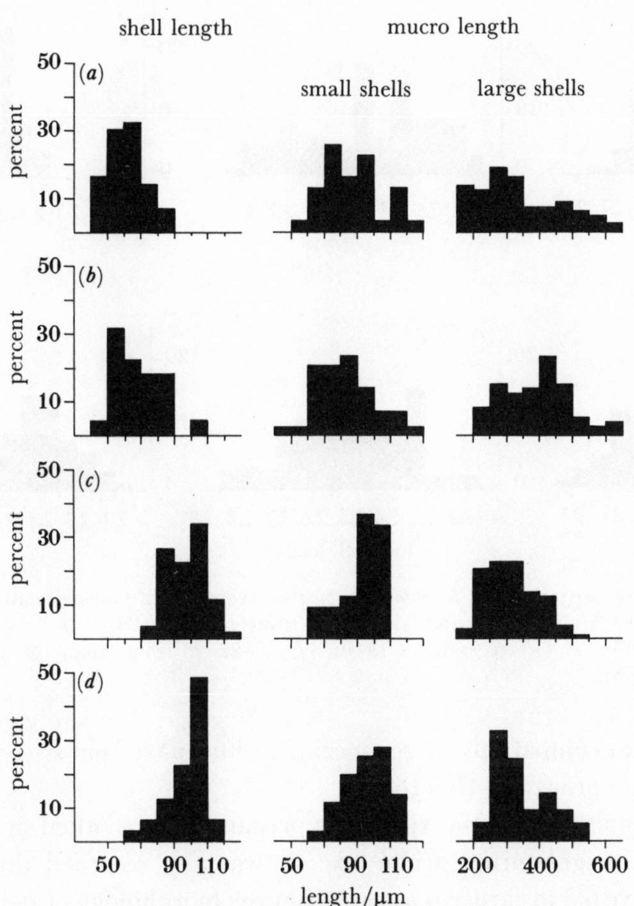

FIGURE 2. Size distribution of body shell and mucro of *Bosmina longispina* from animals of different size classes (small body shell length ⩽ 300 μm) related to pH and predation. Lakes 13 (*a*), 15 (*b*) have medium densities of planktivorous fish and pH 6.2 and 6.4, lakes 3 (*c*), 7 (*d*) are fishless and of pH 4.6 and 4.8.

without fish (3, 7). Generally the size range of *Bosmina* with planktivorous fish followed a normal (Gaussian) distribution, whereas acid fishless lakes showed a skewed size range pattern. Small specimens of *Bosmina* had comparably larger mucro length in acid fishless lakes, probably an adaptation to increased invertebrate predation. The change in the size distribution of *Bosmina* in Gulspettvann took place at the same time as pH decreased in this lake (around 4–5 cm depth) (figure 3). The mucro length of the small *Bosmina* showed comparable changes as indicated in figure 2. However, rostrum length remained constant throughout the core (S. Sandøy & J. P. Nilssen, unpublished data).

Laboratory and field studies have shown *Bosmina* to develop larger mucro and rostrum in response to copepod predation (Kerfoot 1977). In other studies, only the mucro length increased (Wong 1981). In all acid lakes in this study, mucro length increased in small-sized individuals, probably as a response to predation by invertebrates, such as *Heterocope* spp. (cf. Burckhart 1944).

We would have also expected an increase in body and rostrum size with acidification; the first as a response of decreased size-selective predation from fish and the latter due to increased invertebrate predation. In the less acidic lakes we recorded all size groups of *Bosmina*, whereas

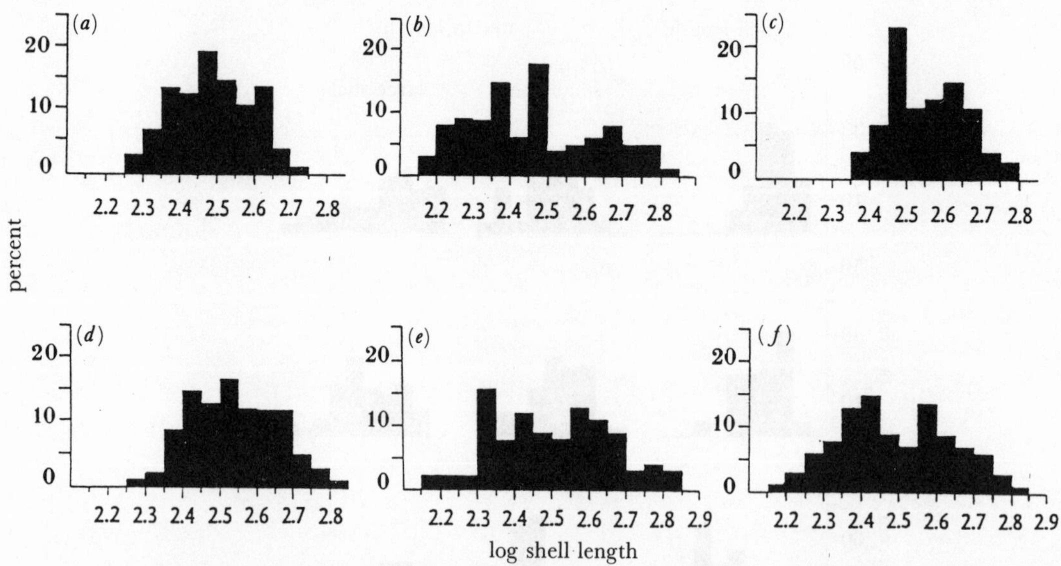

FIGURE 3. Size distribution of body shell of *Bosmina longispina* recovered from Gulspettvann (lake 6) at different depths, compared to lake 3 (*a*) (fishless) and lake 13 (*b*) (trout–perch lake); (*c*) 0–1 cm (present day: 1985); (*d*) 2–3 cm (around 1967), (*e*) 4–5 cm (around 1910), (*f*) 20–22 cm (more than 150 years) (dates from El-Daoushy, this symposium).

the most acidic lakes had comparably larger specimens but maximum sizes were smaller than in the lakes with planktivorous fish (figure 2).

For a lake with strong fish predation Nilssen (in preparation) recorded smaller body sizes in zooplankton than in a neighbouring acidic lake. It was also recorded that the acidic lake probably had a pH above 5.5 in earlier times and that the morphology of *Bosmina* had changed because older sediments contained specimens adapted to fish predation (Nilssen 1984).

(*d*) *Relations between Cladocera and lake* pH

The relation between lake pH and the Cladocera remains is shown in figure 4. The observation that a specific species decreases with decreasing pH does not mean in most cases that it cannot endure low pH. In general, species number and diversity in the planktonic community decrease with decreasing pH, but the littoral–benthic community diversity may decrease, remain stable or even increase depending upon changes in habitat (see above).

The interval of pH change is of critical importance for species succession and abundance patterns; a change from pH 6.0 to 5.0 has greater consequences for the communities than a change from pH 7.0 to 6.0. A particularly sensitive pH interval for many aquatic organisms seems to be pH 5.2–5.5, in the case of a clear water lake with aluminium content of about 150–200 $\mu g\ l^{-1}$. If the lake is strongly coloured, most toxic metal ions (e.g. aluminium) may be chelated and the changes in the lake community are less conspicuous.

With increasing acidification, there is an increasing tendency for some littoral species to be collected in the plankton: e.g., *Alonella nana*, *A. exisa*, *Acroperus harpae*, *A. elongatus*, *Alona affinis* and *Chydorus sphaericus*, together with some copepods. These species belong to the so-called pioneer species (early immigrants after ice withdrawal), common in a variety of environments.

The best pH indicators are the genus *Daphnia* (cf. Nilssen *et al.* 1984) and *Bosmina longirostris* (decrease or disappear at low pH) and *Acantholeberis curvirostris* (increases at low pH). Other

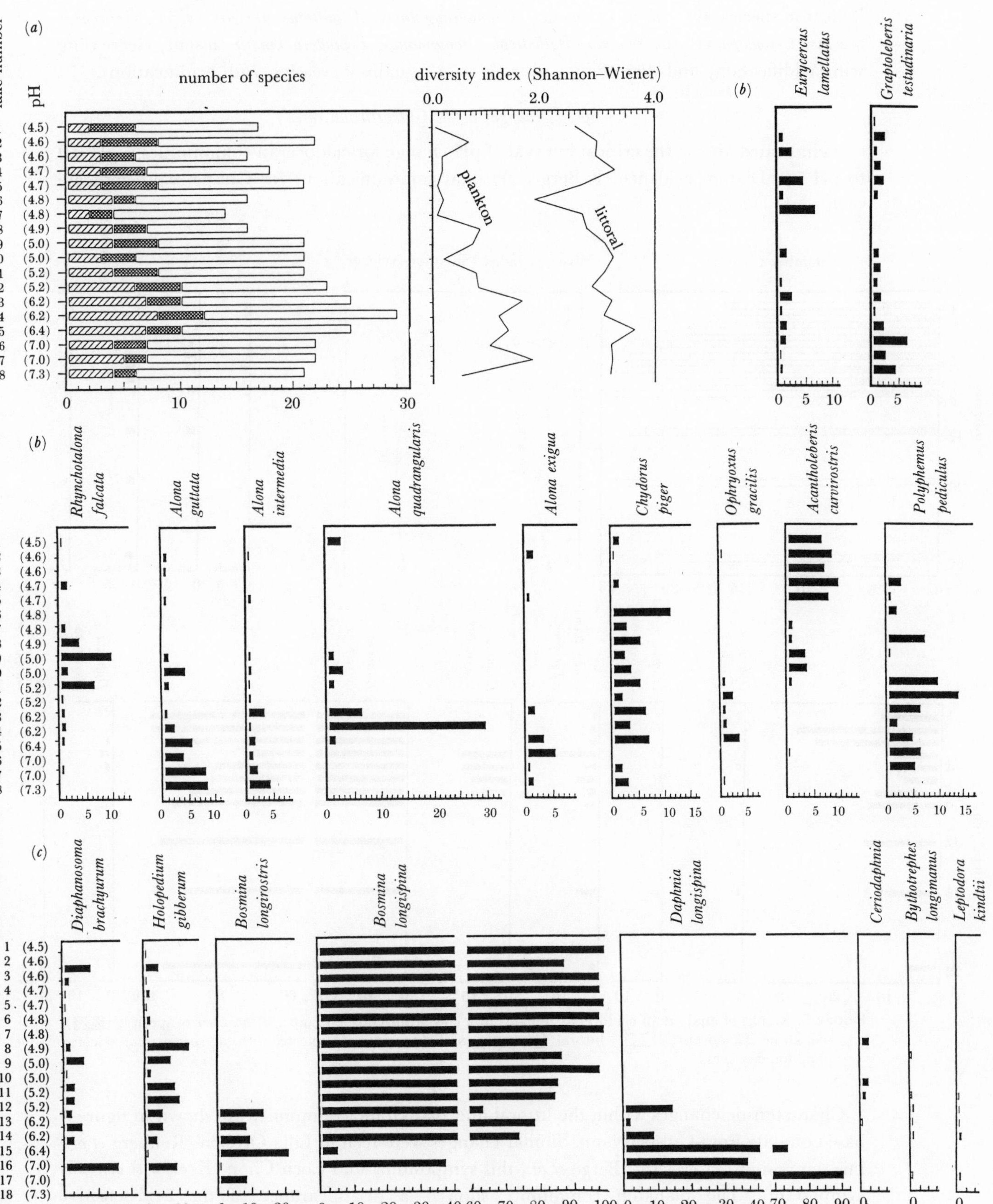

FIGURE 4. Results of analysis of cladoceran remains in surface sediment samples from 18 lakes with pH from 4.5 to 7.3; (a) number of species; (▨), planktonic Cladocera; (▩), non-chydorids; (□), Chdoridae and diversity; (b) selected littoral species; (c) selected planktonic species.

indicator species are: *Alona intermedia*, *A. quadrangularis*, *A. guttata*, *Alonella exigua*, *Ophryoxus gracilis*, *Ceriodaphnia quandrangula*, *Bythotrephes longimanus*, *Leptodora kindtii* (usually decreasing with acidification) and *Alona rustica*, *Alonella exisa* (usually increasing with acidification).

(*e*) *Species changes in the Gulspettvann core*

As indicated above, the critical interval of pH change for cladoceran communities is pH 6.0 to pH 5.0. Diatom evidence (F. Berge, personal communication) for Gulspettvann indicate such a pH change.

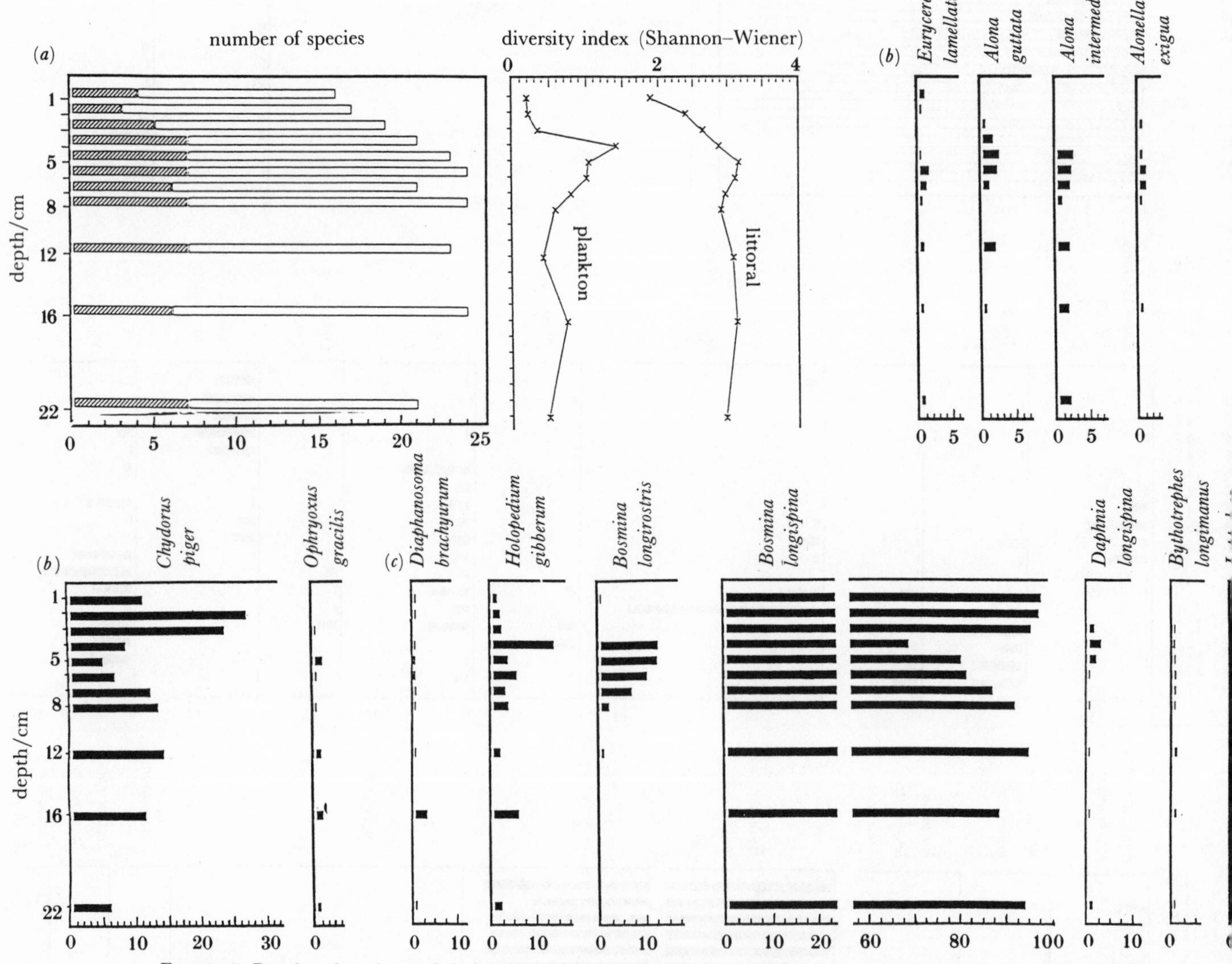

FIGURE 5. Results of analyses of cladoceran remains in a core from Gulspettvann; (*a*) number of species; (hatched bar), planktonic Clodocera; (open bar), littoral Cladocera and diversity; (*b*) selected littoral species; (*c*) selected planktonic species.

Characteristic changes within the littoral and planktonic community are shown in figure 5 based on data from Gulspettvann. Similar changes were seen in Lilla Öresjön (Renberg *et al.*, this symposium), Verevatn (Berge *et al.*, this symposium) and Loch Chon (Kreiser *et al.*, this symposium). The plankton community showed a disappearance of the acid-sensitive

D. longispina, *B. longimanus*, *L. kindtii* and *B. longirostris*. This agrees well with the distribution of animals from field studies (Sandøy & Nilssen 1986) and surface sediments (figure 4). The littoral species showed a disappearance of *A. intermedia*, *A. exigua*, *A. guttata* and *Ophryoxus gracilis*, comparable to the findings in the biogeographical samples and surface sediment samples. Crustacean changes took place at times comparable to changes in the diatom community (F. Berge, personal communication).

(*f*) *Cluster analyses and environmental reconstruction*

To reconstruct the pH history of Gulspettvann (figure 5) from the cladoceran remains, cluster analyses of both the core assemblages and the surface sediment dataset were done.

The dendrogram based on surface sediments of planktonic remains (not shown) divided the lakes into four different groups: acid fishless lakes, acid lakes with moderate fish populations, lakes with pH 6.2–6.4 and lakes with very small fish predation with pH ranging from 6.2 to 7.5. The dendrogram based on the littoral species (not shown) did not classify the lakes into so clearly delimited groups.

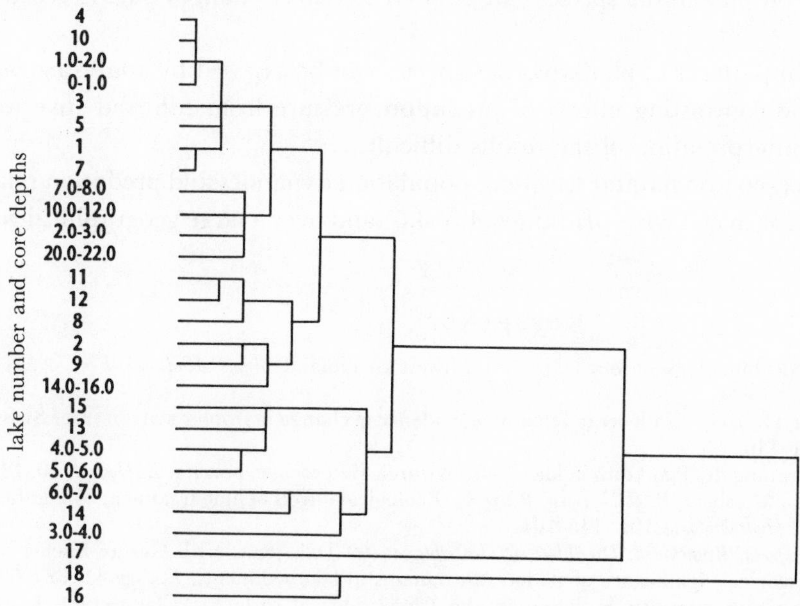

FIGURE 6. Cluster analyses (average linkage between groups) of planktonic species of the Gulspettvann core (0–22.0) and planktonic species in the surface sediment assemblages (lakes 1–18).

When surface sediment samples from the dataset and core samples from Gulspettvann were combined (figure 6), planktonic species from the upper 0–3 cm were grouped together with the most acidic lakes, whereas the strata from 3 to 7 cm were clustered with less acidic lakes in the same region. The littoral–benthic species did not show this relation, but were grouped in an isolated branch. This supports the suggestion that planktonic species may be more suited to study large geographical acidification patterns. Littoral assemblages may be more helpful to study single lakes, where other supporting data (e.g. from diatoms) are available.

Conclusions

1. Cladoceran remains are useful in reconstructing past environments and events in lakes. Changes in crustaceans occurred simultaneously with pH changes as assessed by diatoms or other palaeolimnological methods.

2. Interpretation of cladoceran remains demands a thorough knowledge of their ecology, including habitat selection and relation to predators and abiotic factors, like pH (cf. Nilssen & Sandøy 1986). Because acidification of lakes is a multi-causal phenomenon, in most cases species change is probably not directly related to pH.

3. The pelagic species assemblage gives information on general pH change, whereas the littoral community seems primarily useful in interpreting the more detailed history of a specific lake.

4. Knowledge of the changes in habitat structure (vegetation, sediment structure) of littoral species is necessary for a more thorough development of littoral species as indicators of past lake environment.

5. Cluster analyses on planktonic species can be used to detect changes during recent lake acidification.

6. Former predation patterns of planktivorous species can be assessed by analysing *Bosmina* remains. However, the contrasting effects of predation pressure from fish and invertebrate predators may make interpretation of the results difficult.

7. More work is necessary on habitat selection, population dynamics and predation relations of littoral–benthic species over a wide pH range (4.5–6.5) and over a large geographical region.

References

Alhonen, P. 1970 The paleolimnology of four lakes in southwestern Finland. *Annls Acad. Sci. Fenn.* A. III. **105**, 1–39.

Boucherle, M. M. & Züllig, H. 1983 Cladoceran remains as evidence of change in trophic state in three Swiss lakes. *Hydrobiologia* **103**, 141–146.

Burchkart, G. 1944 Verärmung des Planktons in kleinen Seen durch Heterocope. *Schweiz. Z. Hydrol.* **10**, 121–124.

Eriksson, F., Hörnström, E., Mossberg, P. & Nyberg, P. 1983 Ecological effects of lime treatment of acidified lakes and rivers in Sweden. *Hydrobiologia* **101**, 145–164.

Flössner, D. 1972 *Branchiopoda. Branchiura. Die Tierwelt Deutschlands*, 60 Teil. Jena: VEB Gustav Fischer-Verlag.

Frey, D. G. 1960 The ecological significance of cladoceran remains in lake sediments. *Ecology* **41**, 684–699.

Fryer, G. 1968 Evolution and adaptive radiation in the Chydoridae (Crustacea: Cladocera): A study in comparative functional morphology and ecology. *Phil. Trans. R. Soc. Lond.* B **254**, 221–385.

Hofmann, W. 1978 *Bosmina* (*Eubosmina*) populations of Grosser Plöner See and Schöhsee during late-glacial and postglacial times. *Pol. Arch. Hydrobiol.* **25**, 167–176.

Hörnström, E. & Ekström, C. 1983 pH-, närings- och aluminiums- effekter på plankton i västkustsjöar. *Rep. Statens naturvårdsverk*, SNV PM **1704**, 1–124. (In Swedish, summary and figures in English.)

Kerfoot, W. C. 1974 Net accumulation rates and the history of cladoceran communities. *Ecology* **55**, 51–61.

Kerfoot, W. C. 1977 Implication of copepod predation. *Limnol. Oceanogr.* **22**, 316–325.

Nilssen, J. P. 1978 Selective vertebrate and invertebrate predation – some paleolimnological implications. *Pol. Arch. Hydrobiol.* **25**, 307–320.

Nilssen, J. P. 1980 Acidification of a small watershed in southern Norway and some characteristics of acidic aquatic environments. *Int. Revue ges. Hydrobiol.* **65**, 177–207.

Nilssen, J. P. 1984 An ecological jig-saw puzzle: reconstructing aquatic biogeography and pH in an acidified region. *Res. Rep. Freshwat. Inst. Drottningholm* **61**, 139–147.

Nilssen, J. P. & Sandøy, S. 1986 Acidification history and crustacean remains: some ecological obstacles. *Hydrobiologia* **143**, 349–354.

Nilssen, J. P., Østdahl, T. & Potts, W. T. W. 1984 Species replacements in acidified lakes: physiology, predation or competition. *Res. Rep. Freshwat. Inst. Drottningholm* **61**, 148–153.

Sandøy, S. & Nilssen, J. P. 1986 A geographical survey of littoral crustacea in Norway and their use in paleolimnology. *Hydrobiologia* **143**, 277–286.

Skogheim, O. K. 1979 Beskrivelse av en sedimenthenter konstruert for prøvetakning av korte sedimentkjerner. *Rapp. Årungen prosjekt* nr. **4**, 1–65. (Mimeograph, in Norwegian.)

Stenson, J. A. E. 1985 Biotic structure and relations in the acidified Lake Gårdsjön system – a synthesis. *Ecol. Bull.* **37**, 319–326.

Wallin, J.-E. & Renberg, I. 1985 Vegetation history of the Lake Gårdsjön area, Bohuslän, SW Sweden. *Ecol. Bull.* **37**, 31–34.

Whiteside, M. C. 1970 Danish chydorid Cladocera: modern ecology and core studies. *Ecol. Monogr.* **40**, 79–118.

Whiteside, M. C. & Swindoll, M. R. 1988 Guidelines and limitations to cladoceran paleoecological interpretations. *Paleogeog. Paleoclim., Paleoecol.* **62**, 405–412.

Wong, C. K. 1981 Cyclomorphosis in Bosmina and copepod predation. *Can. J. Zool.* **59**, 2049–2052.

Phil. Trans. R. Soc. Lond. B **327**, 311–317 (1990)

Printed in Great Britain

Sediment chemistry and atmospheric contamination

By B. Rippey

University of Ulster, Freshwater Laboratory, Traad Point, Ballyronan, Northern Ireland BT45 6LR, U.K.

The trace metal, sulphur and polycyclic aromatic hydrocarbon concentration–depth profiles in dated lake-sediment cores are used to establish the history of contamination of the atmosphere above the study lakes. The results from three chemical groups give the same qualitative description of contamination. The atmosphere became contaminated in the areas of high present day acid deposition early last century in Scotland and late last century in southern Scandinavia. Contamination increased this century and the sulphur, polycyclic aromatic hydrocarbon and sometimes the trace metal fluxes to the sediment drop over the past 10–30 years. There was little or no contamination at the low recent acid-deposition sites in both study regions.

Introduction

The concentration–depth profiles of trace metals are frequently used in surface water acidification studies to establish if a lake has received contaminants deposited from the atmosphere (Galloway & Likens 1979; Norton *et al.* 1981; Wong *et al.* 1984; Battarbee *et al.* 1985). This trace metal contamination of the atmosphere and surface waters is part of a global pattern (Rippey *et al.* 1982) and, although the metals do not cause acidification, it is assumed that several trace metals and the acidic components do have the same deposition history. The time when the atmosphere over the lake became contaminated and the change in level of contamination can at least be established from the trace metal profiles.

Sulphur, one of the main components of acid deposition, has been measured in some palaeolimnological studies (Nriagu & Coker 1983; Holdren *et al.* 1984; Mitchell *et al.* 1985) and is potentially a more direct indicator of acid stress on the lake. However, because the main sulphur sedimentation process, sulphate reduction (Nriagu & Soon 1985; Rudd *et al.* 1986), is prone to changes in efficiency as lake conditions change, the concentration–depth or flux–time profiles do not always accurately record the sulphur input history. Polycyclic aromatic hydrocarbons (PAH) have been used as a more reliable record of the deposition history of the products of fossil fuel combustion (Furlong *et al.* 1987). Their main source in the environment is fossil-fuel combustion and they are little altered during transport through the atmosphere or during burial in the sediment (Hites 1981). A few studies have included trace metals, sulphur and polycyclic aromatic hydrocarbons in their palaeolimnological investigation of surface water acidification (Furlong *et al.* 1987; Charles *et al.* 1987).

We also use these sediment properties to establish the timing and extent of contamination of the atmosphere by these chemical species to help provide evidence for the start and change of acid stress on the lakes in the Surface Water Acidification Project (SWAP). Lakes in the United Kingdom, Sweden and Norway were chosen to establish the patterns of atmospheric contamination in areas of high and low present-day acid deposition. The Round Loch of

Glenhead (Galloway), Lochs Tinker and Chon (Trossachs, central Scotland), Verevatn (southern Norway) and Lilla Öresjön (southern Sweden) are in areas of high acid deposition. Loch Doilet and Lochan Dubh (Strontian/Loch Sheil, Northwest Scotland), Lochan Uaine (Cairngorms, Northeast Scotland) and Röyrtjörna (mid-Norway) are in areas of low acid deposition. Site details are given by Battarbee & Renberg (this symposium).

Methods

In the U.K., sediment cores were taken with a mini-Mackereth corer and in Scandinavia cores were taken with a freeze-corer (for trace metals and S) or a modified Kajak corer (PAH). Laboratory methods are described in Stevenson *et al.* (1987) and are only outlined briefly here. The trace metals were determined by flame atomic absorption spectrophotometry after digestion of the sediment by hydrofluoric, nitric and perchloric acids. Total sulphur was determined by turbidity (Tabatabi 1974) after half fusion of the sediment (Grant & Yeung 1971). The polycyclic aromatic hydrocarbons were determined by liquid chromatography with fluorescence detection after Soxhlet extraction of the freeze-dried sediment with cyclohexane. The extracts were cleaned-up by using neutral alumina. In the U.K. work, one core, which was dated, was used for the trace metal and sulphur analyses and another for the trace organics. This core was cross correlated with the dated one by using dry mass and loss on ignition profiles. In the Scandinavian work, trace metal, sulphur, PAH and ^{210}Pb were analysed on different cores, but these were carefully cross-correlated by using similar techniques.

Results and discussion

Figure 1 shows the lead and zinc concentration–depth profiles from a long core from the Round Loch of Glenhead in Galloway. As there is little change in sediment dry mass, loss on ignition and accumulation rate in the core, the shape of the flux–depth and concentration–depth profiles are identical. This core covers the last 9000 years (Jones *et al.* 1986) and shows that zinc and lead contaminate only the most recent sediment. Lead contamination starts above 40 cm (extrapolates to the late 18th century), zinc at 28 cm (extrapolates to around 1820) and the concentrations are highest during the 20th century. As this is a remote lake, the source of contamination is deposition from the atmosphere. The drop in concentration towards the sediment surface indicates that the quality of the atmosphere has improved recently. The lead improvement starts around the 1920s (8.25 cm). However, because the efficiency of zinc sedimentation is less at lower pH values (Tessier *et al.* 1989), the drop in sedimentary zinc concentration above 5.5 cm (1950) is probably due to both lake acidification (Jones *et al.* 1986) and to a real drop in flux from the atmosphere. The deposition flux of trace metals from the atmosphere is known to have dropped recently in the U.K. (Cawse 1987).

The dry mass, loss on ignition, accumulation rate and sediment constitution (grain size and mineralogy) are not always constant in a core and this makes interpretation of the trace metal profiles more difficult. Interpretation of the profiles from Loch Tinker is not as easy as with the Round Loch of Glenhead core. The lead and zinc concentrations in Loch Tinker are constant up to 22.5 cm (extrapolates to early 19th century), and then increase. Lead is constant above 10 cm, whereas zinc drops a little above 5 cm. The broad contamination pattern is similar to that in the Round Loch of Glenhead.

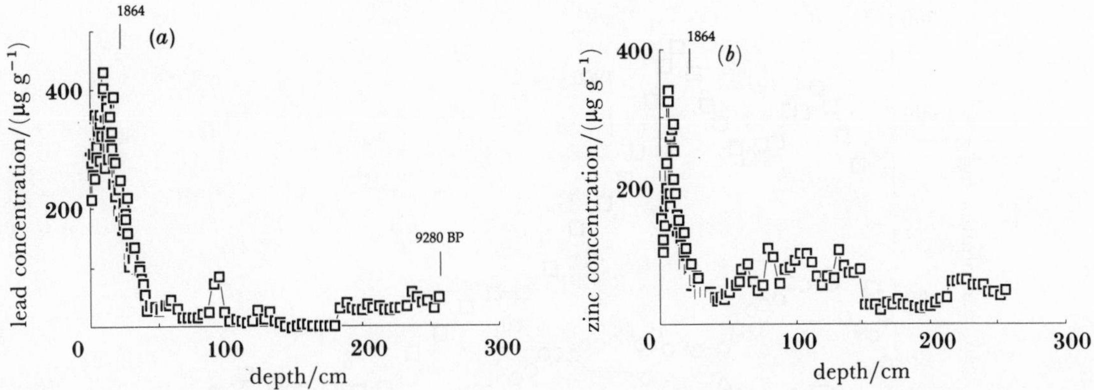

FIGURE 1. The variation of lead (*a*) and zinc (*b*) concentration with depth in the sediments of the Round Loch of Glenhead in Galloway shows that only the most recent sediments are contaminated by material deposited from the atmosphere.

However, superimposed on this pattern there is a trough in the lead and zinc concentrations between 13 and 20 cm. This coincides with changes in sediment composition and accumulation rate. Specifically, the sodium and magnesium concentrations and the sediment accumulation rate are higher in this interval. However, there is a steady increase in lead and zinc fluxes during this interval (figure 2). Although the temporary change in sediment accumulation rate in Loch Tinker did not alter the trace-metal fluxes, this is not always so (Johnston & Nichols 1988). The sulphur and zinc concentration–depth profile shapes are similar and the flux–depth behaviour shows that the input of sulphur to the sediment increased until 3 cm (1960) after which it falls a little (figure 2). In this case, as the zinc and sulphur behaviour is similar, the zinc profile is a good surrogate for acid stress on the lake (Holdren *et al.* 1984).

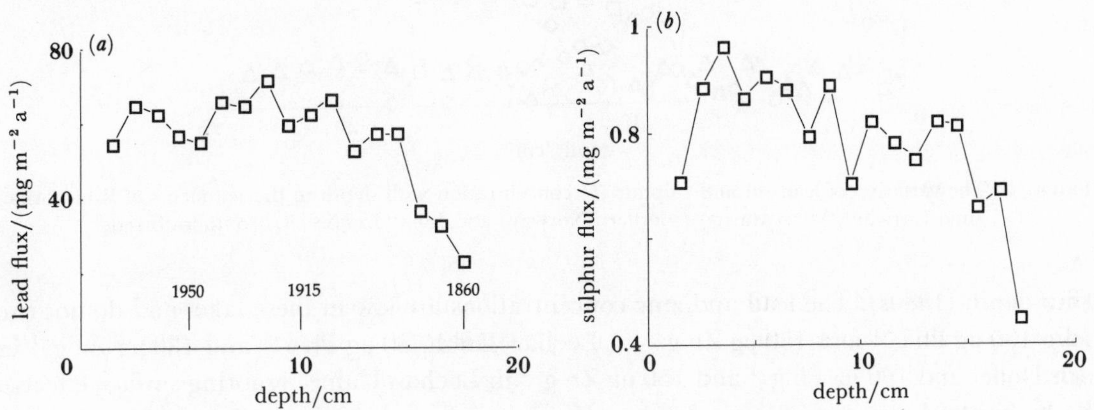

FIGURE 2. The variation of lead (*a*) and sulphur (*b*) fluxes to the sediment with depth in Loch Tinker in the Trossachs, central Scotland.

The behaviour and concentrations of lead and zinc in Loch Chon are similar to nearby Loch Tinker. Contamination started early last century. The results for Lochan Dubh and Loch Doilet in the Strontian–Loch Sheil area of Northwest Scotland and for Lochan Uaine in the Cairngorms show that there is only a little zinc contamination in Lochan Dubh that starts at

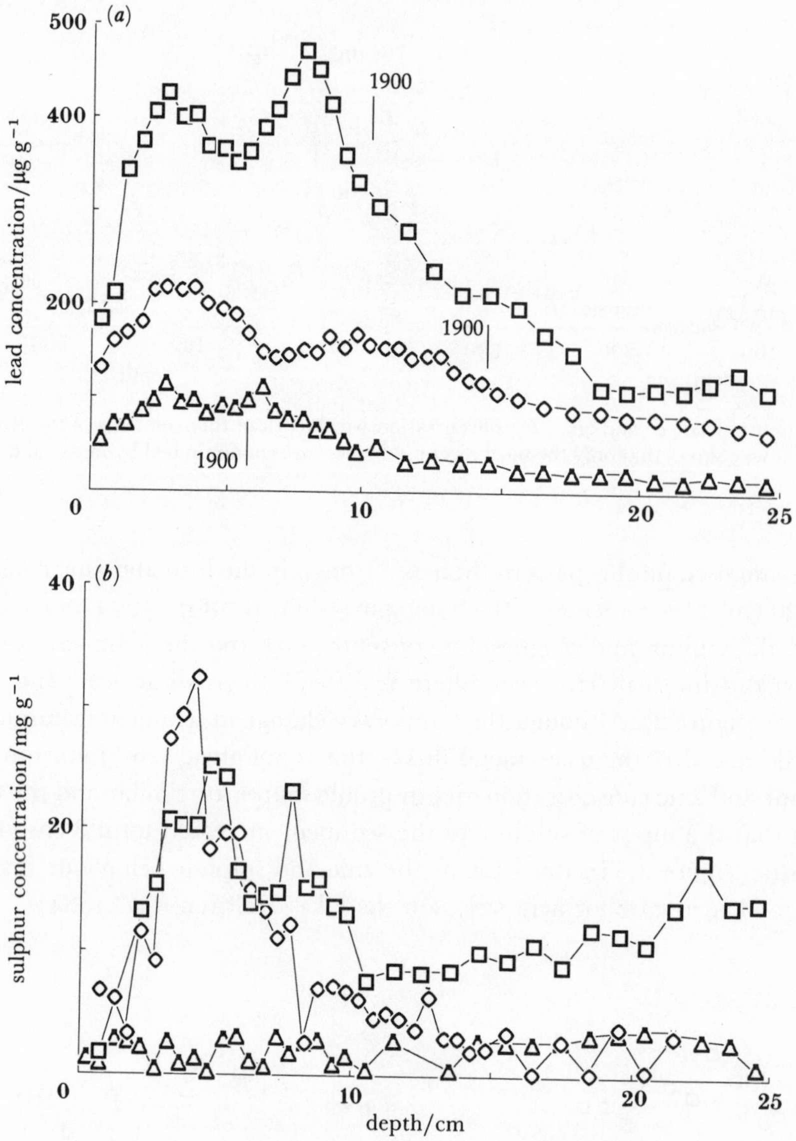

FIGURE 3. The variation of lead (*a*) and sulphur (*b*) concentration with depth in the sediments of Röyrtjörna (△) (mid-Norway), Verevatn (□) (southern Norway) and Lilla Öresjön (◇) (southern Sweden).

10 cm depth (1880s). The lead and zinc concentrations are low in these lakes and do not rise above 100 μg Pb g^{-1} and 150 μg Zn g^{-1} in Lochan Dubh, 80 μg Pb g^{-1} and 130 μg Zn g^{-1} in Loch Doilet and 160 μg Pb g^{-1} and 150 μg Zn g^{-1} in Lochan Uaine (ignoring surface effects). The higher lead concentrations in Lochan Uaine are due to granite in the catchment.

The SWAP lakes in Norway and Sweden were chosen to cover the range from high acid deposition in southern Norway (Verevatn) and southern Sweden (Lilla Öresjön) to low deposition in mid-Norway (Röyrtjörna). The trace metal and sulphur results confirm this contamination pattern (figure 3). Lead and zinc contamination is highest in Lilla Öresjön and Verevatn. Lead and zinc contamination started round 1880 in Lilla Öresjön (16 cm), zinc at the same time (10 cm) and lead earlier in Verevatn. There is a small amount of trace metal contamination in Röyrtjörna. The sulphur profiles show that there is no contamination in

Röyrtjörna but contamination starts in the 1880s in the other two lakes and increases strongly around 1940 (8 cm) in Lilla Öresjön and 1924 (8 cm) in Verevatn. The sulphur concentrations in Lilla Öresjön and Verevatn are quite high (compare with a maximum of 5.2 mg S g^{-1} in Loch Tinker). Although the trace metal and sulphur profiles provide the same qualitative history of atmospheric contamination at these lake sites, there are important quantitative differences. For example, the lead concentration profiles suggest that Verevatn is more contaminated than Lilla Öresjön, whereas the sulphur profiles indicates that there is not much difference. Furthermore, the lead fluxes indicate that there is not much difference between the two lakes, but the sulphur fluxes indicate that Lilla Öresjön is more contaminated.

The trace metal and sulphur results confirm that the atmosphere was contaminated in those areas receiving high present-day acid deposition early last century in Scotland and late last century in southern Scandinavia. There is little or no contamination in the low acid-deposition areas in Scotland and Scandinavia.

We found many polycyclic aromatic hydrocarbons in many of the lake sediments (mostly over 40 compounds). The main compounds, naphthalene, fluorene, phenanthrene, anthracene, fluoranthene, pyrene, benz[a]anthracene, chrysene, benzo[b]fluoranthene, benzo[k]fluoranthene, benzo[a]pyrene and dibenz[a,h]anthracene, comprise a group that is found in lake sediments throughout the northern hemisphere (Laflamme & Hites 1978; Furlong *et al.* 1987) and are the result of long-distance transport of the products of fossil fuel combustion (Laflamme & Hites 1978; Bjørseth *et al.* 1979; Hites 1981). The concentrations of PAH in all the lakes examined were highly correlated and one of the compounds found at highest concentration, benzo[a]pyrene, is used to illustrate the degree of PAH contamination between the sites (figure 4). As the concentrations in Verevatn are around twice those in Lilla Öresjön, the concentrations in Loch Tinker and Loch Chon similar, and similar in Loch Doilet and Lochan Dubh, this figure summarizes the relative contamination in areas of high acid deposition in southern Scandinavia (Lilla Öresjön, Verevatn) and central Scotland (Loch Tinker, Loch

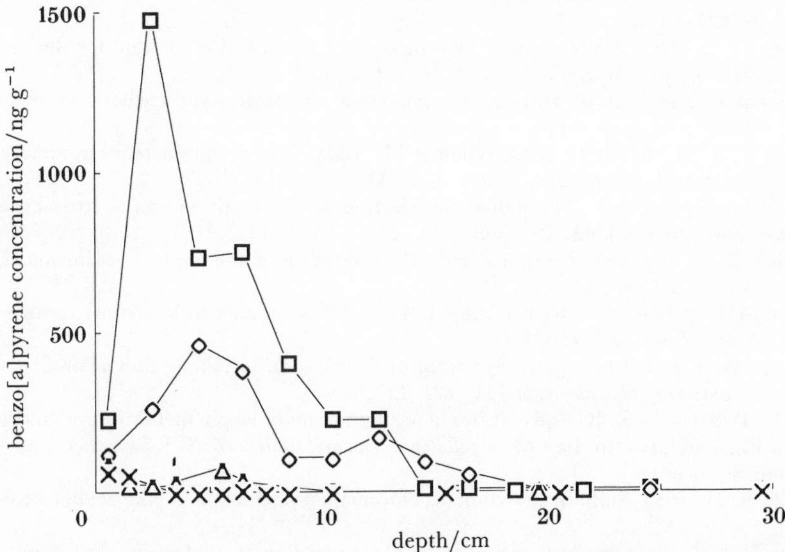

FIGURE 4. The variation of benzo[a]pyrene concentration with depth in the sediments of Lilla Öresjön (southern Sweden), Loch Tinker (Trossachs, central Scotland), Lochan Dubh (northwest Scotland) and Lochan Uaine (Cairngorms, Scotland). (□), Lilla Öresjön; (◇), Loch Tinker; (△), Lochan Dubh; (×), Lochan Uaine.

Chon) and in two areas of low deposition in Northwest Scotland (Loch Doilet, Lochan Dubh) and the Cairngorms (Lochan Uaine). The two areas of low acid deposition have much lower benzo[a]pyrene concentrations, and all other PAH, than the areas of high deposition in Scotland and southern Scandinavia. Loch Doilet, Lochan Dubh and Lochan Uaine do show a small amount of contamination, whereas contamination started early last century in Loch Tinker (and Loch Chon) and late last century in Lilla Öresjön (and Verevatn). There is an improvement at all sites over the past 10–30 years.

The trace metal, sulphur and PAH results give similar qualitative descriptions of the history of atmospheric contamination at the SWAP sites. They all confirm that the atmosphere has been contaminated in the areas of highest recent acid deposition in Scotland since early last century and late last century in southern Scandinavia. Although small, there is a little trace metal contamination at the low deposition sites in both study regions. Contamination by all three chemical groups increased strongly this century and the sulphur, PAH and sometimes the trace contamination drops over the past 10–30 years. Acidification of the lakes coincides with or post-dates the start of atmospheric contamination (Battarbee, this symposium).

References

Battarbee, R. W., Flower, R. J., Stevenson, A. C. & Rippey, B. 1985 Lake acidification in Galloway: a palaeoecological test of competing hypotheses. *Nature, Lond.* **314**, 350–352.

Bjørseth, A., Lunde, G. & Lindskoog, A. 1979 Long-range transport of polycyclic aromatic hydrocarbons. *Atmos. Environ.* **13**, 45–53.

Cawse, P. A. 1987 Trace and major elements in the atmosphere at rural locations in Great Britain, 1972–81. In *Pollutant transport and fate in ecosystems* (ed. P. J. Coughtrey, M. H. Martin & M. H. Unsworth), pp. 89–112. Oxford: Blackwell Scientific Publications.

Charles, D. F., Whitehead, D. R., Engstrom, D. R., Fry, B. D., Hites, R. A., Norton, S. A., Owen, J. S., Roll, L. A., Schindler, S. C., Smol, J. P., Uutala, A. J., White, J. R. & Wise, R. J. 1987 Paleolimnological evidence for recent acidification of Big Moose Lake, Adirondack Mountains, N.Y., U.S.A. *Biogeochemistry* **3**, 267–296.

Furlong, E. T., Cessar, L. R. & Hites, R. A. 1987 Accumulation of polycyclic aromatic hydrocarbons in acid sensitive lakes. *Geochim. cosmochim. Acta* **51**, 2965–2975.

Galloway, J. N. & Likens, G. E. 1979 Atmospheric enhancement of metal deposition in Adirondack lake sediment. *Limnol. Oceanogr.* **24**, 427–433.

Grant, C. J. & Yeung, H. L. 1971 A preliminary investigation of a half-fusion method for the determination of total sulphur in acid sulphate soil. *Agric. Sci. Inst. Hong Kong* **4**, 256–264.

Hites, R. A. 1981 Sources and fates of atmospheric polycyclic aromatic hydrocarbons. *ACS Symp. Ser.* **167**, 187–196.

Holdren, G. R., Brunelle, T. M., Matisoff, G. & Whalen, M. 1984 Timing the increase in atmospheric sulphur deposition in the Adirondack Mountains. *Nature, Lond.* **311**, 245–248.

Laflamme, R. E. & Hites, R. A. 1978 The global distribution of polycyclic aromatic hydrocarbons in recent sediments. *Geochim. cosmochim. Acta* **42**, 289–303.

Johnson, M. G. & Nicholls, K. H. 1988 Temporal and spatial trends in metal loads to sediments of Lake Simcoe, Ontario. *Wat. Air Soil Pollut.* **39**, 337–354.

Jones, V. J., Stevenson, A. C. & Battarbee, R. W. 1985 Lake acidification and the land-use hypothesis: a mid-post-glacial analogue. *Nature, Lond.* **322**, 157–158.

Mitchell, M. J., David, M. B. & Uurl, A. J. 1985 Sulphur distribution in lake sediment profiles as an index of historical deposition patterns. *Hydrobiologia* **121**, 121–127.

Norton, S. A., Hess, C. T. & Davis, R. B. 1981 Rates of accumulation of heavy metals in pre- and post-European sediments in New England lakes. In *Atmospheric pollutants in natural waters* (ed. S. J. Eisenrich), pp. 409–421. Ann Arbor: Ann Arbor Science.

Nriagu, J. O. & Coker, R. D. 1983 Sulphur in sediments chronicles past changes in lake acidification. *Nature, Lond.* **303**, 692–694.

Nriagu, J. O. & Soon, Y. K. 1985 Distribution and isotopic composition of sulphur in lake sediments of northern Ontario. *Geochim. cosmochim. Acta* **49**, 823–834.

Rippey, B., Murphy, R. J. & Kyle, S. W. 1982 Anthropogenically derived changes in the sedimentary flux of Mg, Cr, Ni, Cu, Zn, Hg, Pb, and P in Lough Neagh, Northern Ireland. *Environ. Sci. Technol.* **16**, 23–30.

Rudd, J. W. M., Kelly, C. A. & Furutani, A. 1986 The role of sulphate reduction in long term accumulation of organic and inorganic sulphur in lake sediments. *Limnol. Oceanogr.* **31**, 1281–1291.
Stevenson, A. C., Patrick, S. T., Kreiser, A. & Battarbee, R. W. 1987 Palaeoecological evaluation of the recent acidification of susceptible lakes: methods utilised under DoE contract PECD 7/7/139 and the Royal Society SWAP Project. Palaeoecology Research Unit, University College London.
Tabatabai, M. A. 1974 Determination of sulphate in water samples. *Sulph. Inst. Jl* **10**, 11–13.
Tessier, A., Carignan, R., Dubreuil, B. & Rapin, F. 1989 Partitioning of zinc between the water column and the oxic sediments in lakes. *Geochim. cosmochim. Acta* **53**, 1511–1522.
Whalen, M. & Thompson, R. C. 1980 Pollution records from sediments of three lakes in New York State. *Geochim. cosmochim. Acta* **44**, 333–339.
White, J. R. & Driscoll, C. T. 1987 Zinc cycling in an acidic Adirondack lake. *Environ. Sci. Technol.* **21**, 211–216.
Wong, K. T., Nriagu, J. O. & Coker, R. D. 1984 Atmospheric input of heavy metals chronicled in lake sediments of the Algonquin Provincial Park, Ontario, Canada. *Chem. Geol.* **44**, 187–201.

Discussion

D. F. Charles (*United States Environmental Protection Agency, Oregon, U.S.A.*). I understand that the nature, amount and proportion of PAHs varies among PAH emission sources (for example, coal versus oil) and generally from one geographical region to another. Can Dr Rippey interpret the PAH profiles from any of his studied lakes to detect these differences, for example, between the U.K. and Scandinavia?

Secondly, and related to the first question, does Dr Rippey think that any of the decline in PAH concentration in the top 5 cm of some of the cores is due to increased use of emission controls?

B. Rippey. We have not detected any major differences in the relative proportions of the main PAHs either from sample to sample within a core or between sites. The concentrations of the main compounds are highly correlated. As the lakes are contaminated by long-distance transport from the main emission sources in urban and industrial areas, it may be that there is an integration of the various sources during transport through the atmosphere to form a homogeneous mixture.

The decline in PAH concentrations in the top 3–5 cm of some of the cores is probably due to an improvement in atmospheric quality due to improved emission control measures. The improvement starts in the 1950s in Loch Chon and Loch Tinker and this coincides with the introduction of legislation to control emissions in the U.K. The reductions in PAH concentration start around 1960 in Verevatn and in the mid-1970s in Lilla Öresjön.

Phil. Trans. R. Soc. Lond. B **327**, 319–323 (1990)
Printed in Great Britain

British and Scandinavian lake sediment records of carbonaceous particles from fossil-fuel combustion

By M. Wik[1] and J. Natkanski[2]

[1] *Department of Ecological Botany, University of Umeå, S-901 87 Umeå, Sweden*
[2] *Palaeoecology Research Unit, University College London, 26 Bedford Way, London WC1H 0AP, U.K.*

Spheroidal carbonaceous particles are emitted to the atmosphere during oil and coal combustion. The sedimentary record of these particles has been analysed for six Scottish, two Norwegian and one Swedish lake. Concentration profiles in the sediments parallel fuel-consumption trends. There are also large differences in carbonaceous particulate concentrations indicating geographical differences in loading of air pollutants from fossil-fuel combustion.

Introduction

During oil and coal combustion, particulate matter together with SO_2, NO_x, polycyclic aromatic hydrocarbons (PAH) and metals are emitted into the atmosphere. Most of the particulate matter emitted from oil combustion, and some of the particles from coal combustion, are carbonaceous particles. The carbonaceous particles analysed in this investigation are more than 5–10 μm in diameter, black, porous and spheroidal (figure 1*a*). They are formed when fuel drops or particles are incompletely burnt and the volatile components vaporized, leaving a spheroidal skeleton of nonvolatile elemental carbon (McCrone & Delly 1973). As these particles are mainly composed of elemental carbon, they are chemically very resistant, well preserved in sediments, and not affected by diagenesis as are many other pollutant indicators e.g. sulphur (Holdren *et al.* 1984) and zinc (Carignan & Tessier 1985). The sedimentary spheroidal carbonaceous particle (SCP) record can therefore serve as an indirect record of other air pollutants originating from fossil-fuel combustion. The particle record in lake sediment cores reflects the history of particle deposition. Such stratigraphic investigations have been done in the U.S.A. (Griffin & Goldberg 1983), Sweden (Wik *et al.* 1986) and Great Britain (Battarbee *et al.* 1988). Surface sediment samples (Renberg & Wik 1985*a*) and soil samples (Wik & Renberg 1987) have been used to detect geographical differences in deposition.

This investigation aimed to study the historical deposition pattern of SCPs in nine Surface Water Acidification Project (SWAP) lakes, and assess loading differences between these lakes. The lakes are: Loch Chon, Loch Doilet, Loch Tinker, Lochan Uaine, Lochan Dubh and Round Loch of Glenhead in Scotland, Verevatn and Röyrtjörna in Norway and Lilla Öresjön in Sweden (figure 1*b*). See Battarbee & Renberg (this symposium) for further site details.

Methods

Cores from the three Scandinavian lakes were sampled with a freeze-corer and cut in contiguous 0.5 cm subsamples (Renberg 1981). The Scottish cores were taken with a Mackereth mini-corer and 0.5 cm, occasionally 1.0 cm, subsamples taken at varying, but mostly 1 cm, intervals. Sediment preparation and counting procedures followed the method described by Renberg & Wik (1985*b*) with the samples analysed at times 50 magnification for the Scandinavian sites and times 40 for the Scottish.

Results and discussion

Spheroidal carbonaceous particle profiles have been analysed for 26 British lakes. Common features are the presence of few particles in sediments older than 1900, and a notable sharp increase in concentrations at about 1940, continuing to the surface sediment (Battarbee *et al.* 1988). The six Scottish SWAP lakes show reasonable agreement with these general features, although there is some variability between sites (figure 1 *c–h*). The three northernmost lakes show a slightly reduced surface concentration, a feature recorded for the first time. This decrease indicates that these lakes may now be less exposed to pollutants from fossil-fuel combustion than about ten years ago.

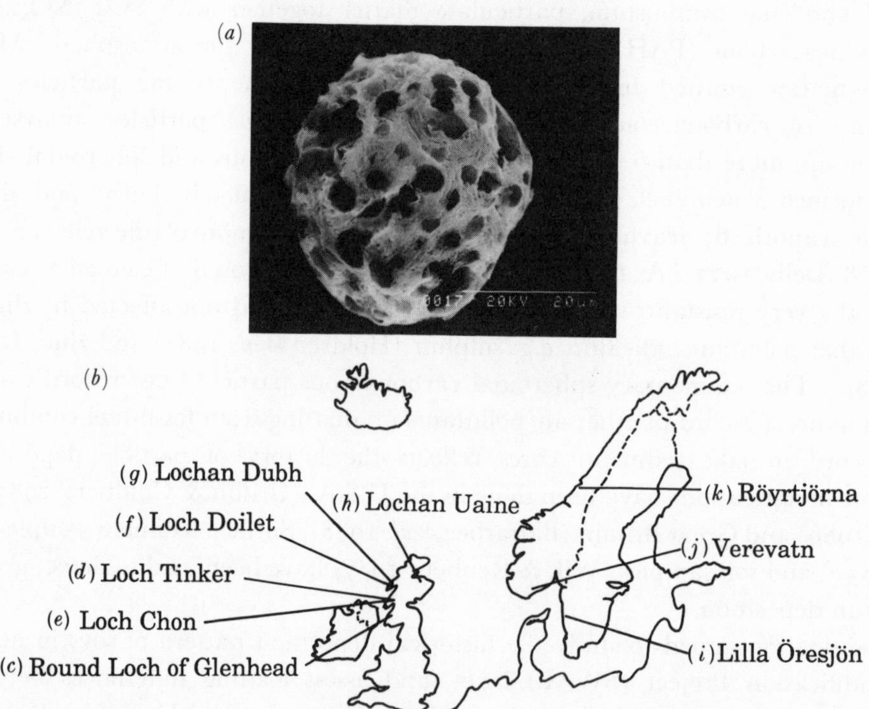

Figure 1. (*a*) A spheroidal carbonaceous particle (SCP). (*b*) Map showing the location of investigated lakes; SCP concentration (particles gds^{-1}) plotted against depth (cm) with ^{210}Pb dates (Appleby and El-Dauoshy, this symposium) for; (*c*) Round Loch of Glenhead (cored 1984), (*d*) Loch Tinker (cored 1985), (*e*) Loch Chon (cored 1987), (*f*) Loch Doilet (cored 1986), (*g*) Lochan Dubh (cored 1986), (*h*) Lochan Uaine (cored 1986), (*i*) Lilla Öresjön (cored 1986), (*j*) Verevatn (cored 1986) and (*k*) Röyrtjörna (cored 1987). Profiles indicating trends in consumption of; (*l*) oil (○) and coal (●) in U.K. power stations (Electrical Council 1988), (*m*) fuel oils (○) and coal (●) in Sweden (Statistiska Centralbyrån 1972, Statistical papers series J 1971–1978, Energy statistics yearbook 1983–1986, S. Lundberg, Swedish Petroleum Institute, personal communication) and (*n*) fuel oils (○) and coal (●) in Norway (A. G. Furuset Central Bureau of Statistics Norway, personal communication).

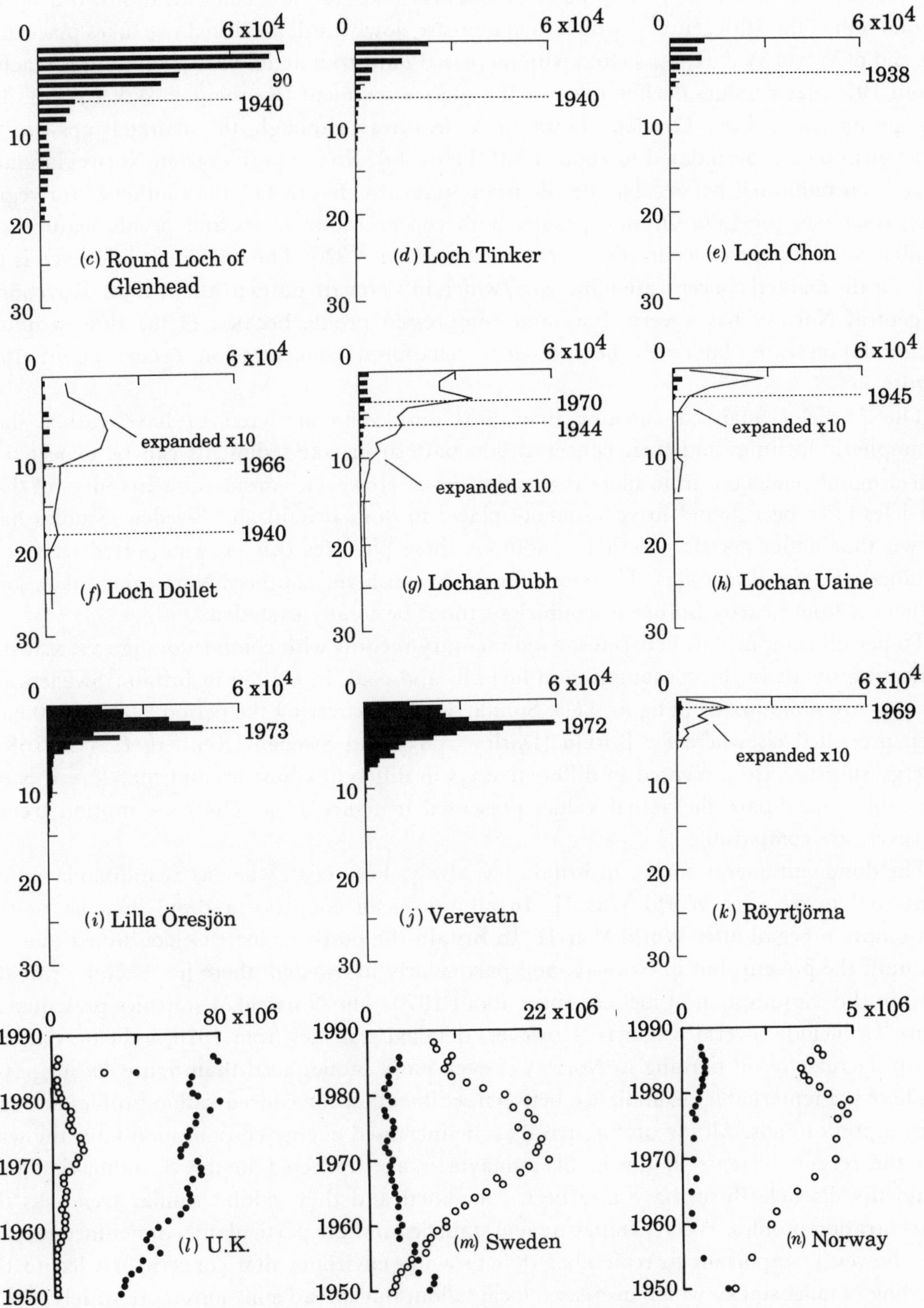

FIGURE 1. For description see opposite.

Characteristic features of SCP profiles in Swedish lakes are low concentrations, during the second half of the 19th century, which then increase slowly until a marked rise takes place after the end of World War II, associated with increased industrial activity. A maximum is reached about 1970; later values decline towards the surface sediment (Renberg & Wik 1985*a*). The SCP profile from Lilla Öresjön shows these features, although the marked upswing in concentration has been dated to about 1960 (figure 1*i*). No SCP profiles from Norwegian lakes have been published before. The profile from Verevatn (figure 1*j*), the southern Norwegian lake, resembles the Lilla Öresjön profile. Both concentration levels and profile features are similar, with a clear concentration maximum at about 1970. The only real difference is the date for the marked concentration increase, which in Verevatn dates to about 1930. Röyrtjörna in central Norway has a very short and compressed profile because of the slow sediment accumulation rate, but even here a clear maximum concentration occurs about 1970 (figure 1*k*).

The particles analysed (greater than 5–10 μm) are considered to have rather short atmospheric lifetimes and their concentration pattern in lake sediments can be expected to reflect mainly emissions from more regional sources. However, considerable amounts of these particles have been found in very remote places in both Britain and Sweden. Studies have shown that under certain weather conditions these particles can be transported over long distances (Davies *et al.* 1984). Therefore, for the Swedish and southern Norwegian lakes, some influences from nearby European countries cannot be totally excluded.

To permit comparisons between SCP sedimentary records with combustion figures, statistics indicating trends in the consumption of fuel oils and coal since 1950 in Britain, Sweden and Norway are summarized in figure 1*l–n*. Similar statistics covering the period before 1950 have been presented elsewhere for Britain (Darley 1985) and Sweden (Renberg & Wik 1984). Energy statistics are presented in different ways in different countries and therefore it is not advisable to compare the actual values presented in figure 1*l–n*. The consumption trends, however, are comparable.

The dominant energy source in Britain has always been coal, whereas Scandinavia shifted from coal to oil after World War II. In all European countries a rapid increase in fuel consumption began after World War II. In Britain the post-war increase continued more or less until the present, but in Norway, and particularly in Sweden, there has been a dramatic drop in the consumption of fuel oils since about 1970. The Norwegian statistics presented in figure 1*n* include several products. However, detailed statistics from 1970, indicate that the recent decrease in oil burning in Norway is even more pronounced than figure 1*n* suggests.

There is a remarkable resemblance between sedimentary SCP concentration profiles and fuel consumption trends. All SCP profiles parallel the increased energy consumption after the war, and the recent decrease in use in Scandinavia is also reflected in the Scandinavian lake sediments. Particle fluxes have also been calculated and they exhibit similar trends as the concentration profiles. When comparing fuel statistics and the particulate sedimentary records it is, however, important to remember that growing environmental concern first led to the building of taller stacks, which decreased local fallout but spread emissions more widely. More recently control devices have been installed to reduce emission levels and improved combustion techniques have had a similar effect.

The SCP concentration values for the lakes vary, indicating regional differences in the amount of air pollutants deposited from combustion sources. Among the Scottish lakes the concentrations for Lochan Uaine, Loch Doilet and Lochan Dubh in the north are significantly lower than for Loch Chon and Loch Tinker, which are in turn lower than for the Round Loch of Glenhead, the southernmost lake. The maximum value in the Round Loch of Glenhead (93×10^3 particles g^{-1} dry sediment (gds^{-1})) is about 45-times higher than in Lochan Uaine, the lake with the lowest maximum value (2.1×10^3 particles gds^{-1}). The concentration for Round Loch of Glenhead is the highest recorded so far in Britain. In Scotland the geographical concentration pattern found for the SWAP lakes generally agrees with other work carried out (Battarbee *et al.* 1988), with the exception of Lochan Uaine, which has a low particle concentration compared with other lakes from the same area. However, the trace metal concentrations (Rippey, this symposium) are also very low for this lake and the fact that it is a very remote, high-altitude lake might explain these results.

Among the Scandinavian lakes the particle concentration levels for Lilla Öresjön and Verevatn are similar although the maximum concentration is a little higher in Verevatn (59×10^3 compared with 48×10^3 particles gds^{-1}). Both lakes have high SCP concentrations compared with other sites previously studied in Scandinavia. The maximum concentration in Röyrtjörna is low (1.6×10^3 particles gds^{-1}), about 35 times lower than in Verevatn. The SCP concentration of the surface sediment from Lilla Öresjön fits well into a SCP map for Sweden (Wik & Renberg (unpublished)). The map is based on analyses of more than 100 lakes and shows a good agreement with maps of atmospheric sulphate deposition. The concentration in Röyrtjörna is comparable to lakes from low deposition areas in N. Sweden and N. Scotland.

References

Battarbee, R. W., Anderson, N. J., Appleby, P. G., Flower, R. J., Fritz, S. C., Haworth, E. Y., Higgitt, S., Jones, V. J., Kreiser, A., Munro, M. A. R., Natkanski, J., Oldfield, F., Patrick S. T., Richardson, N. G., Rippey, B. & Stevenson, A. C. 1988 *Lake acidification in the United Kingdom 1800–1986*. London: ENSIS Publishing.

Carignan, T. & Tessier, A. 1985 Zinc deposition in acid lakes: the role of diffusion. *Science, Wash.* **228**, 1524–1526.

Darley, J. 1985 Particulate soot in Galloway lake sediments; its application as an indicator of environmental change and as a technique for dating recent sediments. Department of Geography, University College London. Unpublished dissertation.

Davies, T. D., Abrahams, P. W., Tranter, M., Blackwood, I., Brimblecombe, P. & Vincent, C. E. 1984 Black acidic snow in the remote Scottish Highlands. *Nature, Lond.* **312**, 58–61.

Electrical Council 1988 *Handbook of electricity supply statistics*. London: Electrical Council.

Energy statistics yearbook 1983–1986 New York: United Nations.

Griffin, J. J. & Goldberg, E. D. 1983 Impact of fossil fuel combustion on sediments of Lake Michigan: a reprise. *Environ. Sci. Technol.* **17**, 244–245.

Holdren, G. R. Jr., Brunelle, T. M., Matisoff, G. & Wahlen, M. 1984 Timing the increase in atmospheric sulphur deposition in the Adirondack Mountains. *Nature, Lond.* **311**, 245–248.

McCrone, W. C. & Delly, J. G. 1973 *The particle atlas*, 1–4. Ann Arbor: Ann Arbor Science Publishers.

Renberg, I. 1981 Improved methods for sampling, photographing and varve-counting of varved lake sediments. *Boreas* **10**, 255–258.

Renberg, I. & Wik, M. 1984 Dating recent lake sediments by soot particle counting. *Verh. internat. Verein. Limnol.* **22**, 712–718.

Renberg, I. & Wik, M. 1985*a* Carbonaceous particles in lake sediments – pollutants from fossil fuel combustion. *Ambio* **14**, 161–163.

Renberg, I. & Wik, M. 1985*b* Soot particle counting in recent lake sediments: an indirect dating method. *Ecol. Bull.* **37**, 53–57.

Statistical papers series J 1971–1978 *World energy supplies*. New York: United Nations.

Statistiska Centralbyrån 1972 *Historisk statistik för Sverige*. Del 3, Utrikeshandeln 1932–1970. (In Swedish.)

Wik, M. & Renberg, I. 1987 Distribution in forest soils of carbonaceous particles from fossil fuel combustion. *Wat. Air Soil Pollut.* **33**, 125–129.

Wik, M., Renberg, I. & Darley, J. 1986 Sedimentary records of carbonaceous particles from fossil fuel combustion. *Hydrobiologia* **143**, 387–394.

Phil. Trans. R. Soc. Lond. B **327**, 325–330 (1990)
Printed in Great Britain

Lake sediment magnetism and atmospheric deposition

By F. Oldfield and N. Richardson

Department of Geography, University of Liverpool, P.O. Box 147, Liverpool, L69 3BX, U.K.

Many recent lake sediment profiles contain atmospherically derived fly ash and various particles from industrial processes. All these include a magnetic fraction that can be studied by subjecting subsamples to controlled magnetic fields in the laboratory and measuring the isothermal remanences acquired. These provide a basis for partially characterizing and roughly quantifying the magnetic minerals preserved in the sediments. The results presented illustrate those obtained from some 70% of the 39 profiles taken from 32 sites mostly in upland Wales and the Scottish Highlands. They show widespread increases in magnetite and haematite deposition beginning from the mid-nineteenth century onwards and steepening in the last three to five decades.

Introduction

Fly ash from solid-fuel fired power stations, together with the particulates emitted by industrial processes such as iron and steel manufacture and non-ferrous metal smelting, contains high concentrations of magnetic minerals. Those in fly ash arise from the conversion of iron impurities in the feed coal through high temperature combustion. They include both ferrimagnetic ('magnetite') and imperfect anti-ferromagnetic ('haematite') components in concentrations and proportions that vary with coal source and combustion procedures. The upper layers of peat bogs (Oldfield *et al.* 1978) and of lake sediments contain a historical record of atmospherically deposited magnetic particulates that, in most cases, are indistinguishable under scanning electron microscopy (SEM) from power-station fly ash (Hunt 1988).

The magnetic properties of most lake sediments are largely controlled by the nature of the magnetic minerals washed in from the catchment. Only where the contributions from these and from any authigenic components are consistently sparse and relatively uniform will it be easy to distinguish an atmospherically deposited component. The magnetic properties of all the lake sediment profiles used in both the Surface Water Acidification Project (SWAP) and the U.K. Department of Environment research programmes were measured to assess the value of magnetic records as indicators of the deposition of air-borne pollutants from combustion and industrial sources. One of the main advantages of magnetic measurements is their non-destructive character. This allows the same subsamples to be used for dating by γ assay (also non-destructive) and subsequent trace-metal or other analyses. The main disadvantage arises from the failure of the technique to give precise quantitative information on unambiguously identified mineral phases.

Methods and interpretation

The most frequent approach to establishing magnetic concentrations in samples involves measurement of magnetic susceptibility. The majority of samples used in this study were too small or too poor in ferrimagnetic minerals to make routine susceptibility measurements reliable or informative. Magnetic remanence measurements alone were used.

Dried and powdered sediment samples were weighed into 10 ml polystyrene pots that had been acid washed, pre-measured and selected for minimum magnetic contamination. In all cases the samples were given an anhysteretic remanent magnetization (ARM) by using a peak AF field of 100 mT and a DC field of 0.04 mT. In some cases stepwise acquisition of isothermal remanent magnetization (IRM) was measured by using forward fields of 20 mT and 300 mT. 'Saturation' isothermal remanent magnetization (SIRM) was grown for all samples in a DC field of 1 T. A partial stepwise demagnetization of SIRM was done on all samples by using reverse fields of 20 mT, 40 mT, 100 mT and 300 mT; ARM acquisition was achieved by means of a suitably adapted Molspin AF demagnetizer and IRMs were generated by using Molspin pulse magnetizers. At each step, the remanence retained by the sample was measured by using a Minispin slow-speed spinner fluxgate magnetometer. Measurements of laboratory remanences such as ARM and IRM can be used both to characterize and, within the limits set by the between-sample variations in magnetic-grain size and mineralogy, to quantify magnetic mineral assemblages; SIRM measurements as defined and measured in this study integrate contributions from all the isothermal remanence bearing components of the magnetic mineral assemblages in a sample. These different components can, to some degree, be differentiated by using the approach outlined below.

In presenting and interpreting the results of the magnetic remanence studies it has been useful to distinguish three mutually independent measurements each one related to the concentration of one or more magnetic components.

1. That part of the SIRM that can be demagnetized in a reverse DC field of 20 mT ($\text{SIRM} - \text{IRM}_{-20\text{ mT}}$). For the samples measured in this study, this 'soft' remanence component provides the best available approximate indication of the relative importance of magnetite. Thompson's (1986) calculations suggest that this measurement will be roughly proportional to the concentration of magnetite across a wide range of grain sizes with diameters above 0.0625 μm.

2. That part of the SIRM that remains unreversed in a reverse DC field of 300 mT ($\text{SIRM} + \text{IRM}_{-300\text{ mT}}$). This 'hard' remanence component can be used as a rough guide to the relative importance of haematite in the sample as the remanence held by almost all forms of magnetite saturates in fields lower than this.

These two calculated remanence properties provide the main basis for reconstructing the record of atmospheric deposition at sites where it is possible to distinguish either or both components from the catchment input. Simpler calculations by using remanences grown during stepwise acquisition of IRM can be used for the same purpose, but reverse-field measurements have been used in this study, largely because they can be precisely remeasured and confirmed much more easily. Moreover, the forward field ratios are available only for the cores measured towards the end of the programme.

3. The ARM values. For a given concentration of magnetite, ARM values reach a maximum both in absolute terms and also relative to IRM values, in true stable single domain grains with diameters around 0.02–0.04 μm (Maher 1988). The magnetic properties of most fly-ash samples and of most igneous rocks are dominated by coarser grains whereas secondary ferrimagnetic oxides formed in soils often include higher concentrations of these fine grains. A catchment-derived input of magnetic minerals may therefore have a wide range of ARM and SIRM/ARM values depending on the sources and types of material represented. Both catchment and atmospheric sources will contribute to ARM values; moreover, SIRM/ARM quotients will be

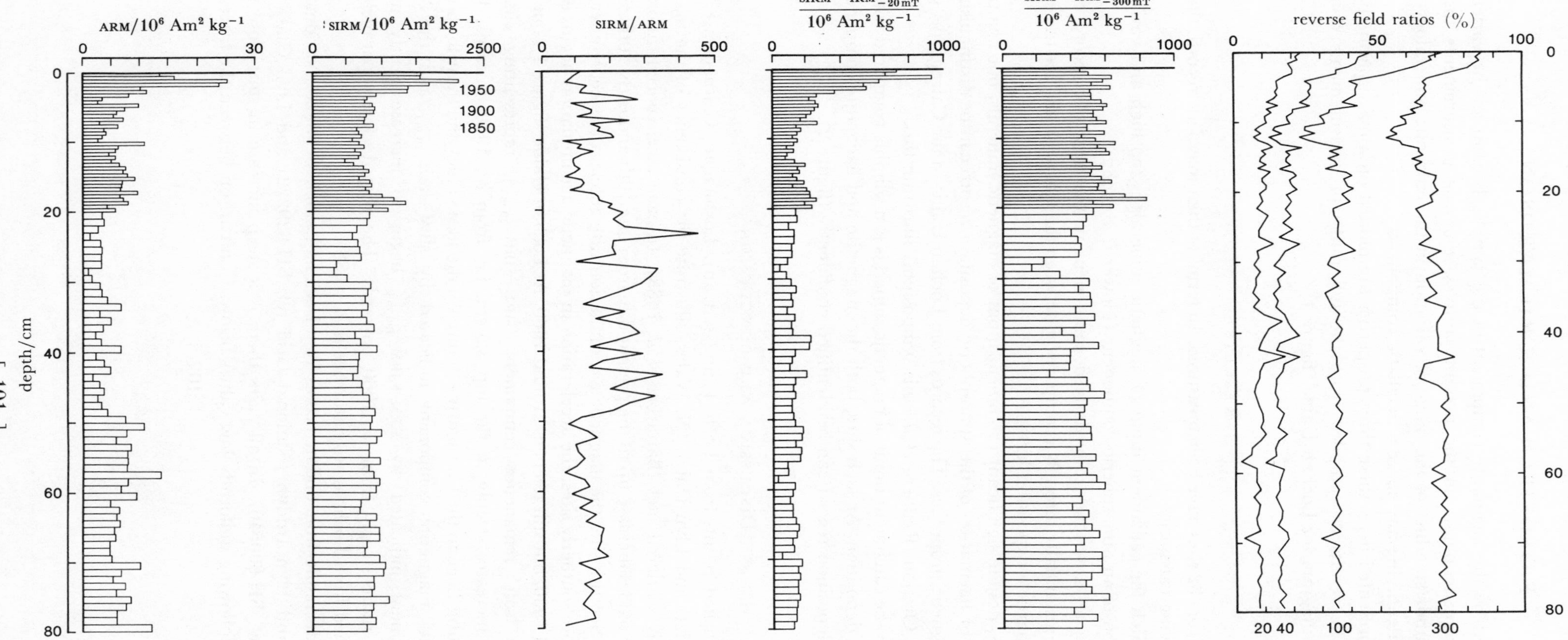

FIGURE 1. Magnetic remanence measurements done on subsamples from Lochan Uaine, Core UAI2. The sequence of measurements is described and explained in the text. In the reverse-field ratio plot the upper scale signifies percentage reverse saturation. Thus 50% represents the stage at which demagnetization of the original SIRM has reduced net remanent magnetization to zero; 100% represents the point at which the original SIRM is fully reversed. The figures below the graph are the reverse fields in millitesla (mT) used at each stage in demagnetization. The dates shown are based on a ^{210}Pb chronology derived from gamma measurements (Appleby *et al.*, this symposium).

strongly influenced by the haematite component of the sample. Because of the variety and complexity of magnetic phases in the present samples, the ARM measurements therefore contribute to an understanding of the range of variation in the magnetic mineralogy of the samples without identifying any specific magnetic component.

In the figures presented here, these three properties are plotted on a mass specific basis as 10^{-6} Am^2 kg^{-1}. The results as compiled from the full range of measurements done are illustrated by the diagram for Lochan Uaine (figure 1).

Results

In all, 39 cores from 32 sites have been measured. In terms of their magnetic record, the cores fall into the following categories.

1. Those in which the catchment input of magnetic minerals is too high and variable to permit the isolation of an atmospheric component (Flower *et al.* 1987).

2. Those where an atmospherically derived component in the magnetic record can be inferred only circumstantially through a comparison between the magnetic and the trace metal or carbonaceous particle deposition histories.

3. Those where, despite significant catchment input of magnetic minerals, one component (either magnetite or haematite) of the atmospheric deposition record can be distinguished on the basis of its magnetic properties. The records from Lochan Uaine in the Cairngorms (figure 1) and from Lilla Öresjön (Renberg *et al.*, this symposium) illustrate this.

4. Those where the catchment input of magnetic minerals is negligible compared with that from atmospheric deposition. At such sites, both the magnetite and haematite components of the atmospheric deposition record can be identified confidently (figure 2).

Discussion and conclusions

Previously published results from Loch Tanna (Arran), Lochnagar (Cairngorms), Scoat Tarn (Lake District) and Llyn Dulyn (N. Wales) illustrate the consistency of the magnetic record from widely scattered sites (Battarbee *et al.* 1988). In each lake, concentrations and fluxes of magnetic oxides increase up to the present day from late 19th and early 20th century levels. At the two Scottish sites the magnetic accumulation rate accelerates steeply after 1960, whereas at the more southerly sites, the acceleration in magnetic accumulation begins earlier, between 1915 and 1930, but still steepens around 1960. At Lochan Uaine (figure 1), one of the SWAP sites, the 'soft' remanence component ($\mathrm{SIRM} - \mathrm{IRM}_{-20\,\mathrm{mT}}$), representing changing magnetite input, increases steeply in the top 3.5 cm, i.e. from *ca.* 1940 onwards. In the sediments from Dubh Loch in the Cairngorms (figure 2), the SIRM values and those for both the magnetically 'soft' magnetite component indicated by $\mathrm{SIRM} - \mathrm{IRM}_{-20\,\mathrm{mT}}$ and the 'hard' haematite component indicated by $\mathrm{SIRM} + \mathrm{IRM}_{-300\,\mathrm{mT}}$ begin to increase gently around 1920–1930, then more steeply from *ca.* 1960 onwards. The record closely parallels that previously published from Lochnagar (Battarbee *et al.* 1988).

Figure 2 also plots results from undated cores from Loch na Larach, Scotland (National Grid ref. NC 217583 and Llyn Irddyn (National Grid ref. SH 629222) and Llyn Glas, Wales (National Grid ref. SH 600546). In all cases there is a steep increase in SIRM close to the sediment surface following uniformly low values below. Comparison between the traces from

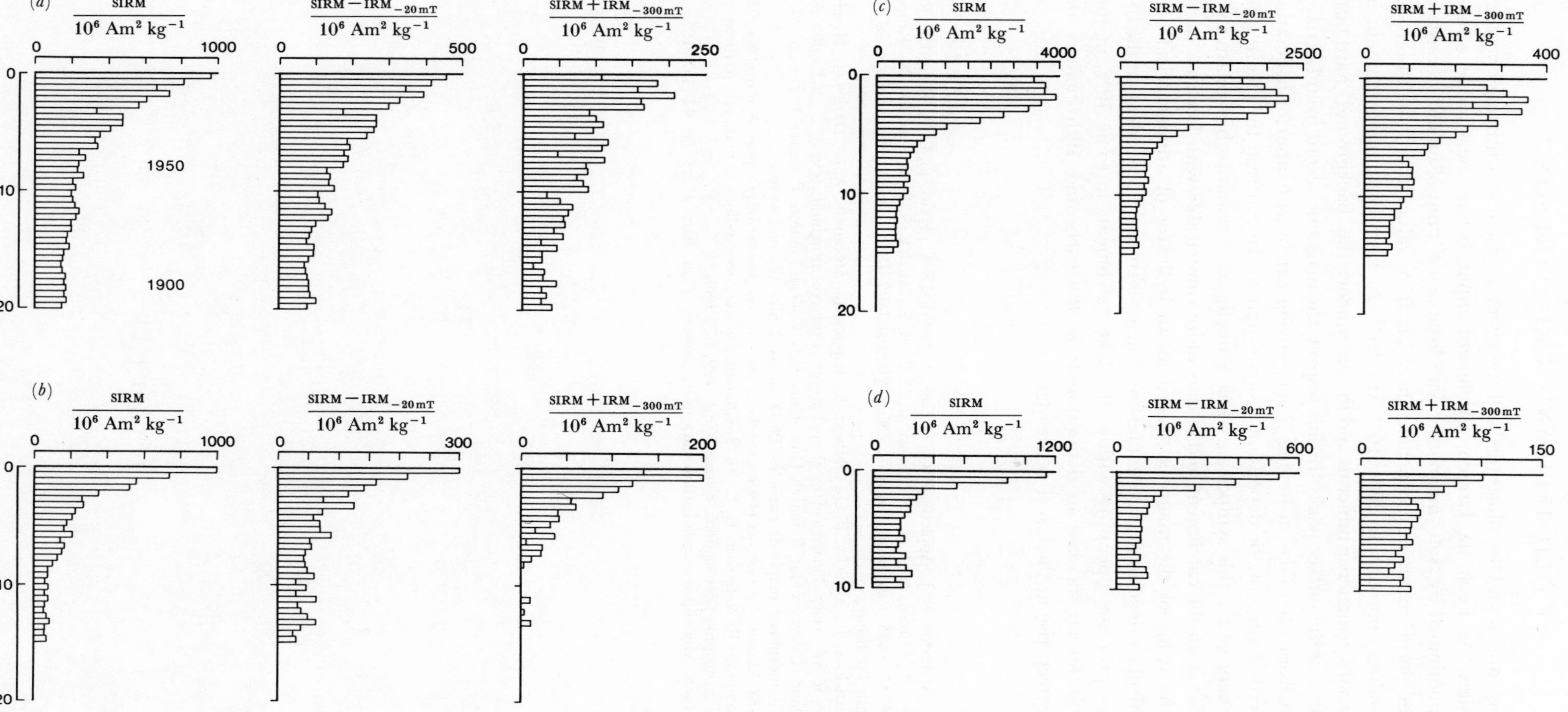

FIGURE 2. Profiles of SIRM, SIRM − IRM$_{-20\,mT}$ and SIRM + IRM$_{-300\,mT}$ for cores from (*a*) Dubh Loch (Grid ref. NO 238825) and (*b*) Loch na Larach (Grid ref. NC 217583) in the Scottish Highlands and from (*c*) Llyn Irddyn (Grid ref. SSH 629222) and (*d*) Llyn Glas (Grid ref. SH 600546), in upland Wales. The dates on the Dubh Loch graph are based on a ^{210}Pb chronology derived from γ measurements (Appleby *et al.*, this symposium). The other three cores, which form part of the U.K. Department of Environment programme, have not yet been dated.

Loch na Larach and Llyn Glas illustrates well the effect of catchment lithology on the record at different sites. At Loch na Larach, catchment input before measurable atmospheric deposition is dominated by 'soft' magnetite, with little or no input of unambiguously defined haematite. The 'hard' magnetic component then rises from values at or close to zero to near-surface peak values approaching $200 \times 10^{-6}\ Am^2\ kg^{-1}$. At Llyn Glas, the catchment input is dominated by hard remanence minerals and in consequence the 'background' hard IRM values average 30–40 % of the surface peaks. In this respect, the magnetic record from Lochan Uaine resembles that from Llyn Glas in having a very strong catchment input of haematite upon which the record of atmospheric deposition is superimposed. In contrast, the record from Lilla Öresjön (Renberg *et al.*, this symposium) has a negligible haematite but relatively strong magnetite input from the catchment and is thus more comparable with Loch na Larach.

Although the value of the magnetic record as an indicator of atmospherically derived industrial particulate deposition in recent lake sediments is strongly dependent on the lithology of, and surface processes operating within, the lake catchment, in some 70 % of the cores studied it indicates an increase in deposition from the early–mid 19th century onwards followed by a steep rise in the last 3–5 decades.

References

Battarbee, R. W., Anderson, N. J., Appleby, P. G., Flower, R. J., Fritz, S. C., Haworth, E. Y., Higgitt, S. R., Jones, V. J., Kreiser, A., Munro, M. A. R., Natkanski, J., Oldfield, F., Patrick, S. T., Richardson, N., Rippey, B. & Stevenson, A. C. 1988 *Lake acidification in the United Kingdom 1800–1986: evidence from analysis of lake sediments.* London: Ensis Publishing.

Flower, R. J., Patrick, S. T., Appleby, P. G., Oldfield, F., Rippey, B., Stevenson, A. C., Darley, J., Higgitt, S. R. & Battarbee, R. W. 1987 Palaeoecological evaluation of the recent acidification of Loch Laidon, Rannoch Moor, Scotland. Palaeoecology Research Unit, University College London, Research Paper no. 29.

Hunt, A. 1988 Atmospheric magnetic particles. Ph.D. thesis, University of Liverpool.

Maher, B. A. 1988 Magnetic properties of some synthetic sub-micron magnetites. *Geophys. R. astron. Soc.* **94**, 83–96.

Oldfield, F., Thompson, R. & Barber, K. E. 1978 Changing atmospheric fallout of magnetic particles recorded in recent ombrotrophic peat sections. *Science, Wash.* **199**, 679–680.

Thompson, R. 1986 Modelling magnetization data using SIMPLEX. *Phys. Earth planet. Int.* **42**, 113–127.

Phil. Trans. R. Soc. Lond. B **327**, 331–338 (1990)
Printed in Great Britain

The record of atmospheric deposition on a rainwater-dependent peatland

By R. S. Clymo[1], F. Oldfield[2], P. G. Appleby[3], G. W. Pearson[4], P. Ratnesar[1] and N. Richardson[2]

[1] *School of Biological Sciences, Queen Mary and Westfield College, London E1 4NS, U.K.*
[2] *Department of Geography and*
[3] *Department of Applied Mathematics and Theoretical Physics, The University, Liverpool L69 3BX, U.K.*
[4] *Palaeoecology Centre, The Queen's University, Belfast BT17 1NN, U.K.*

Rainwater-dependent peatlands retain a record of atmospheric deposition. Unlike lake sediments they record both particulate and soluble influxes, and they are not complicated by processes in the catchment or by mineral particle influx from the catchment. They do, however, have their own difficulties some of which are considered here.

The timescale for cores from a suitable peatland in Southwest Scotland was established by a combination of ^{14}C 'wiggle matching', pollen events, ^{210}Pb dating and the ^{241}Am event. Retention of deposited elements varied greatly from less than 1% (Na) to complete retention (N). Hummocks retained more than hollows: the quotient was 1.2–1.8 for elements such as Al (associated with particles) and up to 5–10 for Mn, Fe and Zn. The vertical scale in profiles should be as cumulative dry mass or, better, as dry mass after reconstructing losses by decay. These give vertical scales that are approximately linear with age. Elements differ greatly in the shape of their concentration profile as a result of varying influx and as a result of relocation in the peat.

Introduction

The record of deposition of atmospheric contamination in lake sediments may be difficult to read because the constituents have reached the sediments by a variety of processes and by paths of differing tortuosity at different speeds from different parts of the catchment. Atmospheric deposition is often swamped by the contribution to sediments of mineral particles from the catchment soils and rocks. Rainwater-dependent (ombrotrophic) peatlands do not have these problems and, because of their high cation-exchange abilities, may retain solutes that would never reach lake sediments at all. But they have their own difficulties connected with uptake by plants, with decay of the peat, with chemical change in the peat, and with flow of water in the peat. Here we report an exploration of the possibilities. We consider timescales (essential for calculating fluxes), retention efficiency, how best to present results, and a few of the 50000 results that this work has generated.

Site and methods

Fifteen cores were collected from an ombrotrophic raised bog, Ellergower Moss (National Grid reference NX 482795), at the northeast outlet of Loch Dee, Galloway, southwest

Scotland. The bog is approximately elliptical with radii of about 330 and 350 m. At its centre, where we took samples, it is about 6 m deep. Basal samples have low concentrations of pollen of *Corylus*, and may be cross-referred to a similar site on a peninsula in Loch Dee with a ^{14}C age of 9000 years (P. Newell, personal communication) similar to basal dates for peat in a small basin in the catchment of Round Loch of Glenhead close by (V. Jones, personal communication). Most of the Ellergower peat is humified and homogeneous. The surface has a variety of hummocks and hollows and a few small pools. It contrasts with the nearby Silver Flowe on which pools are abundant.

Cores EM1–EM15 of 20 cm diameter and about 50 cm depth were taken from surface features of various sorts by using apparatus (Clymo 1988) that retains the water in place. They were later cut into 1 cm thick slices and the values of about 60 variables measured including dry bulk density, water content, pH, E_{H5}, the concentrations of about 45 elements, activity of ^{210}Pb, ^{137}Cs, ^{241}Am and several magnetic properties.

Comparisons are possible with the adjacent Loch Dee sediments (B. Rippey, personal communication) but are too complex for this article.

Core structure

The cores all show a downward increase in dry bulk density as a result of compaction (figure 1*b*). This is associated with the development of waterlogging and anoxia (Clymo 1987). It is convenient to recognize two layers. The upper one, extending down to the maximum depth reached by the water-table in dry summers, is porous and is called the acrotelm (Ingram 1978). The lower, much thicker and anoxic layer is the catotelm. In the acrotelm aerobic decay is relatively rapid and water movement, both vertical and horizontal, is rapid. In the catotelm anaerobic decay and water movement are very slow. At the boundary are high concentrations of sulphide, with which many metals form highly insoluble salts.

In hummocks the porous acrotelm is relatively deep and one might expect substantial relocation of solutes. In hollows the acrotelm is much shallower. In the work reported here the boundary between acrotelm and catotelm is defined as the point where E_{H5} became negative. The cores were all collected in early November when the water-table was probably within 2 cm of its mean position (Bragg 1982).

Timescales

The ^{14}C 'wiggle-matching' method was applied to one core (EM3) from a *Sphagnum capillifolium* hummock. This method relies on the pattern of fluctuations in ^{14}C in the atmosphere over the most recent 400 years. The ^{14}C age of a single sample in this range is ambiguous at best, but a series may allow the pattern of fluctuations to be matched with that known from tree-rings (Stuiver & Pearson 1986). The results are shown in figure 1.

The calibration curve shows troughs at 1712 and 1900, both now in the catotelm. These were matched with what seem to be corresponding points in the sequence of peat samples. The other peat samples are distributed in proportion to the cumulative mass. The matching of *shape* is fairly good, though some of the ^{14}C ages are rather high.

The most conspicuous local pollen event is the great increase in *Pinus*. It is shown as a proportion of the sum of *Pinus*, *Alnus*, *Betula* and *Corylus* (figure 1*b*). The depth at which this

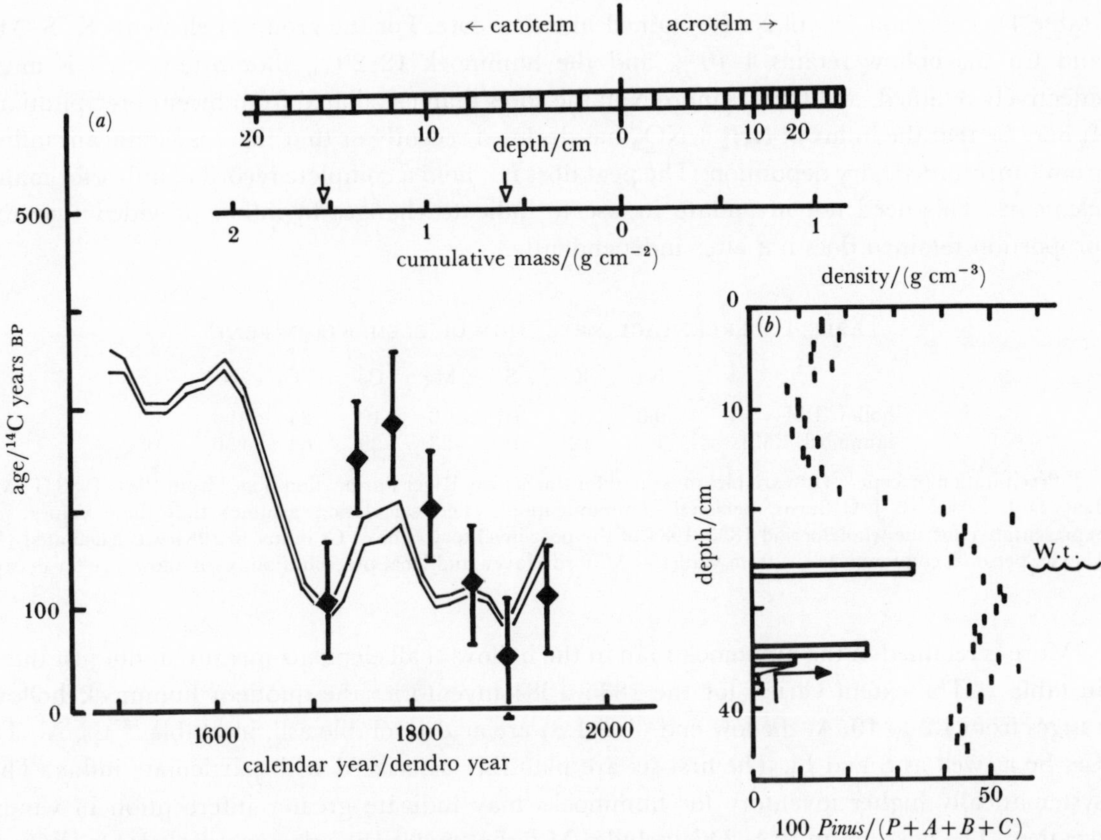

FIGURE 1. Hummock core EM3; (*a*) outer bounds of the relation between ^{14}C age and true (dendro) age. Superimposed lozenges and counting precision bars are for core EM3. Above is a horizontal scale of cumulative mass. Arrows show points at which the EM3 and calibration lines were forced to coincide. At top, the corresponding (nonlinear) scale of depth. Each block represents 2 cm. Both upper scales start at the acrotelm–catotelm boundary. (*b*) Profile of dry matter bulk density (vertical bars) and (histogram) of the pollen quotient *Pinus*/(*Pinus*+*Alnus*+*Betula*+*Corylus*). The point where this rises above 5% is shown by a reflecting arrow. (W.t., watertable.)

variable rises above 5% can be located in all the cores to within 1 cm. The wiggle-matched ^{14}C dates this to about 1835.

The results of ^{210}Pb dating of a core from a hollow are shown in figure 2*a*. The 1835 *Pinus* rise agrees fairly closely with the ^{210}Pb chronology, confirming the assumption implicit in this method that there is relatively little redistribution of Pb in this core with a shallow acrotelm. The assumption of uniformity of processes is confirmed in figure 2*b* where the same results are plotted against cumulative mass. The line is almost straight, with a slight concavity at the top where the decay rate might be expected to be rather higher. Also consistent are the recent rise in conifer pollen (as a result of planting) in about 1973 and of the peak in ^{241}Am attributable to peak influxes from aerial nuclear weapons testing in 1954 and especially in 1963.

RETENTION IN PEAT

The inventory in cores EM3 and EM4 down to the 1835 *Pinus* event is compared with the precipitation influx from 1981–1988, provisionally assumed to hold for the 150-year period (table 1). Less than 1% of Na is retained in either core. For the group of elements K, S, Mg and Ca the hollow retains 4–10% and the hummock 12–29%. Bomb-test ^{137}Cs is more effectively retained, and there is more N in the cores than calculated from recent precipitation. It may be that the influx of $NH_4^+ + NO_3^-$ has declined recently or that there is significant influx from (unrecorded) dry deposition. The peat does not hold a complete record of influx for many elements. This need not invalidate its use to indicate changes in influx provided that the proportion retained does not alter independently.

Table 1. Percentage retention of elements in peat[a]

	Na	K	S	Mg	Ca	^{137}Cs	N
hollow EM4	0.3	4	10	6	10	25	120
hummock EM3	1	12	16	23	29	63	250

[a] Precipitation (except ^{137}Cs) variables measured for the Solway River Purification Board from 1981–1988 (F. M. Lee, D. J. Tervet & J. C. Burns, personal communication). The calculation assumes that these values are representative for the whole period 1835–1984 of the peat inventory. The ^{137}Cs influx to 1984 was calculated (P. Cawse, personal communication) from values at Milford Haven and local precipitation, with allowance for decay.

More is retained in the hummock than in the hollow of all elements measured, not just those in table 1. The extent varies: for the 1835–1984 inventories the quotient hummock:hollow ranges from 1.2 to 10. At the low end (1.2–1.8) are acid-insoluble ash, insoluble ^{137}Cs, Al, Ti, Ce, Sc as well as S and Li. The first six are plausibly associated with particulate influx. The systematically higher inventory for hummocks may indicate greater interception in windy weather. The next group (2.1–2.8) includes Mg, the 'metabolic' elements K, soluble ^{137}Cs, P and N and Pb and Cu. In the range 3.5–5.0 are Cd, Na, Ca, Sr and Ba. Finally, with large differences, are Mn (5.1), Fe (7.7) and Zn (10.0). The main difference between the cores is that the hummock has a deeper unsaturated layer than the hollow has. Retention of some elements is very dependent on processes in the unsaturated layer.

Presenting concentration profiles

Lake sediment profiles are usually shown with depth as distance. In peat, however, compression may make this very misleading. Figures 2*a*, *b* and 3 show this effect. Cumulative mass is easily measured and involves no assumptions. But even this can be misleading. During the time that it takes for the catotelm to rise and engulf a piece of organic matter, originally at the surface, aerobic decay will have removed a lot of the matter. Estimates (Clymo 1984) give values of about 90% loss. If an element were conserved in position its concentration on a dry mass basis would increase tenfold. There are two solutions: firstly, one may use only those cores, such as in figure 2*b*, where there is a linear age against cumulative mass relation. (The most plausible, but not the only possible, explanation of such linearity is constant rate of peat accumulation.) Secondly, one may try to reconstruct the lost mass. In figure 3*c*, for the hummock core EM3, is shown a case where this would be essential. The top 32 cm of this profile (strongly condensed by the choice of axis in figure 3*c*) would have had a much steeper slope than the lower part. On the assumptions that, in the acrotelm, $\mathrm{d}m/\mathrm{d}t = -\alpha m$ and $\mathrm{d}M/\mathrm{d}T = p - \alpha M$, where m = dry mass of peat, t = time, M = cumulative dry mass on an area basis below a datum, T = time in the past below the same datum, p = rate of addition

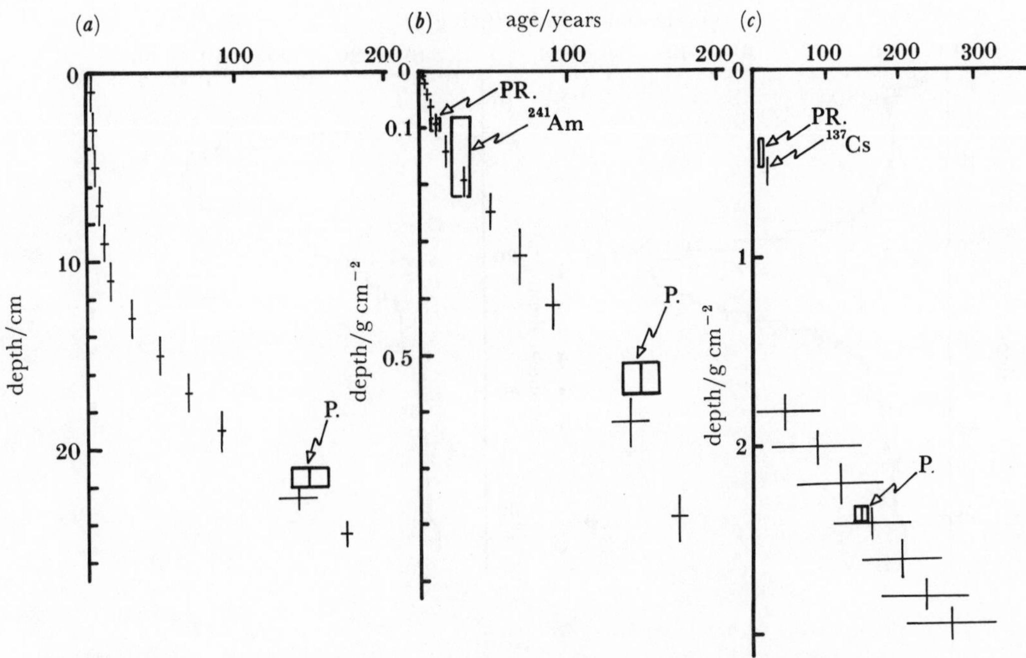

FIGURE 2. Profiles of age against depth. (*a*) Hollow core EM4, ^{210}Pb derived age. (P., *Pinus* event (see figure 1).) (*b*) Same data as in (*a*) but plotted against depth as cumulative dry mass. Not shown in (*a*) are PR., a recent increase in conifer pollen attributed to Forestry Commission plantings, and ^{241}Am, attributed to aerial nuclear weapons testing. (*c*) Axes as in (*b*) but for the hummock core EM3 by using the ^{14}C derived ages from figure 1. The vertical ^{137}Cs line is for acid-insoluble (probably particulate) material, but may be unreliable. Note that though (*b*) shows only a small concavity near the origin, (*c*) has a marked break in slope even though the effects of compression and differing bulk density are removed by this sort of plot. The remaining effect is attributed to decay in the acrotelm (see figure 3).

of dry mass on an area basis and α = proportional rate of decay then it follows that $M_a = (p/\alpha)[1-\exp(m_a/m_0)]$, where the subscript 'a' indicates conditions at the acrotelm–catotelm boundary. The value of M_a can be measured; m_a/m_0 ('survival') could be measured but in practice must be guessed; and p/α can then be calculated. This is then used in $M = (p/\alpha)[1-\exp(m/m_0)]$ at other positions in the acrotelm to calculate m/m_0 and hence to reconstruct m_0. For the catotelm the rate of decay is so much lower that for periods of a few hundred years (only) one can ignore it. The results of using these three methods of presentation (linear, mass and reconstructed mass) are shown in figure 3. The value $m_a/m_0 = 0.05$ gave a line that points, approximately, to the origin in figure 3*c*. Two points are clear. First, the method of plotting has a substantial effect on the apparent meaning of the results. Secondly, the plot in (*d*) is such that if an element had been coming in at constant rate and had not moved after it was deposited then one would see a straight line parallel to the vertical axis. For iron this is not the case. The peak is associated with the water-table where there are large chemical (and probably microbiological) changes as well. It is unlikely that there was a short-lived 20-fold increase in influx during the 1950s; transport and local accumulation on a large scale within the peat core are likely explanations.

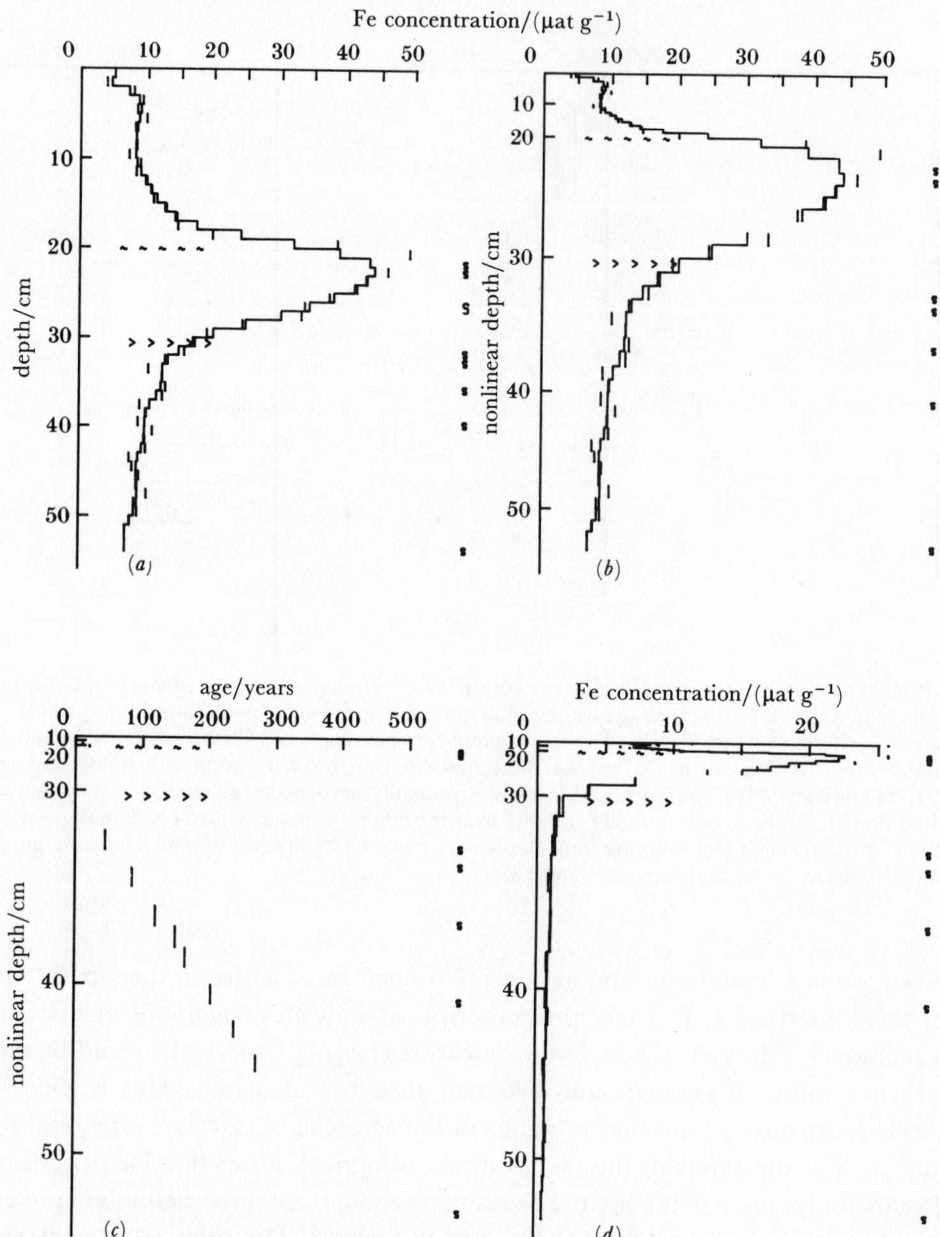

FIGURE 3. Profiles in hummock core EM3 of age (*c*) inferred from figure 1 and of concentration of iron (*a*), (*b*), (*d*). Measured values and a smoothed line are shown. In (*a*) the depth scale is linear distance. In (*b*) depth is linear with cumulative dry mass but has been marked with appropriate distance units (cm). Depth scales in (*c*) and (*d*) are similar to (*b*) but the dry mass includes estimated losses during decay assuming $m_a/m_0 = 0.05$ (see text). The line of (∼ ∼) indicates the watertable. The line of (>) indicates the depth at which E_{H5} becomes negative. The column of scattered symbols at the right of each graph show where a moderate to strong smell of sulphide was recorded.

BEHAVIOUR OF SELECTED ELEMENTS

An example of the variety of patterns in one hollow is shown in figure 4. The vertical scale is linear with cumulative mass and approximately linear with age (figure 2*b*) and the whole core spans about 600 years.

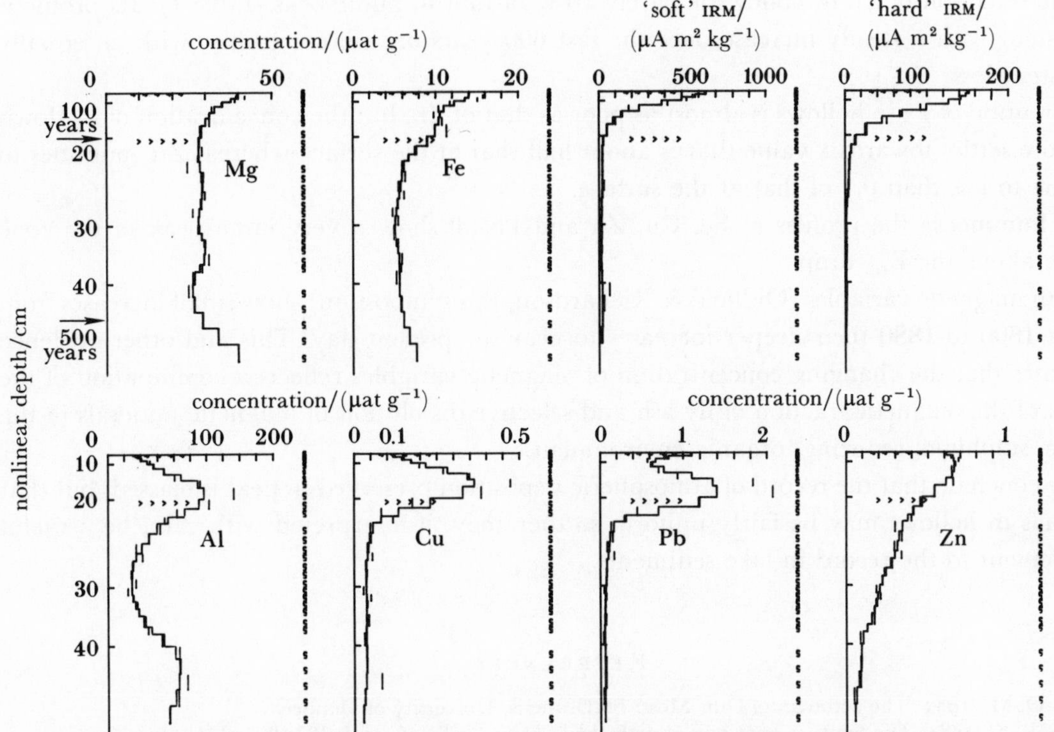

FIGURE 4. Profile of concentrations on a dry mass basis (μat g^{-1}) of six elements and two magnetic variables in hollow core EM4. Conventions as in figure 3. The vertical scale is linear for cumulative dry mass but is marked in (nonlinear) distance units for convenience. For this core cumulative mass is approximately linear with age (figure 2*b*), so on these plots vertical distance on the plot is approximately linear with age too. The arrow at about 19 cm depth is at approximately 100 years; that at about 46 cm depth is five times further down (in cumulative mass) and is therefore at about 500 years (about 1500 A.D.); 'soft' IRM ($\text{SIRM}-\text{IRM}_{-20\,\text{mT}}$) reflects changes in the concentration of magnetite; 'hard' IRM ($\text{SIRM}+\text{IRM}_{-300\,\text{mT}}$) reflects haematite (Oldfield & Richardson, this symposium). (Isothermal remanent magnetization, IRM; 'saturation' isothermal remanent magnetization, SIRM.)

The concentration of Mg, which we assume to be derived mainly from sea spray, is approximately constant though with small increases at the core base and recently. As barely 6% of the incident Mg is retained (table 1) this relative constancy in concentration of an element whose influx has probably been fairly constant is important. The elements Ca, Sr and Ba (not figured) show a similar pattern to that of Mg except that their concentrations double during the last 50 years.

The profile of Al is similar to Ti and V with peaks in about 1500 and 1880. We suspect these elements arrived mainly as particles, but the decline during the present century suggests that power-station fly ash may contribute rather little compared with other sources. The peak centred on 1880, however, is related to the E_{H5} drop and to a sharp increase in dry bulk density (not shown). The chemistry of Al is not much affected by redox or sulphide concentration, but the movement of particles may be affected by sharply reduced hydraulic conductivity (consequent on increased bulk density).

Both Pb and Cu form very insoluble sulphides, and their downward movement may be retarded in horizons with a high concentration of H_2S thus giving peaks in their concentration profiles. There is a doubling of concentration of Pb (parallel with that of Ba and Sr) during the last 50 years. This is consistent with the increase in emission of these elements.

The retention of Zn in hollows is barely 10% of that in hummocks (table 1). Its profile is consistent with a steady increase over the last 600 years or, more credibly, with an equally persistent loss.

Retention of Fe in hollows is almost as poor as that of Zn, but the concentration of Fe down the core settles towards a value that is about half that at the surface whereas Zn continues to decline to less than 0.1 of that at the surface.

In hummocks the profiles of Fe, Cu, Zn and Pb all show a very large peak in the zone 10 cm above the E_{H5} drop.

Both magnetic variables (Oldfield & Richardson, this symposium) show small increases from about 1800 to 1880 then steeper increases to near the present day. This and other evidence indicates that the changing concentration of magnetic variables reflects a combination of the influx of the magnetic fraction of fly ash and selective dissolution of magnetic minerals in the acidic, sulphidic, reducing, organic environment.

We conclude that the record of atmospheric deposition preserved in peat is biassed, but that the bias in hollows may be fairly uniform so they may, if interpreted with care, be a useful supplement to the record in lake sediments.

References

Bragg, O. M. 1982 The acrotelm of Dun Moss. Ph.D. thesis, University of Dundee.
Clymo, R. S. 1984 The limits to peat bog growth. *Phil. Trans. R. Soc. Lond.* B **303**, 605–654.
Clymo, R. S. 1987 The ecology of peatlands. *Sci. Prog., Oxf.* **71**, 593–614.
Clymo, R. S. 1988 A high-resolution sampler of surface peat. *Func. Ecol.* **2**, 425–431.
Ingram, H. A. P. 1978 Soil layers in mires: function and terminology. *J. Soil Sci.* **29**, 224–227.
Stuiver, M. & Pearson, G. W. 1986 High precision calibration of the radiocarbon time scale, AD 1950–500 BC. *Radiocarbon* **28**, 805–838.

Phil. Trans. R. Soc. Lond. B **327**, 339–347 (1990)
Printed in Great Britain

The causes of lake acidification, with special reference to the role of acid deposition

By R. W. Battarbee

Palaeoecology Research Unit, Department of Geography, University College London, 26 Bedford Way, London WC1H 0AP, U.K.

Acid surface waters (pH < 5.5) occur throughout western and northern Europe. The claim that many of these waters have been acidified in recent decades and that the acidification results from acid deposition has been well-substantiated by palaeolimnological studies. At almost all sites acidification post-dates 1800 A.D.; it is accompanied by increases in the concentration of trace metals and carbonaceous particles and the spatial pattern of acidified lakes coincides with areas of high acid deposition (greater than 0.5 g sulphur m^{-2} a^{-1}). Very sensitive sites (Ca^{2+} < 50 μeq l^{-1}) in areas of low acid deposition are not acidified.

Palaeolimnological tests to evaluate the contribution of other factors suggest that leaching and paludification processes are important on a post-glacial time scale but imperceptible over the last 200 years, and that alterations to catchment burning and grazing regimes over this time scale have little or no effect. Only the afforestation of sensitive catchments in areas of high sulphur deposition appears to be significant, an effect attributed to the enhanced sulphur-scavenging efficiency of the forest canopy rather than to the direct effect of forest growth.

Introduction

Palaeolimnologists have shown that recent (post-1800) lake acidification is a common phenomenon in many parts of Europe and North America (Renberg & Hellberg 1982; Davis *et al.* 1983; Flower & Battarbee 1983; Charles 1985). They have used the lake sediment record to evaluate alternative explanations for the causes of lake acidification (Battarbee *et al.* 1985). In addition to the acid deposition hypothesis initially proposed by Odén (1968), these have included land-use change (Rosenqvist 1977, 1978; Krug & Frink 1983) and the long-term effect of natural processes (Pennington 1984).

Although there is now overwhelming palaeolimnological evidence for the importance of acid deposition as the main cause of recent acidification (Battarbee *et al.* 1988*a*) it is nevertheless important to assess the extent to which these other factors may have contributed to the overall result.

The Surface Water Acidification Project (SWAP) Palaeolimnology Programme has included two studies that describe the post-glacial history of acidified or sensitive lakes (Atkinson & Haworth and Renberg, this symposium) and several studies that were designed to assess the impact of land-use and land-management change (Patrick *et al.*, Birks *et al.*, Anderson & Korsman, Kreiser *et al.* and Renberg *et al.*, this symposium). This paper summarizes the results of these studies and describes the palaeolimnological evidence that directly supports the acid-deposition hypothesis.

Long-term acidification

Long-term lake acidification has been a theme in palaeolimnological research for over 50 years. There are now many studies, reviewed by Battarbee (1984) and Charles & Norton (1986), mainly based on diatom analysis, showing that many presently acidic lakes were characterized in their early history by alkaline conditions. Some, however, have been acidic throughout their history (Jones *et al.* 1989). In all cases where acidification has taken place, the period of most rapid change occurs in the earliest stage following deglaciation (Whitehead *et al.* 1986; Atkinson & Haworth and Renberg, this symposium). Most authors, by using pollen analysis and sediment chemistry (Pennington *et al.* 1972; Digerfeldt 1972; Engstrom & Wright 1985) attribute this change to a combination of the removal of easily leached base cations from unweathered catchment soils and the development of acidic organic soils as a vegetation succession from arctic tundra to forest took place in the early Post-glacial period.

Although detailed trajectories in the latter part of the Post-glacial period vary from site to site depending on geology, soils, vegetation and early human influence, recent studies by using pH-inference techniques have shown that acidification during this period is very slow indeed (Renberg & Hellberg 1982; Atkinson & Haworth and Renberg, this symposium), with rates often less than 0.1 pH unit per 1000 years. In some cases, pH has not changed despite acidification and paludification of catchment soils (Jones *et al.* 1989). This mismatch between soil acidity and lake acidity in pre-industrial periods may be due to a combination of in-lake neutralizing processes, the inflow of relatively alkaline groundwater to lakes, the high partial pressure of CO_2 in soils and the lack of additional mobile anions to transfer acidity in surface soil horizons to watercourses.

Land-use and land-management change

Heathland and/or forest regeneration

The possibility that recent lake acidification is caused by changes in catchment land-use and management was proposed most explicitly by Rosenqvist (1977, 1978). He argued that a decline in farming intensity, especially in burning and grazing, would lead to regeneration of heathland and forest vegetation causing an increase in the accumulation of acid humus in soils and the release of protons into surface waters by cation exchange processes.

There have been many attempts to test this hypothesis by using palaeolimnological techniques, either by careful choice of sites or by using past analogues. It can be argued that the hypothesis cannot have universal validity as recent lake acidification has occurred in regions where there has been either no change or, in some cases, an increase in farming intensity (Timberlid 1980; Battarbee *et al.* 1985; Patrick *et al.*, this symposium). In addition, sites with only very small catchments in relation to their surface area (Birks *et al.*, this symposium) have been recently acidified as have montane sites above the limit of summer sheep grazing (Patrick *et al.* 1989, this symposium). In all these cases there is a clear evidence of atmospheric contamination.

At sites where a decrease in burning and grazing has occurred in the catchments of acidified lakes, it is sometimes possible to test the hypothesis by comparing the timing of land-use change with the timing of acidification. For example at Llyn y Bi in Wales Fritz *et al.* (1990) showed that acidification began in the late-nineteenth century well before the landowner's decision to stop *Calluna* burning in the 1930s.

Although these examples illustrate cases where land-use changes cannot have caused lake acidification, none examine the efficacy of the mechanism itself. Where there has been a decrease in burning and grazing and an increase in acid deposition over approximately similar timescales, the effect of the former can be assessed by using analogues in space or in time. A space analogue would involve a study of land-use effects in sensitive systems in an area of very low acid deposition (less than 0.5 g S m^{-2} a^{-1}). There have been no palaeolimnological studies of this kind, but it can be observed that very acid clear-water lakes ($pH < 5.5$) do not occur in areas of very low acid deposition despite well-documented histories of land-use change.

An alternative approach is to use past analogues, employing palaeoecological techniques to examine the relation between vegetation and land-use changes, inferred from pollen analysis, and lake response, inferred from diatom analysis, at times well before the increase in acid deposition (pre 1800 A.D.). Although detailed land-use inferences are more conjectural with past analogues the advantage is that lakes that are currently acidified, and therefore of proven sensitivity, can be used. In this way Jones *et al.* (1986) showed that a major shift from woodland to peatland in the catchment of the Round Loch of Glenhead approximately 5000 years BP caused little change in lake pH. Renberg *et al.* (this symposium) did pollen and diatom analysis of eight sensitive sites in Sweden and showed that there was little or no water pH response to the spread of *Picea* forest 2500–3000 years ago, and Anderson & Korsman (this symposium) similarly showed that no acidification followed the decline in farming that took place in an area of northern Sweden during Iron Age times.

The heathland and forest regeneration hypothesis is irrelevant at many sites and where and when an appropriate land-use change has taken place there is no related evidence for significant water acidification.

Conifer afforestation in the United Kingdom

In this discussion it is appropriate to separate afforestation of moorland and its effects from the land-use changes described above because afforestation processes involve an intensification of catchment interference and management, often including deep drainage of soils, hydrological manipulation, use of fertilizers and pesticides and closely-spaced planting of trees. Moreover it has been observed that forests are efficient scavengers of dry sulphur deposition (D. Fowler, personal communication) and that streams with afforested catchments have more acidic water and poorer fisheries than adjacent streams with moorland catchments (Harriman & Morrison 1982; Stoner & Gee 1985).

Diatom analysis of sediments from very sensitive lakes ($Ca^{2+} < 50$ μeq l^{-1}) have shown that acidification invariably precedes afforestation (Flower & Battarbee 1983; Flower *et al.* 1987), but the study of Kreiser *et al.* (this symposium) comparing the diatom histories of afforested and moorland lakes at higher Ca^{2+} levels (80 μeq l^{-1}) indicates that afforestation led to a rapid acceleration in acidification at a time when the moorland control site (Loch Tinker) changed little.

To evaluate whether the forest effect was caused by forest growth factors or by scavenging Kreiser *et al.* (this symposium) then compared a sensitive afforested and moorland site in an area to the north with lower acid deposition. Although it was not possible to separate clearly the forest effect from the direct effect of acid deposition, as the moorland site was also slightly acidified, the results show that the afforested site in the north (Loch Doilet) was much less acidified than the afforested site (Loch Chon) in the south, despite the presence of a more mature forest at the former site. These data require replication but nevertheless support the scavenging hypothesis as the main mechanism to explain the 'forest effect.'

Acid deposition

A major effort has been made to consider the role of factors other than acid deposition as a cause of lake acidification. As these factors have been shown to be of very minor importance it is now necessary to assess how well acid deposition can explain recent lake acidification. Potential cause-effect relations are easier to disprove than to prove, but the palaeolimnological evidence supporting the acid deposition hypothesis is substantial. It can be demonstrated that recent lake acidification is almost perfectly correlated with acid deposition surrogates in both time and space; we can show that a dose–response relation exists between sulphur loading and the sensitivity of lakes to acidification.

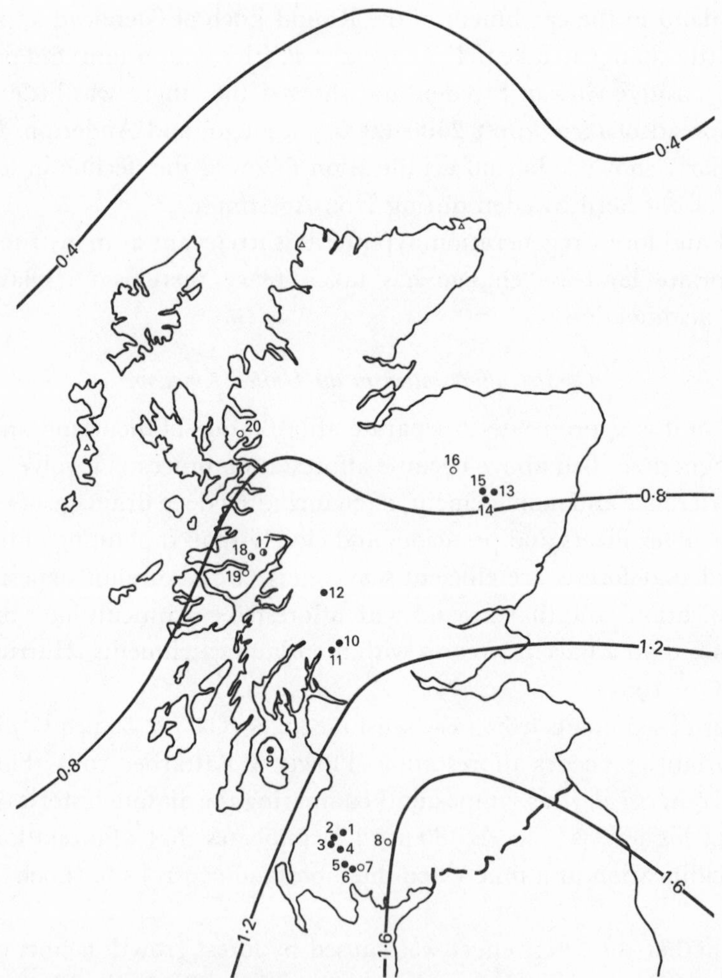

FIGURE 1. Change of pH at core sites in relation to the modelled deposition of S (g m^{-2} a^{-1}) for Scotland (from Derwent *et al.* (1988)); (●), pH decrease 0.4–1.2; (◑), pH decrease < 0.4; (○), no decrease; (△), work in progress.

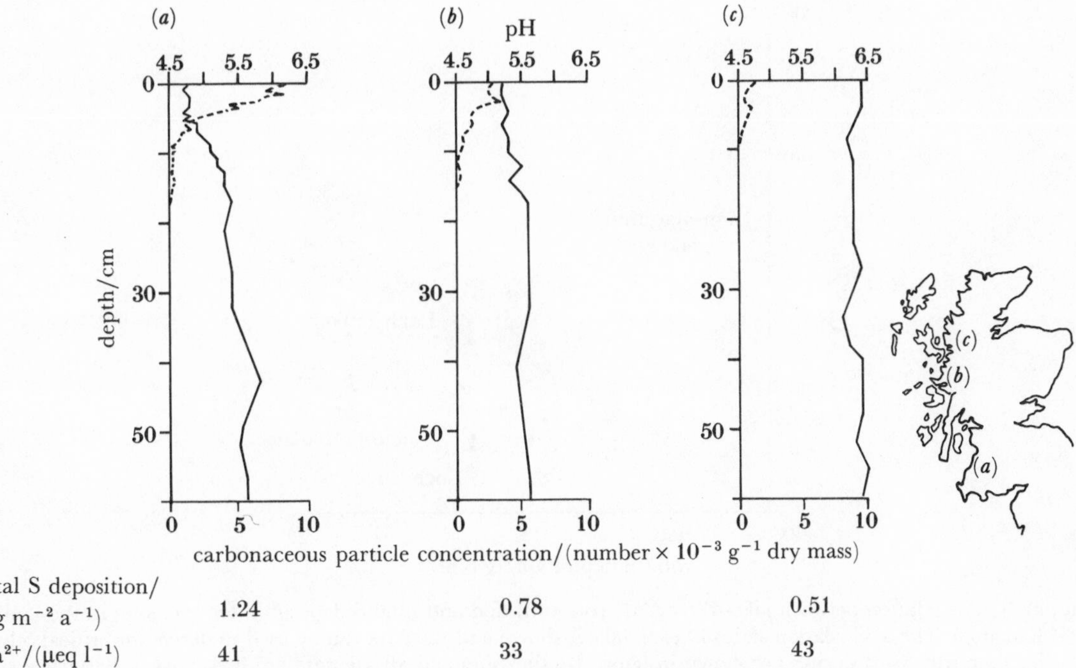

FIGURE 2. Comparison of pH trends (——) and carbonaceous particle profiles (– – – –) for three sites with moorland catchments from high to low S deposition and approximately constant lake-water Ca^{2+} values. (*a*) Round Loch of Glenhead, (*b*) Lochan Dubh, (*c*) Loch Corrie nan Arr.

These relations can be illustrated by data from Scotland where there is a strong sulphur deposition gradient from south to north. Figure 1 shows the distribution of sites for which we have diatom-based pH reconstructions and indicates the extent of estimated pH decline at each site. At each acidified site the first point of pH decrease is never before 1800 (cf. Battarbee *et al.* 1988*a*) and no acidified sites have been found in the areas of low acid deposition.

If lake sensitivity is kept constant, but sulphur loading is varied, it can also be shown (figure 2) that the degree of pH decline is correlated with the degree of atmospheric contamination. The three sites shown in figure 2 are all extremely sensitive to acidification with Ca^{2+} between 30 and 50 $\mu eq\ l^{-1}$. The Round Loch of Glenhead lies in an area of high sulphur deposition ($1.2\ g\ m^{-2}\ a^{-1}$), has undergone a pH decline of approximately 1 pH unit and is strongly contaminated by carbonaceous particles. At Lochan Dubh in an area of medium sulphur deposition ($0.8\ g\ m^{-2}\ a^{-1}$) acidification and atmospheric contamination are correspondingly lower, and at Loch Corrie nan Arr there is only slight atmospheric contamination and no evidence of a pH decline.

If the data-set is enlarged to cover all sites that have diatom-based pH reconstructions (cf. Battarbee *et al.* 1988*a*), the acidification status of any one site can be determined by using this relation of sensitivity (as Ca^{2+} concentration) and loading (as sulphur deposition). Figure 3 shows data for moorland sites where a line describing a Ca^{2+}:sulphur deposition ratio of between approximately 50 and 70:1, effectively separates acidified from non-acidified sites. All sites where the diatom data indicate questionable or very slight acidification fall within the bounds of the ratio.

This empirically derived relation has not yet been independently validated, and it has not been modified to include sites with afforested catchments, where sulphur deposition may be

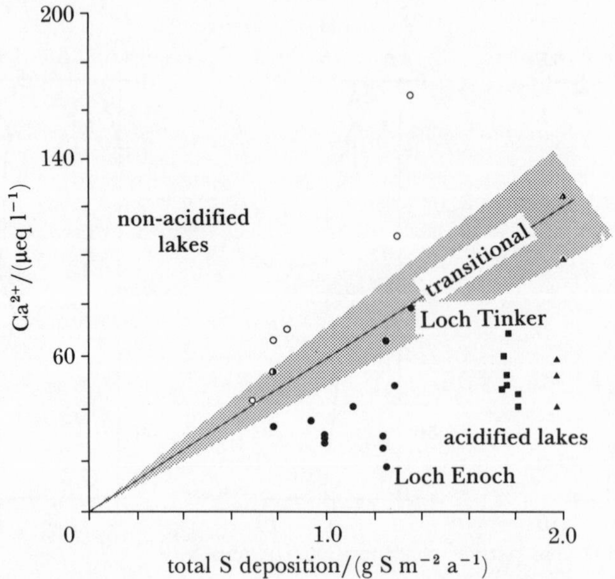

FIGURE 3. The relation between lake-water Ca^{2+} concentration and total S deposition for core sites in the United Kingdom. The acidification status of each lake is shown and the data can be used to derive the critical S load for each site. Scottish sites are shown in figure 1, other sites and all site data are presented in Battarbee *et al.* 1988*a*; (○◑●), Scottish sites; (△▲▲), English sites; (■), Welsh sites; (●▲■), pH decrease 0.4–1.2; (◑▲), pH decrease < 0.4; (○△), no decrease.

enhanced, but it does underline the importance of sulphur deposition as the main cause of lake acidification.

The ratio can also be regarded as the 'critical ratio' for the acidification of moorland sites as it allows the critical sulphur load for any one site to be calculated. On this basis the critical load for Loch Enoch, assuming no change in Ca as S is reduced, is about 0.3 g S m^{-2} a^{-1} (75% lower than the present sulphur deposition).

The ultimate dose–response test of this relation is the recovery of lakes following a reduction in deposition. Already there is evidence to suggest that following the decline in U.K. and European emissions of SO_2 in the last decade, lake acidification has stopped and in some cases is reversing (Battarbee *et al.* 1988*b*).

I thank all members of the Palaeoecology Research Unit at University College London and other colleagues in the SWAP Palaeolimnology Programme for providing the data and contributing to the ideas in this paper. I am also grateful to Ron Harriman, Ron West and David Tervet for chemical analyses; sulphur deposition data were kindly provided by Dick Derwent.

REFERENCES

Battarbee, R. W. 1984 Diatom analysis and the acidification of lakes. *Phil. Trans. R. Soc. Lond.* B **305**, 451–477.

Battarbee, R. W., Flower, R. J., Stevenson, A. C. & Rippey, B. 1990 Lake acidification in Galloway: a palaeoecological test of competing hypotheses. *Nature, Lond.* **314**, 350–352.

Battarbee, R. W., Anderson, N. J., Appleby, P. G., Flower, R. J., Fritz, S. C., Haworth, E. Y., Higgitt, S., Jones, V. J., Kreiser, A., Munro, M. A. R., Natkanski, J., Oldfield, F., Patrick, S. T., Richardson, N. G., Rippey, B. & Stevenson, A. C. 1988*a* *Lake acidification in the United Kingdom 1800–1986: evidence from analysis of lake sediments*. London: Ensis Publishing.

Battarbee, R. W., Flower, R. J., Stevenson, A. C., Jones, V. J., Harriman, R. & Appleby, P. G. 1988*b* Diatom and chemical evidence for reversibility of acidification of Scottish lochs. *Nature, Lond.* **332**, 530–532.

Charles, D. F. 1984 Recent history of Big Moose Lake (Adirondack Mts, N.Y., U.S.A.) inferred from sediment diatom assemblages. *Verh. internat. Verein. Limnol.* **22**, 559–566.

Charles, D. F. & Norton, S. A. 1986 Paleolimnological trends for evidence for trends in atmospheric deposition of acids and metals. In *Atmospheric deposition: historical trends and spatial patterns*, ch. 9, pp. 335–434. Washington, D.C.: National Academy Press.

Davis, R. B., Norton, S. A., Hess, C. T. & Brakke, D. F. 1983 Paleolimnological reconstruction of the effects of atmospheric deposition of acids and heavy metals on the chemistry and biology of lakes in New England and Norway. *Hydrobiologia* **103**, 113–124.

Derwent, R. G., Hopper, S. & Metcalfe, S. E. 1988 *Computer modelling studies of the origins of the acidity deposited in Scotland.* Harwell: Atomic Energy Research Establishment, report no. 13328.

Digerfeldt, G. 1972 The post-glacial development of Lake Trummen. Regional vegetation history, water-level changes, and palaeolimnology. *Fol. Limnol. Scand.* **16**, 1–104.

Engstrom, D. R. & Wright, H. E. 1985 Chemical stratigraphy of lake sediments as a record of environmental change. In *Lake sediments and environmental history* (ed. E. Y. Haworth & J. W. G. Lund), pp. 1–68. University of Leicester Press.

Flower, R. J. & Battarbee, R. W. 1983 Diatom evidence for recent acidification of two Scottish lochs. *Nature, Lond.* **20**, 130–133.

Flower, R. J., Battarbee, R. W. & Appleby, P. G. 1987 The recent palaeolimnology of acid lakes in Galloway, south-west Scotland: diatom analysis, pH trends and the role of afforestation. *J. Ecol.* **75**, 797–824.

Fritz, S. C., Kreiser, A. M., Appleby, P. G. & Battarbee, R. W. 1990 Recent acidification of upland lakes in North Wales: palaeolimnological evidence. In *Acid waters in Wales* (ed. R. Edwards). Cardiff: Welsh. (In the press.)

Harriman, R. & Morrison, B. R. S. 1982 The ecology of streams draining afforested and non-forested catchments in an area of central Scotland subject to acid precipitation. *Hydrobiologia* **88**, 251–263.

Jones, V. J., Stevenson, A. C. & Battarbee, R. W. 1986 Lake acidification and the land-use hypothesis: a mid-post-glacial analogue. *Nature, Lond.* **322**, 157–158.

Jones, V. J., Stevenson, A. C. & Battarbee, R. W. 1989 Acidification of lakes in Galloway, Southwest Scotland: a diatom and pollen study of the post-glacial history of the Round Loch of Glenhead. *J. Ecol.* **77**, 1–23.

Krug, E. C. & Frink, C. R. 1983 Acid rain on acid soil, a new perspective. *Science, Wash.* **221**, 520–525.

Odén, S. 1968 *The acidification of air precipitation and its consequences in the natural environment.* Energy Committee Bulletin, 1. Stockholm: Swedish Natural Sciences Research Council.

Patrick, S. T., Flower, R. J., Appleby, P. G., Oldfield, F., Rippey, B., Stevenson, A. C., Darley, J., Raven, P. J. & Battarbee, R. W. 1989 Palaeoecological evaluation of the recent acidification of Lochnagar, Scotland. Palaeoecology Research Unit, University College London, Research paper no. 34.

Pennington, W. 1984 Long-term natural acidification of upland sites in Cumbria: evidence from post-glacial lake sediments. *Freshwat. Biol. Ass. Ann. Rep.* **52**, 28–46.

Pennington, W., Haworth, E. Y., Bonny, A. P. & Lishman, J. P. 1972 Lake sediments in northern Scotland. *Phil. Trans. R. Soc. Lond.* B **264**, 191–294.

Renberg, I. & Hellberg, T. 1982 The pH history of lakes in southwestern Sweden, as calculated from the subfossil diatom flora of the sediments. *Ambio* **11**, 30–33.

Rosenqvist, I. T. 1977 *Acid soil – acid water* Oslo: Ingeniørforlaget.

Rosenqvist, I. T. 1978 Alternative sources for acidification of river water in Norway. *Sci. Tot. Envir.* 10, 39–49.

Stoner, J. H. & Gee, A. S. 1985 The effects of forestry on water quality and fish in Welsh rivers and lakes. *J. Inst. Wat. Engineers Scientists* **39**, 125–157.

Whitehead, D. R., Charles, D. F., Reed, S. E., Jackson, S. T. & Sheehan, M. C. 1986 Late-glacial and Holocene acidity changes in Adirondack (N.Y.) lakes. In *Diatoms and lake acidity* (ed. J. P. Smol, R. W. Battarbee, R. B. Davis, & J. Meriläinen), pp. 251–274. Dordrecht: Dr. W. Junk

Discussion

G. Howells (*University of Cambridge, Cambridge, U.K.*). Is the interpretation by Dr Battarbee of the acidifying effect of forestry at Loch Fleet correct? Ploughing and planting at Loch Fleet took place in 1961–62 and acidification did not occur until the mid 1970s. Further, the area afforested covers only 10% of the catchment, yielding significantly less than this to the runoff, as evapotranspiration from the forest is significantly greater than that from the moorland. The acidity of runoff from the forest, before liming treatment in 1986, was only slightly less than that from the rest (90%) of the catchment and so this contribution could not be responsible for the shift in pH of the loch.

R. W. Battarbee. Loch Fleet and Loch Chon are the only two afforested sites we have studied where the main period of acidification follows afforestation. For Loch Chon, which has a largely afforested catchment, we attribute the acceleration in acidification to enhanced scavenging of S by the canopy. I did not give an explanation for the acidification of Loch Fleet. I agree that an insufficient proportion of the catchment has been afforested at Loch Fleet for this interpretation to be valid. We need an additional mechanism. We know that the groundwater in parts of the catchment is extremely Ca^{2+} rich and that a layer of post-1960 peaty sediment up to 1.2 m thick now covers the main bed of the lake, so we have proposed that peat inwash that followed the deep ploughing of the catchment (before planting) has sealed off the lake-water from neutralising contact with sediments. With Dr W. M. Edmunds from BGS we are presently testing this hypothesis by examining pore-water chemistry of cores before and after the inwash period.

R. A. Skeffington. (*National Power Technology and Environmental Centre, Leatherhead, Surrey, KT22 7SE, U.K.*). The evidence seems overwhelming that acid deposition has been the major factor in recent lake acidification. But this does not preclude land-use change having a contributory effect in places. Inferences that the effect of afforestation on water quality is mediated only through pollutant capture seem to be being made on the basis of only one site in the 'afforested, low deposition' category. This is surely unsatisfactory and I wonder whether further studies are planned? Our modelling work indicates that afforestation on poor sites should affect water quality simply through cation uptake. I would not like it to be thought that one conclusion of the SWAP palaeoecology programme was that lake catchments could be misused with impunity, acid deposition being the only factor that can affect water quality.

R. W. Battarbee. We would like to replicate our Loch Doilet study at sites further north, but unfortunately (or perhaps fortunately!) there are very few afforested sites in Scotland with low Ca^{2+} waters in these areas of low acid deposition in Scotland. Cation uptake may have a role to play but on the basis of the Loch Doilet study, and from observations of water chemistry of lakes with forested catchments in low S deposition areas of Norway, it must be very minor. This does not imply that afforestation has little effect on surface water quality and aquatic ecosystems. On the contrary, we were only concerned with acidification in this study, but we have other data that demonstrate problems of soil erosion and nutrient enrichment associated with afforestation.

A. D. Bradshaw, F.R.S. (*Department of Environmental and Evolutionary Biology, University of Liverpool, Liverpool L69 3BX, U.K.*) Our memories are often made very short by the pressure of new problems and new experiences. Nowhere is this more true than in science, where ideas can become old in five years. Yet it is those ideas, not long ago so very new, that are the steps to the present.

I was brought up to a tradition of paleoecology – it was called pollen analysis in those days – as an esoteric historical discipline of appeal to an academic few.

So it was, also, with palaeolimnology, until about ten years ago. Then, suddenly, it began to provide some very interesting evidence for the effects of acid rain, an environment problem that was unclear and disbelieved by many, especially in the U.K. This was because the direct evidence, from lake acidification, was based on poor historical data and rather inadequate comparisons of different lakes.

Then, suddenly, I clearly remember, our ideas changed, because palaeolimnology gave clear evidence of major changes in lake quality in recent times that could only be due to acid deposition (Battarbee 1984). Not only were the changes able to be correlated in time with developing industrial activity, but other pieces of evidence could be found, such as carbonaceous particles, to make the arguments incontrovertible. The crucial point was that this evidence was, then, not only enough to persuade ecologists that acid rain was a problem, but politicians also. The need for control of sulphur emissions suddenly became clear.

As a result of all this, palaeolimnology has become an important, practically oriented, area of work, with a great deal of financial support. This has, however, not destroyed palaeolimnology as a scientific discipline, as some academics might have thought, but has strengthened it. The many excellent papers of this meeting make this very clear. There is now a very healthy two-way exchange between the demands of studying acid rain and the science of palaeolimnology, which shows well the value of combining science and practice so that each can feed on the other.

This pleases me greatly, as it is something that has been argued for on previous occasions (Dunnett 1980; Bradshaw 1982). I would like to compliment not only the organizers of this meeting and the speakers, but also the many other scientists, who, together, have taken palaeolimnology into new rewarding areas.

References

Battarbee, R. W. 1984 Diatom analysis and the acidification of lakes. *Phil. Trans. R. Soc. Lond.* B **305**, 415–477.
Bradshaw, A. D. 1982 Presidential viewpoint: achieving useful ecology. *Bull. Br. Ecol. Soc.* **13**, 112–114.
Dunnett, G. M. 1980 Presidential viewpoint. *Bull. Br. Ecol. Soc.* **11**, 94–96.

Phil. Trans. R. Soc. Lond. B **327**, 349–355 (1990)
Printed in Great Britain

Devoke Water and Loch Sionascaig: recent environmental changes and the post-glacial overview

By K. M. Atkinson and E. Y. Haworth
Institute of Freshwater Ecology, Ambleside, Cumbria LA22 0LP, U.K.

Diatoms from postglacial sediments of two oligotrophic lakes, one in northwest England and one in northwest Scotland, have been examined. Apart from the decline of alkalinity in the early post-glacial period at both sites, the only evidence for further increase in acidity occurs in the post-1900 sediments of Devoke Water (Cumbria). There has been no such change in Loch Sionascaig, in a region of lower acid deposition in northwest Scotland.

Introduction

The aquatic ecosystem is a reflection of the state of both the terrestrial and atmospheric environment, with catchment soils (where sufficient) intervening as buffers or ion-exchange mechanisms. The state of the lakes is therefore indicative of wider environmental conditions. Within the last *ca.* 150 years, there have been considerable changes to many of the lakes in the U.K., Scandinavia and elsewhere (Johnson 1982). Many considered as oligotrophic, undisturbed systems have recently become more acidic and no longer support certain plants and animals, especially fish.

Recent changes in many lakes that apparently result from increasing air pollution have to be considered within the context of the long-term changes in post-glacial history as a whole, to observe which has the greater influence and to assess the likelihood of lake recovery. We have made an analysis of the most recent sediments of two oligotrophic lakes for which earlier post-glacial records were already available, Devoke Water (Evans 1961) and Loch Sionascaig (Pennington *et al.* 1972), and have compared the modern rates and extent of change with previous changes.

Methods

Cores of the upper 1 m of sediment were collected from Devoke Water, in 1985, and Loch Sionascaig, in 1986, by using a Mackereth minicorer. These were collected from the mid-lake area in 9 m, and towards the eastern end in 21 m of water, respectively. Site locations and characteristics are given in Battarbee & Renberg (this symposium).

Radio-isotope analyses were done by Appleby *et al.* (this symposium) and diatom analysis has followed the methods in Haworth (1984). The nomenclature follows Hartley (1986) and Surface Water Acidification Project (SWAP) guidelines (Munro *et al.*, this symposium). A more detailed methodology appears in Haworth and Atkinson (in preparation).

Material for the long-core studies by Evans (1961) and Haworth (Pennington *et al.* 1972) was collected by using the 6 m Mackereth corer. Despite problems of sampling the upper sediment by using this corer, and the incomplete description of methods, the stratigraphy outlined by Evans clearly includes these upper sediments; 20 cm was assumed lost from the top of the Loch Sionascaig core. In figures 1 and 2, sample levels in the upper 1 m have been adjusted to match with the later minicores. Evans' diatom counts were expressed as concentrations per mg dry mass of sample and his data have been recalculated as percentages (figure 1). His pH classifications have been changed here to conform with SWAP guidelines and units. The pH categories are as used in our investigation of the 1986 minicore.

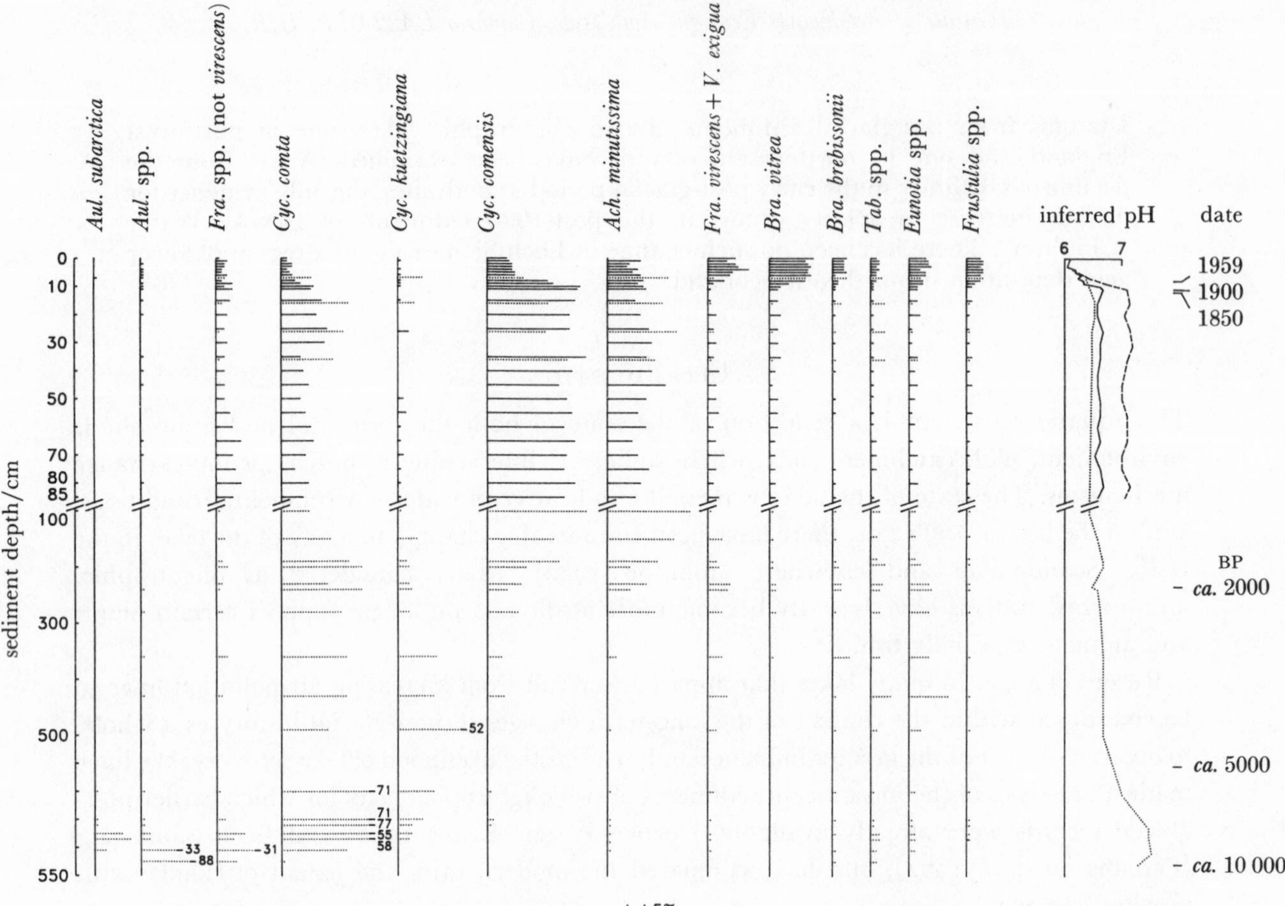

Figure 1. Devoke Water. Percentages of major diatom taxa and the inferred pH with the recent minicore (0–85 cm) superimposed upon a recalculation of the 1959 profile of the whole Post-glacial. Depths below 90 cm relate to long-core stratigraphy, whereas those above 90 cm relate to minicore stratigraphy and long-core samples have been adjusted accordingly. Diatoms: (......), 1959 long core and (—), 1985 minicore. Inferred pH: (......), Index B calculation of 1959 profile and (—), Index B calculation of 1985 profile; (------), weighted averaging of 1985 profile. Dates according to ^{210}Pb and ^{14}C. (*Aul.*, *Aulacoseira*; *Fra.*, *Fragilaria*; *Cyc.*, *Cyclotella*; *Ach.*, *Achnanthes*; *Bra.*, *Brachysira*; *Tab.*, *Tabellaria*.)

Results

Devoke Water is an oligotrophic lake in a glacial hollow on the western fells of Cumbria, close to the coast; this raises the salt content slightly whereas alkalinity is low (table 1). Pennington (1964, 1984) showed that the now treeless catchment supported woodland until clearances by Bronze Age and subsequent farmers. The sharp rise in *Calluna* pollen, together with an increase in the iodine:carbon ratio is interpreted, by her, as the increased input of humus during the Romano-British period. Soil erosion was such that there was a tenfold increase in sediment accumulation above the Elm Decline. Evans (1961) found a high proportion of alkaliphilous

Table 1. Characteristics of Devoke Water, southwest Cumbria and Loch Sionascaig, northwest Scotland

lake	Devoke Water	Loch Sionascaig
grid reference	SD 163972	NC 120140
altitude/m	233	73
length/km	1.2	4.8
surface area/ha[a]	34	517
drainage area/ha[a]	305	4000
maximum depth/m	14	66
mean depth/m	4	18.5
distance from the sea/km	8.5	4.0
local geology	Borrowdale volcanics and granite	Lewisian gneiss Torridonian sandstone
vegetation	rough grass and bracken	blanket bog and deer grass
soils	shallow and peaty	peat
sodium/(μeq l^{-1})	231	363
calcium/(μeq l^{-1})	108	73
magnesium/(μeq l^{-1})	79	101
potassium/(μeq l^{-1})	10	14
chloride/(μeq l^{-1})	272	433
sulphate/(μeq l^{-1})	111	71
nitrate/(μeq l^{-1})	15	4
alkalinity/(μeq l^{-1})	< 50	50–100
pH	6.3	6.6

[a] 1 ha = 10^4 m^2.

taxa in the immediate post-glacial sediment (table 2, figure 1), mainly *Melosira* (*Aulacoseira*) and *Fragilaria* spp., and suggested that there had been a pH of about 7.0. These taxa declined *ca.* 5000 BP and again just above the horizon that Pennington (1964) ascribes to the Romano–British period. *Cyclotella kuetzingiana* and *C. comta* are abundant throughout the early post-glacial period and circumneutral (= indifferent) diatoms, such as *C. comensis* and *Achnanthes minutissima*, increased steadily in the latter part of the Post-glacial, as in other Cumbrian lakes (Haworth 1985). Evans found little change in the upper part of the core except for some increase in acidic taxa at the surface. Our Index B inferred pH profile (Renberg & Hellberg 1982) of the 1959 core data suggests that the pH of lake water in the immediate Postglacial was about 7.7 but that this declined during the next 5000 years, to pH about 6.7. There was a further drop to 6.5 (figure 1) and then 6.4 in the upper sample, close to the measured pH of 6.3 in 1959.

The close interval analysis of the 1985 1 m core shows that there was little change in diatom percentages below 12 cm with circumneutral taxa dominant, especially *Cyclotella comensis*, *C. comta* and *Achnanthes minutissima* (figure 1). A significant percentage of alkaliphilous taxa was present throughout the profile, e.g. *Fragilaria*, *Nitzschia* and *Asterionella* spp. but this declined, above 12 cm, where more acidic taxa such as *Brachysira vitrea* and *Fragilaria virescens* increase by 20% (table 2, figure 1). The profile inferred from Index B shows that the earlier pH was about 6.6 but there has been a slight but distinct decrease to about 6.35 above 10 cm. The similar calculation based upon the weighted averages of each taxon according to the SWAP calibration set (Birks *et al.*, this symposium) produces a similar profile but infers a higher pH of about 7.0 below 10 cm, where the *Cyclotella* percentage is markedly higher. ^{210}Pb dating identifies the 1959 horizon at 7.5 cm, which has an inferred pH of 6.3, the same as measurements at that time. The pH declined to 6.1 above this. The ^{210}Pb profile of this core suggests a discontinuity at 9 cm with a loss of a section representing up to 50 years, or about 9 cm; calculations to date the profile (figure 1) have therefore been made with reference to ^{137}Cs and ^{241}Am analyses (Appleby *et al.*, this symposium). The pH decline at 10 cm is estimated at about 1900, whereas 9 cm is dated as 1954.

Loch Sionascaig is a large, irregularly shaped lake on the coastal foreland of northwest Scotland, surrounded by bare rock and peatbog. Here, as in Devoke, there is a high NaCl content (table 1). Pennington *et al.* (1972) found that the sedimentary record differed from other U.K. sites in that there was a very gradual transition between the late-glacial and Post-glacial. This study also indicated early peat formation and the decline of the local pine forest at *ca.* 4000 BP.

The diatom assemblages of the core from this site reflect these changes (figure 2) as alkaline taxa declined, and circumneutral ones increased, well before 8500 BP (table 2), which is earlier than elsewhere in the U.K. (Haworth 1985). This change also predates the maximum extension of birch–hazel woodland but coincides with the base of the *Calluna* and *Sphagnum* profiles signifying the onset of peat formation. *Cyclotella comensis*, *C. kuetzingiana* and *Achnanthes minutissima* predominate thereafter, *C. kuetzingiana* increasing as *A. minutissima* decreases. *Aulacoseira* spp. are best represented at the time of the Elm Decline and the expansion of peat. The dominant form, *A. subarctica*, may be up to 5% of the sample between 8500 BP and the present, especially between 6000 and 4000 BP. The diatom-inferred pH declined from more than 7.7 at 10000 BP to less than 6.5 about 8000 BP with little further change, even at the pine decline (Pennington *et al.* 1972). This emphasizes the rapid decline in alkaliphilous taxa at the end of the late-glacial. Although percentages of acidic taxa increased, with a maximum of about 20% at the level of peat expansion at *ca.* 4000 BP, there has been no recent increase in these taxa.

TABLE 2. THE pH-RELATED DIATOM SPECTRUM FROM THREE LEVELS OF POST-GLACIAL LAKE SEDIMENT, SHOWING THE DECLINE IN ALKALIPHILOUS TAXA SINCE THE END OF THE LATE-GLACIAL PERIOD AND THE HIGH PERCENTAGE OF ACIDOPHILOUS TAXA AT THE SURFACE OF DEVOKE WATER

(Depth, below sediment surface; alkb., alkalibiontic; alkf., alkaliphilous; ind., indifferent (= circumneutral); acf., acidophilous; acb., acidobiontic.)

		pH categories/(%)					
	depth/cm	alkb	alkf	ind	acf	acb	date
Devoke Water	0	0	10.6	52.0	26.6	0	1985 A.D.
	85	0	27.6	54.4	5.2	0	*ca.* 1000 BP
	540	2.7	71.5	14.8	4.1	0	*ca.* 10000 BP
Loch Sionascaig	0	0	2.6	78.3	6.6	0.3	1986 A.D.
	80	0.2	5.4	80.4	10.4	0	*ca.* 1000 BP
	540	1.3	61.3	25.7	3.0	0	*ca.* 10000 BP

The diatom profile of the upper 1 m of sediment, collected in 1986, is dominated by *Cyclotella* spp. (figure 2), together with *Achnanthes* and *Brachysira* spp. There is little evidence of change in the upper part; since 1900, *Achnanthes minutissima* and *Aulacoseira distans* var. *tenella* declined and *C. glomerata* and *Stephanodiscus minutulus* (not shown) occurred more consistently and *A. subarctica* increased very recently. There is certainly no equivalent of the increase in acidic taxa found in other, upland sites (Battarbee *et al.* 1988) as the pH spectrum illustrates the

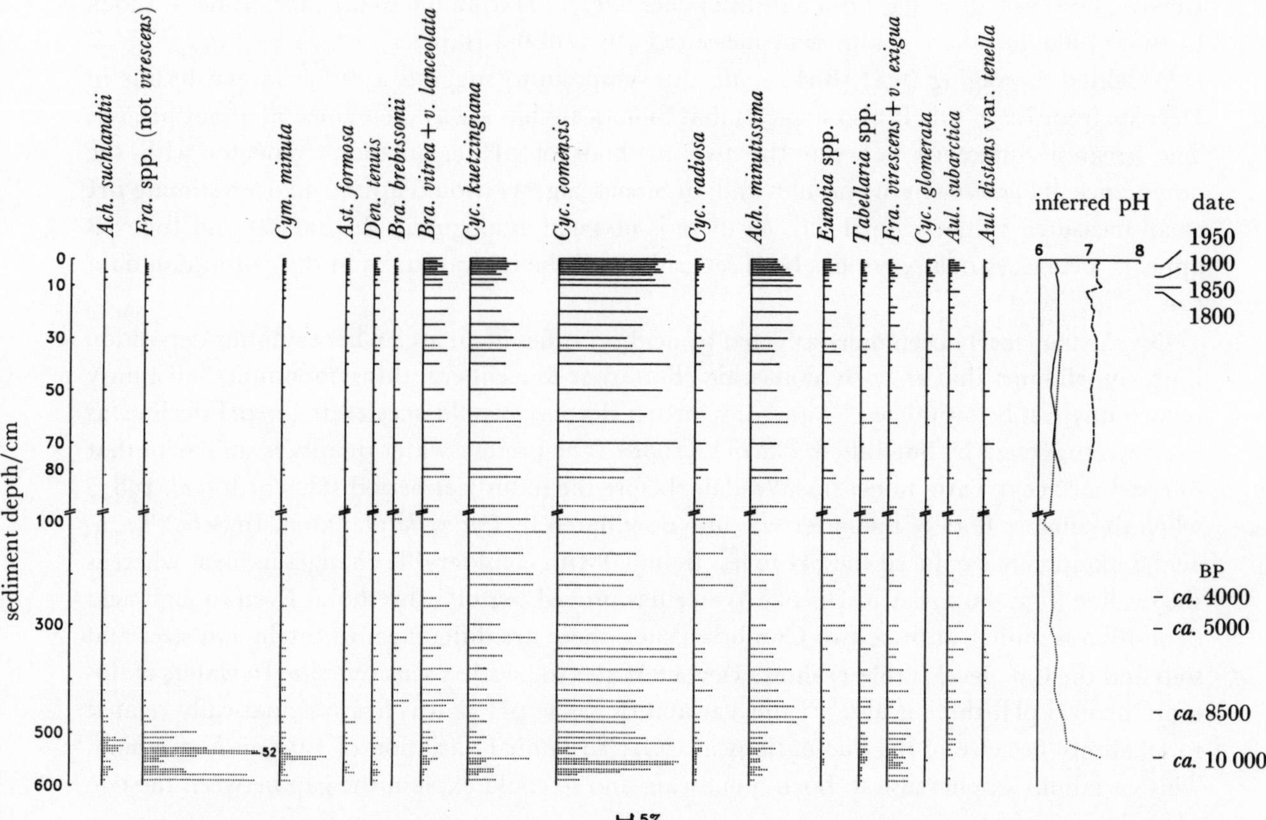

FIGURE 2. Loch Sionascaig. Percentages of major diatom taxa and the inferred pH with the recent minicore (0–80 cm) superimposed on the 1967 Post-glacial profile. Depths below 90 cm relate to the long-core stratigraphy, whereas those above relate to the minicore and the long-core samples have been adjusted accordingly. Diatoms: (......), 1967 long-core and (—), 1986 minicore. Inferred pH: (......), Index B calculation of 1967 profile; (—), Index B calculation of 1986 profile; (------), weighted averaging of 1986 profile. Dates according to ^{210}Pb and ^{14}C. (*Cym.*, *Cymbella*; *Ast.*, *Asterionella*; *Den.*, *Denticula*; *Aul.*, *Aulacoseira*; *Cyc.*, *Cyclotella*; *Ach.*, *Achnanthes*; *Fra.*, *Fragilaria*.)

dominance of circumneutral taxa and the low percentage of acidic taxa. The Index B inferred pH varies between 6.2 and 6.4 throughout (figure 2). Alternatively, inferred pH values by using weighted averaging suggest a higher pH of about 7.1. This difference is currently difficult to explain as the measured pH is about 6.6; there may be a bias as the site is at the upper pH limit of lakes studied or there may be a greater degree of variation in pH at higher levels (W. Davison, personal communication).

Conclusions

Diatom changes indicate that alkaliphilous taxa declined during the immediate Postglacial period, the pH of the lakes becoming stable around 6.5 before 8500 BP in Loch Sionascaig and by 5000 BP in Devoke Water, there being better forest soils on the catchment of the latter.

Diatoms indicate that pH levels of both lakes (figures 1 and 2) have remained circumneutral even to the present day, with floras changing very little. Only in Devoke is there any recent change in floristic composition, with a significant 20% increase in acidic taxa; in Sionascaig, the changes are much less obvious. The inferred pH profile of recent sediments indicates that there has been no change in the acidity of Sionascaig as this has retained a pH of 6.2–6.4. In

Devoke, however, there has been a distinct decrease in pH from 6.6 to 6.1 (according to Index B) since 1900 and there is a present measured mean of 6.3 (table 1).

Weighted Averaging (WA) (Birks *et al.*, this symposium) suggests a rather larger decline in Devoke, from 7.2 to 6.1. It also suggests that Sionascaig has always remained at about pH 7.1. The greatest difference between the two methods of pH calculation coincides with the dominance of *Cyclotella* in the profiles and, in Sionascaig, WA would appear to overestimate pH as all measured values are pH 6.6. As there is no good analogue in the dataset and Index B appears a closer estimate, WA has been set aside until the relevant taxa in the calibration data can be reviewed.

Devoke has clearly been more affected by acidity. It lies in an area where sulphur deposition is nearly ten times that at Loch Sionascaig (Battarbee & Renberg, this symposium); alkalinity is currently just below 50 μeq l^{-1} and any further decrease would accelerate the pH decline, as has been suggested by Sutcliffe & Carrick (1988). The present water quality is similar to that inferred for Scoat Tarn, in nearby Wasdale, before the industrial period (Haworth *et al.* 1987) when the diatom flora of the latter was also dominated by *Cyclotella* plankton. In Scoat Tarn, acid deposition has reduced the pH to less than 5.0 with considerable changes in taxa, whereas the decline from 6.6 to 6.1 in Devoke Water has proved less of a threshold. Even though acid deposition is similar at these two Cumbrian sites, there are differences in catchment sizes and soils and the Ca^{2+} level (table 1) shows Devoke Water to be a less sensitive site. In waters of this more neutral pH, there is also greater variability in the pH as it is less systematically related to alkalinity because of the fluctuations in CO_2; an annual variation of 1.0 unit is common. This variability applies also to Loch Sionascaig and so could explain the gap between the two pH calculations.

Post-glacial profiles show that Devoke Water has always been less sensitive to acidity than the more upland lakes (Haworth *et al.* 1987), as have other lowland Cumbrian lakes (Haworth 1985); Loch Sionascaig too started with better alkalinity and, although this was quickly lost, the lake is less sensitive than many other Scottish sites (Battarbee *et al.* 1988; Battarbee & Renberg, this symposium).

We thank the Nature Conservancy Council and Muncaster Estate, for access to these lakes; also W. Henderson and A. Scott of the Inverpolly National Nature Reserve, P. R. Cubby, P. V. Allen, T. I. Furnass and A. E. Irish for all their help. The study was jointly funded by SWAP and NERC.

References

Battarbee, R. W., Anderson, N. J., Appleby, P. G., Flower, R., Fritz, S. C., Haworth, E. Y., Higgitt, S., Kreiser, A., Munro, M. A. R., Natkanski, J., Oldfield, F., Patrick, S. T., Raven, P. J., Richardson, N., Rippey, B. & Stevenson, A. C. 1988 *Lake Acidification in the United Kingdom 1900–1986*. London: ENSIS Publishing.

Evans, G. H. 1961 *A study of the diatoms in a core from the sediments of Devoke Water*. M. Sc. thesis, University College of Wales, Aberystwyth.

Hartley, B. 1986 A checklist of the freshwater, brackish and marine diatoms of the British Isles and adjoining coastal waters. *J. mar. biol. Ass. U.K.* **66**, 531–610.

Haworth, E. Y. 1984 Stratigraphic changes in algal remains (diatoms and chrysophytes) in the recent sediments of Blelham Tarn, English Lake District. In *Lake sediments and environmental history* (ed. E. Y. Haworth & J. W. G. Lund), pp. 165–190, Leicester University Press.

Haworth, E. Y. 1985 The highly nervous system of the English Lakes: aquatic ecosystem sensitivity to external changes, as demonstrated by diatoms. *Rep. Freshwat. Biol. Ass.* **53**, 60–79.

Haworth, E. Y., Atkinson, K. M. & Riley, E. M. 1987 *Acidification in Cumbrian waters: past and present distribution of diatoms in local lakes and tarns*. Report to Department of the Environment, U.K., 107 pp.

Johnson, R. E. (ed.) 1982 *Acid rain/fisheries*. Proceedings of an international symposium on acidic precipitation and fishery impacts in Northeastern North America, Cornell University Ithaca, New York, August 2nd–5th 1981. Bethesda, Maryland: American Fisheries Soc.

Pennington, W. 1964 Pollen analyses from the deposits of six upland tarns in the Lake District. *Phil. Trans. R. Soc. Lond.* B **248**, 205–244.

Pennington, W. 1984 Long-term natural acidification of upland sites in Cumbria: evidence from post-glacial sediments. *Rep. Freshwat. Biol. Ass.* **52**, 28–46.

Pennington, W., Haworth, E. Y., Bonny, A. P. & Lishman, J. P. 1972 Lake sediments in northern Scotland. *Phil. Trans. R. Soc. Lond.* B **264**, 191–294.

Renberg, I. & Hellberg, T. 1982 The pH history of lakes in southwestern Sweden, as calculated from the subfossil diatom flora of the sediments. *Ambio* **11**, 30–33.

Sutcliffe, D. W. & Carrick, T. R. 1988 Alkalinity and pH of tarns and streams in the English Lake District (Cumbria). *Freshwat. Biol.* **19**, 179–189.

Phil. Trans. R. Soc. Lond. B **327**, 357–361 (1990)
Printed in Great Britain

A 12600 year perspective of the acidification of Lilla Öresjön, southwest Sweden

By I. Renberg

Department of Ecological Botany, University of Umeå S-901 87 Umeå, Sweden

The pH history of Lilla Öresjön was studied by using diatom analyses of a 3.5 m long sediment core (700 contiguous 0.5 cm samples). Four pH periods were distinguished; (i) an alkaline period (12600–7800 BP) following deglaciation, (ii) a naturally acidic period (7800–2300 BP) when pH decreased from 6.0 to 5.2, (iii) a period with higher pH (greater than 6) (2300 BP–1900 A.D.), which started at the same time as agriculture expanded, and (iv) the recent acidification period that began with a deterioration phase around 1900 A.D. and developed into an acute acidification phase during the 1960s (pH 4.5). This post-1960 phase has no similarity with any of the previous periods identified.

Introduction

Several investigations of Holocene lake development have been made in Europe (cf. reviews by Battarbee (1984) and Charles *et al.* (1989)). Except for Jones *et al.* (1989), few studies are from lakes sensitive to acidification and sample intervals in the sediment cores are usually so large that only general trends with a resolution of 10^2–10^3 years are revealed. This project aimed to study the detailed pH history of a 12600 year old lake, which is severely acidified today, and to assess whether the recent acidification is a unique phenomenon, or if any short-term acidification episodes have occurred in the past, for example, due to climatic fluctuations, vegetation and related soil changes, or any other factors.

Study site and methods

Lilla Öresjön is a typical lake of southwest Sweden; many such lakes have acidified. The lake surface area is 0.6 km^2, max. depth 17 m, retention time 10 months, pH 4.5, alkalinity 0, catchment area 4 km^2 of which 60% is spruce and pine forest. The bedrock is gneiss and soils are generally thin. See also Battarbee & Renberg (this symposium).

Overlapping Russian sediment cores (together more than 3 m long) were taken from ice in winter and correlated by stratigraphic changes in sediment colour and texture, or by diatom analysis. Freeze coring was used for recent sediments (see Renberg *et al.*, this symposium). Contiguous 0.5 cm subsamples, prepared for diatom analysis by a modified standard method by using hydrogen peroxide, were analysed. About 100 valves were counted on each slide (*ca.* 500 in the freeze core). Nomenclature follows Williams *et al.* (1988) and pH classifications follow the Surface Water Acidification Project (SWAP) list. Values for pH were inferred by using weighted averaging (Birks *et al.*, this symposium). Radiocarbon dates, here presented as calibrated ages, were done by the Laboratory for Isotope Geology, Swedish Museum of Natural History, and ^{210}Pb dates are from El-Daoushy (this symposium).

Results and discussion

As one of the aims of this investigation was to consider if any short-term acidification periods (less than 10^2 years) had occurred before, it was necessary to take contiguous subsamples, each comprising only a few years. Because of the very large number of samples (700) the valve count for each level was reduced from the SWAP standard of 500 to 100. Although the low number of valves counted caused more variability, it is not particularly large (figure 1). The count of 100 valves is sufficient to identify previous short-term acidification episodes, and is compensated for by the high number of levels, which gives an excellent picture of the long-term trend (figure 2).

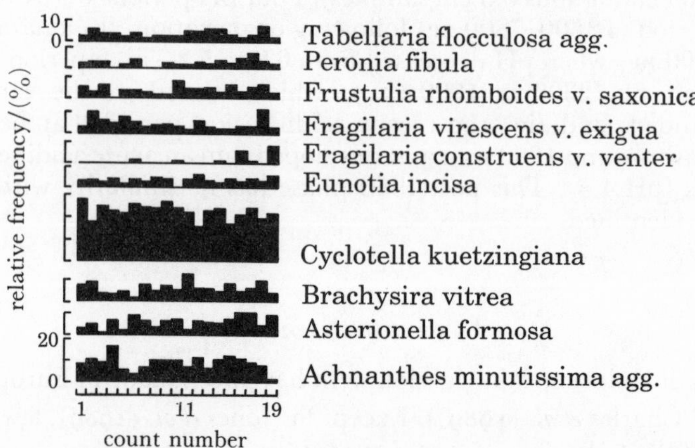

Figure 1. Test of slide preparation and diatom counting methods. Counts 1–10 were made on slides prepared from ten sediment subsamples from one particular level and 11–19 are replicate counts from one of those slides. Taxa with more than 5% in any count are shown.

The lake was formed after deglaciation, about 12600 years ago (Björck *et al.* 1988). Each analysed sample therefore represents about 20 years, or less in the most recent sediment. About 250 taxa were recorded, classified into Hustedt's pH categories, and the relative frequency of diatom valves belonging to each category calculated. The diatom assemblages change considerably during the lake's history. Four major periods are discernible (figure 2).

An alkaline period following deglaciation (*level* 350–275 *cm*, *ca.* 12600–7800 BP) (I)

The bottom 5 cm are characterized by alkaliphilous *Fragilaria* species such as *F. construens*, *F. construens* var. *venter*, *F. brevistriata* and *F. pinnata*. High percentages of *Fragilaria* spp. are often found in sediments deposited at deglaciation and lake isolation stages and this is thought to depend on the alkaline environment and a higher nutrient supply (Haworth 1976; Stabell 1985). The rest of the period is dominated by *Cyclotella* species, particularly *C. kuetzingiana*, but also *C. comensis*, *C. comta* and *C. stelligera* and *Asterionella formosa*. The end of the period is marked by the disappearance of these species and a decline in *Achnanthes minutissima* agg. Acidophilous taxa increase gradually during period I. Inferred pH values decrease from 7.2 to 6.0 (notice weighted averaging is a method independent of Hustedt's categories, but that both give a consistent picture). This pH decrease and oligotrophication is due to a progressive leaching of the catchment and subsequent decrease of the input of base cations and nutrients to the lake and is a process recorded elsewhere (see Battarbee (1984)). The loss of the planktonic *Cyclotella*

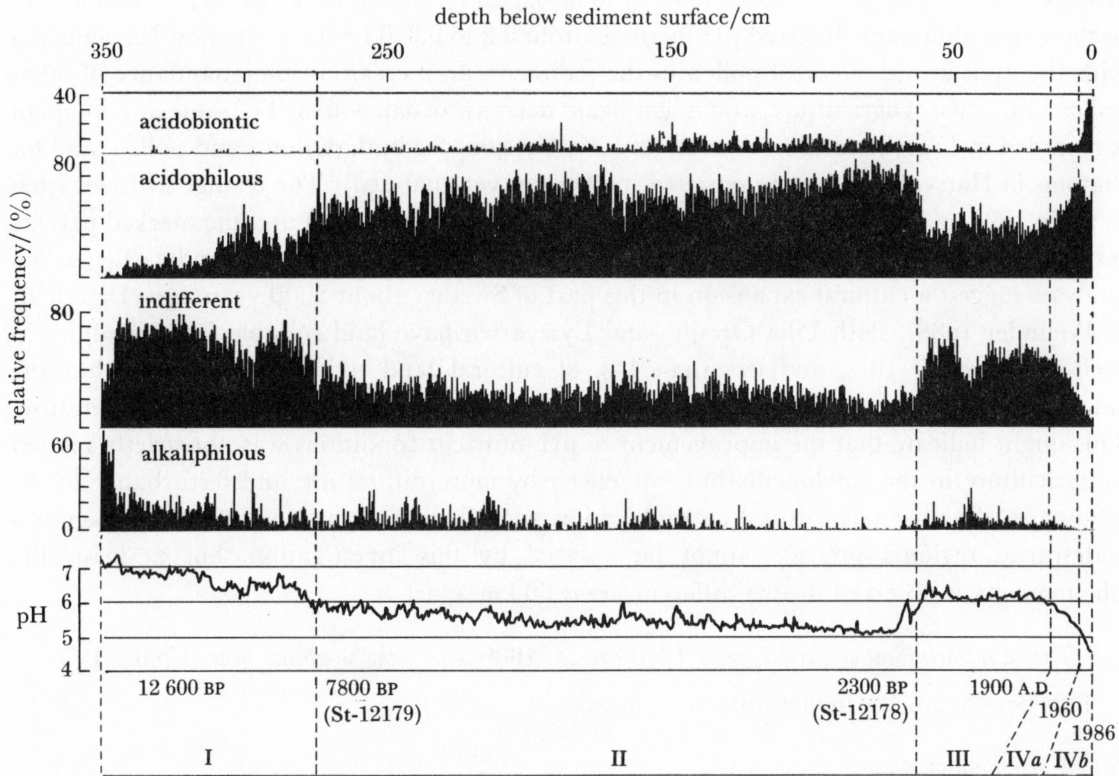

Figure 2. Hustedt pH categories, diatom inferred pH values (weighted averaging), calibrated radiocarbon dates, ^{210}Pb dates and pH periods in the history of Lilla Öresjön, southwest Sweden.

flora took place at later dates in two other studied lakes in S.W. Sweden (Lysevatten 6400 BP and Härsvatten 6000 BP). Gårdsjön (Renberg & Hellberg 1982) never completely lost its *Cyclotella* flora. This indicates that the rate of this pH decrease depended on catchment characteristics, rather than common external forces such as climate.

A period of acid conditions with slightly increasing acidity through time (*level* 275–65 *cm*, *ca.* 7800–2300 *BP*) (II)

Acidobiontic and acidophilous taxa increase slightly and indifferent (= circumneutral) and alkaliphilous taxa decrease, and pH falls from 6.0 to 5.2. This is a very slow natural acidification process over about 5000 years. There are no signs in the diatom record of any episodes with pH values below 5.0 during this naturally acidic period. There are, however, frequent short-term episodes with slightly higher pH values. Common taxa are *Aulacoseira distans* var. *tenella*, *Brachysira vitrea*, *B. brebissonii*, *Eunotia incisa*, *E. naegelii*, *Frustulia rhomboides* var. *saxonica*, *Peronia fibula*, *Tabellaria flocculosa* var. *flocculosa*, and towards the end of the period *Tabellaria flocculosa* agg., *Asterionella ralfsii* var. *americana*, *Navicula leptostriata* and *Tabellaria quadriseptata*.

A period with higher pH (*level* 65–15 *cm*, *ca.* 2300 *BP*–1900 *A.D.*) (III)

Cyclotella kuetzingiana suddenly returns, together with *Achnanthes minutissima* agg. and *Asterionella formosa* and other indifferent and alkaliphilous diatoms. The frequency of acidophilous taxa decreases from *ca.* 70% to 30%, and *Tabellaria quadriseptata* (acidobiontic) becomes less abundant. Inferred pH increases from 5.2 to 6.3. The start of period III coincides with the appearance of cereal pollen in the sediment, an increase in the abundance of other pollen indicative of agriculture, and a significant decrease of oak pollen. The same development is recorded in Lysevatten (60 km north of Lilla Öresjön) for both diatoms and pollen, and for diatoms in Härsvatten (near Lysevatten, pollen not yet analysed). The change in Lysevatten dates to 1800 BP. It is very likely that the changes in the diatom flora and the marked pH rise resulted from an increase in human land use. Archaeological investigations and earlier pollen analyses suggest a cultural expansion in this part of Sweden about 2000 years ago (Digerfeldt & Welinder 1988). Both Lilla Öresjön and Lysevatten have land suitable for agriculture in their catchments (10% and less than 1% of cultural land today, respectively), but the catchment of Härsvatten is very broken and rocky and has no known history of agriculture. This might indicate that the improvement of pH–nutrient conditions was not strictly related to agriculture in the catchments but influenced by more diffuse use and disturbance of the landscape. Whether this cultural eutrophication and alkalinization about 2000 years ago is a widespread regional process cannot be assessed by this investigation, but at least, the phenomenon is observed in two different areas 60 km apart.

The recent acidification period (*level* 15–0 *cm*, *ca.* 1900 A.D. – *the sampling year*, 1986) (IV)

This period can be divided into two phases.

(*a*) *A deterioration phase*

Lasting from *ca.* 1900 A.D. to the 1950s, with decreasing abundance of *Cyclotella kuetzingiana* and other species favoured during the previous period, i.e. a return to the natural conditions prevailing before 2300 BP. Although it cannot be ruled out that changed land use and recovery of forest vegetation and soils, as proposed as a major reason for acidification by Rosenqvist (1977), has contributed to this development, it is more likely that acid deposition plays the most important role already during this phase (see discussion in Renberg *et al.*, this symposium).

(*b*) *An acute acidification phase*

Species such as *Navicula leptostriata*, *Eunotia naegelii*, *Tabellaria quadriseptata*, but also acidobiontic species that were hardly present before, such as *Tabellaria binalis*, become very abundant. *T. binalis*, which is a characteristic species in severely acidified lakes in Fennoscandia, reaches 10%. Acidobiontics exceed 35%, indifferents decrease to 5% and alkaliphilous taxa become extinct. This diatom assemblage never occurred before in the history of the lake. Both inferred pH values and historical data show that pH decreased to *ca.* 4.5 during the 1960s. Acid deposition is the most reasonable explanation (see Renberg *et al.*, this symposium). Although Lilla Öresjön was rather acid before human activity in the catchment caused an increase in pH, it is important to note that no acid period similar to the recent one has occurred before in this lake or in the other studied lakes referred to above.

References

Battarbee, R. W. 1984 Diatom analysis and the acidification of lakes. *Phil. Trans. R. Soc. Lond.* B **305**, 333–355.

Björck, S., Berglund, B. E. & Digerfeldt, G. 1988 New aspects on the deglaciation chronology of south Sweden. *Geog. Polon.* **55**, 37–49.

Charles, D. F., Battarbee, R. W., Renberg, I., van Dam, H. & Smol, J. P. 1989 Paleoecological analysis of lake acidification trends in North America and Europe using diatoms and chrysophytes. In *Acid precipitation vol.* 4. *Soils, aquatic processes, and lake acidification* (ed. S. A. Norton, S. E. Lindberg & A. L. Page). New York: Springer-Verlag. (In the press.)

Digerfeldt, G. & Welinder, S. 1988 The prehistoric cultural landscape in south-west Sweden. *Acta Archaeol.* **58**, 127–136.

Haworth, E. Y. 1976 Two late-glacial (Late-Devensian) diatom assemblage profiles from northern Scotland. *New Phytol.* **77**, 227–256.

Jones, V. J., Stevenson, A. C. & Battarbee, R. W. 1989 Acidification of lakes in Galloway, south west Scotland: a diatom and pollen study of the post-glacial history of Round Loch of Glenhead. *J. Ecol.* **77**, 1–23.

Renberg, I. & Hellberg, T. 1982 The pH history of lakes in southwestern Sweden, as calculated from the subfossil diatom flora of the sediments. *Ambio* **11**, 30–33.

Rosenqvist, I. Th. 1977 *Sur jord – Surt vann* (Acid soil – acid water). Oslo: Ingeniørsforlaget A/S. (In Norwegian.)

Stabell, B. 1985 The development and succession of taxa within the diatom genus *Fragilaria* Lyngbye as a response to basin isolation from the sea. *Boreas* **14**, 273–286.

Williams, D. M., Hartley, B., Ross, R., Munro, M. A. R., Juggins, S. & Battarbee, R. W. 1988 *A coded checklist of British diatoms*. London: Ensis Publishing.

Phil. Trans. R. Soc. Lond. B **327**, 363–367 (1990)
Printed in Great Britain

The significance of land-use and land-management change in the acidification of lakes in Scotland and Norway: an assessment utilizing documentary sources and pollen analysis

By S. T. Patrick[1], J. A. Timberlid[2] and A. C. Stevenson[3]

[1] *Palaeoecology Research Unit, Department of Geography, University College London, 26 Bedford Way, London WC1H 0AP, U.K.*

[2] *O. Hjetlands veg 4, N-5900, Høyanger, Norway*

[3] *Department of Geography, University of Newcastle, Newcastle upon Tyne NE1 7RU, U.K.*

Documentary sources reveal that various land-use and management changes in the catchments of six Scottish lakes during the past 200 years cannot be related to the acidification of specific lakes nor can acidification be related to any general 'land-use' hypothesis. At five of the sites these conclusions are supported by pollen-derived reconstruction of catchment vegetation. In Norway, documentary evidence fails to support a 'land-use' hypothesis of acidification as grazing intensity has actually increased in the area where waters are most strongly acidified. It is considered that the failure to attribute acidification to catchment processes provides further evidence for an explanation in terms of acid precipitation.

Introduction

The recent acidification of surface waters is frequently ascribed to the impact of acidic precipitation in areas of sensitive geology. However, other explanations have been put forward that centre upon changes in land-use and management within lake catchments. To assess the role of changing land-use or management practice, or both, documentary sources and pollen analysis of lake sediment cores, have been utilized to examine the significance of such change in relation to the recent acidification of lakes in Scotland and Norway.

Land-use hypotheses

Rosenqvist (1977, 1978, 1981) proposed that ion exchange reactions in raw humus layers and the uptake of cations by plant growth are the most important factors in determining the acidity of surface waters. The acidification of lakes in southern Norway was attributed to the increase in accumulation of acid humus resulting from the enhanced biomass of acidic heathland (particularly *Calluna*) and forest species, consequent upon a decline in the intensity of pastoral activity in the region. Particular importance was attributed to the decline in burning (Rosenqvist 1981). This hypothesis has found some support as an explanation of contemporary acidification (see, for example, Krug & Frink (1983)).

Study sites

Documentary research was instigated in relation to six specific lake catchments in Scotland and two broad areas in southern and western Norway (figure 1). Palynological analysis was

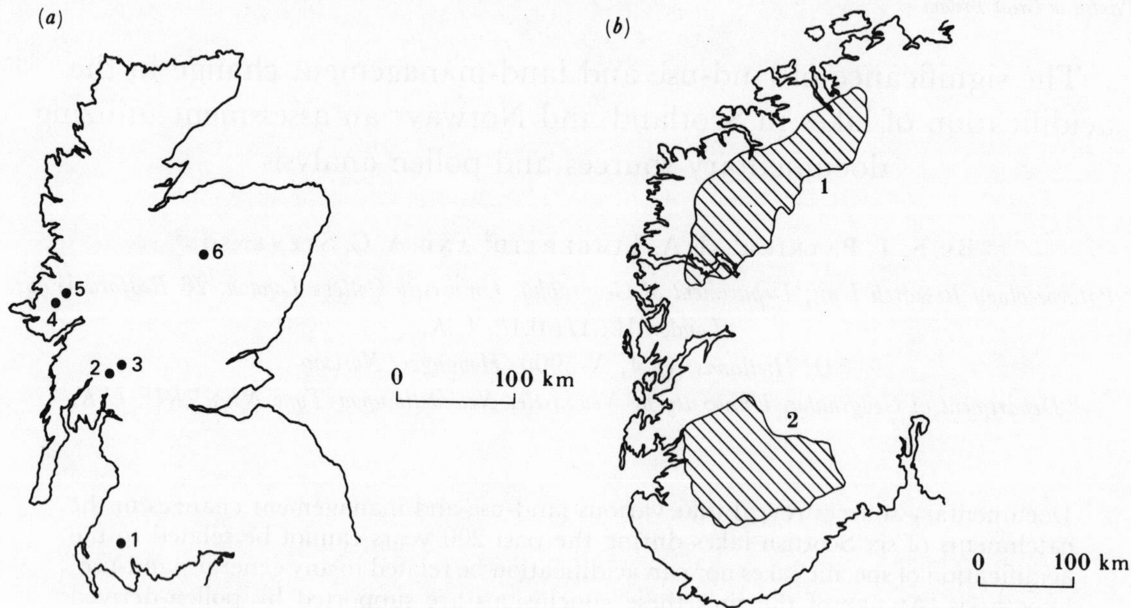

FIGURE 1. Areas of study in (a) Scotland; (1), Round Loch of Glenhead; (2), Loch Chon; (3), Loch Tinker; (4), Loch Doilet; (5), Lochan Dubh' (6), Lochan Uaine. (b) Norway; (1) area 'west'; (2) area 'south'.

carried out on lake sediment cores from the six Scottish sites. Although the sites vary in size and catchment land-use they share the common attribute of experiencing surface water acidification (to a varying degree) within the past 150 years. Of the two Norwegian areas (figure 1), that in the south has been widely influenced by acidification (particularly the higher areas), whereas that in the west has been little affected.

SOURCES AND METHODS

For Scottish sites, documentary information relating to land-use–management was derived from estate plans and records, large scale Ordnance Survey maps, manuscript maps of the 1930s Land Utilization Survey, aerial photographs, Annual Parish Agricultural Returns, the parish-based Statistical Surveys (1790–1798, 1845, 1960s), Forestry Commission records and historical guides and topographies. Similarly, Norwegian histories were compiled by using the agricultural census, land registrations and reports from farming organizations (Timberlid 1989). In both countries a range of miscellaneous site-specific documents were traced and much use was made of personal recollections from farmers, anglers and gamekeepers.

Pollen analysis of lake sediment cores followed standard procedures (Stevenson *et al.* 1987). The results presented here utilize the *Calluna*:Gramineae pollen ratio as an indication of the changing type and proportions of moorland vegetation.

RESULTS

(a) *Scotland*

The three moorland sites of Round Loch of Glenhead, Loch Tinker and Lochan Dubh (figure 1) have a long history of low-intensity grazing. Until the late-eighteenth century, native sheep and cattle characterized the pastoral economy and the rough grazing of these elevated catchments was exploited primarily in summer. The introduction of hardier breeds of sheep facilitated longer grazing periods and by the early-nineteenth century sheep dominated grazing regimes in such areas. Subsequently sheep numbers have fluctuated, but there is no evidence to suggest a decline in grazing intensity in these catchments. Indeed, as adjacent moorland has been lost to afforestation in the twentieth century they have retained their importance for pastoralism. At Round Loch of Glenhead and Lochan Dubh the prevalence of burning as a management practice has declined, but the Loch Tinker catchment is still regularly burnt. The pollen evidence from Round Loch and Lochan Dubh indicates a trend away from *Calluna* since the mid-nineteenth century, presumably because of increased grazing pressure. At Loch Tinker, for as yet unexplained reasons, this trend is reversed in the 1940s (figure 2).

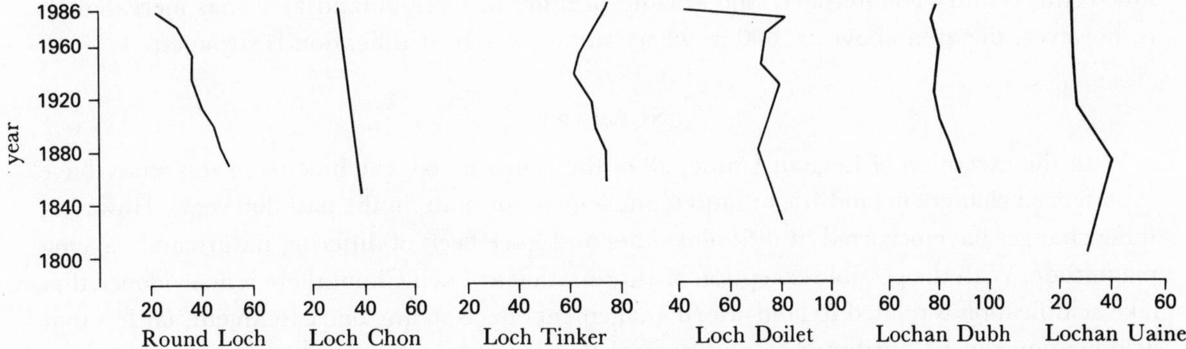

FIGURE 2. ^{210}Pb-dated *Calluna*:Gramineae ratio profiles from lake sediment cores at Scottish sites.

The large, lower-lying and now partly afforested sites, of Loch Chon and Loch Doilet (figure 1) have a history of improvement and management, primarily for animal husbandry. At the peak of agricultural activity in the early–mid-nineteenth century, both catchments contained one or two active farms with plots of arable and meadow land maintained by enclosure, liming and drainage. In addition, the Loch Chon catchment supported a system of deciduous woodland management for charcoal production. Agricultural and silvicultural activity and associated management practices declined from the late-nineteenth century. Conifers were introduced in the Loch Doilet catchment from the 1920s and in the Loch Chon catchment from the 1950s. In the latter catchment there is a suggestion that afforestation may have affected surface water pH, as acidification accelerated in the 1960s (Kreiser *et al.*, this symposium). Since those dates, active land management has been largely confined to practices associated with forestry. Despite the decline in agricultural activity since the mid-nineteenth century, neither the Loch Chon or Loch Doilet *Calluna*:Gramineae ratios exhibit evidence of a more mature heathland vegetation (figure 2).

At 900 m the rocky, sparsely vegetated and exposed catchment of Lochan Uaine lies above the limit of summer sheep grazing in the region. At this altitude there is no evidence for, nor rational expectation of, any land-use change or active land management within the catchment. The catchment may thus be considered a control site in terms of land-use–management effects. Interestingly, since the mid-nineteenth century the *Calluna*:Gramineae ratio has decreased (figure 2), probably reflecting a regional trend rather than a catchment-specific record of vegetation change at this small sparsely vegetated site.

(*b*) *Norway*

Throughout the western area, both grazing by domestic animals and the use of støl (summer-hill) land have decreased since the 1860s (Timberlid 1989). This development has resulted from a demand for better livestock nutrition and for a more rational system of production and has led to the increased use of cultivated pasture on inlying fields. In this western area there are no indications of surface water acidification (Henriksen *et al.* 1988).

In the southern area there has also been a decrease in grazing intensity on land below 600 m, but in the remoter areas above this altitude, sheep are still brought in from other regions for high-level summer grazing. As a result of this practice sheep numbers have changed little since 1896 (Timberlid 1989). Because modern sheep consume twice as much fodder as their nineteenth century counterparts, the grazing pressure in these upland areas has increased. It is, however, the area above *ca.* 600 m where surface water acidification is strongest.

Summary

With the exception of Lochan Uaine, all of the Scottish lake catchments in this study have experienced changes in land-use or land management, or both, in the past 200 years. However, these changes have occurred at different times and have been of differing nature and varying magnitude. With the possible exception of afforestation at Loch Chon, there is no evidence that lake acidification is related to land-use/management effects in any one catchment, far less that acidification can be attributed to any general 'land-use' hypothesis.

At five of the Scottish sites pollen data provide evidence that during the period of recent acidification catchment vegetation has changed little or has shifted towards Gramineae and away from *Calluna*, the antithesis of the 'land-use hypothesis'. Only at Loch Tinker does an increase (unexplained) in the *Calluna*: Gramineae ratio occur.

In Norway the 'land-use hypothesis' also breaks down. In the regions where grazing density has declined (western and southern areas below *ca.* 600 m) there is little evidence of acidification, but in the area where grazing intensity has increased (southern area above *ca.* 600 m) surface waters are strongly acidified.

To date, sources similar to those used in this study have shown no evidence for a land-use/management role in surface water acidification at other sites in the United Kingdom (see, for example, Battarbee *et al.* (1988); Patrick (1987); Patrick & Stevenson (1990)) and Norway (see, for example, Drabløs *et al.* (1980); Timberlid (1980)). Together with evidence of the atmospheric pollution record from lake sediments, the failure to attribute acidification to catchment processes argues strongly for an explanation in terms of acid precipitation.

References

Battarbee, R. W., Anderson, N. J., Appleby, P. G., Flower, R. J., Fritz, S. C., Haworth, E. Y., Higgitt, S., Jones, V. J., Kreiser, A., Munro, M. A. R., Natkanski, J., Oldfield, F., Patrick, S. T., Richardson, N. G., Rippey, B. & Stevenson, A. C. 1988 *Lake acidification in the United Kingdom 1800–1986: evidence from analysis of lake sediments*. London: Ensis Publishing.

Drabløs, D., Sevaldrud, I. & Timberlid, J. A. 1980 Historical land-use changes related to fish status development in different areas in southern Norway. In *Ecological impact of acidic precipitation* (ed. D. Drabløs & A. Tollan), pp. 367–370. SNSF Project Report, Oslo.

Henriksen, A., Lien, L., Traaen, T. S., Sevaldrud, I. S. & Brakke, D. F. 1988 Lake acidification in Norway – present and predicted chemical status. *Ambio* **17**, 259–266.

Krug, E. C. & Frink, C. R. 1983 Acid rain on acid soil in a new perspective. *Science, Wash.* **221**, 520–525.

Patrick, S. T. 1987 Palaeoecological evaluation of the recent acidification of Welsh lakes. V. The significance of land use and land management. Palaeoecology Research Unit, University College London, Research Paper no. 19.

Patrick, S. T. & Stevenson, A. C. 1990 Acidified Welsh lakes: the significance of land use and management change. In *Acid waters in Wales* (ed. R. Edwards *et al.*). (In the press.)

Rosenqvist, I. Th. 1977 *Acid soil–acid water.* Oslo: Ingeniørsforlaget.

Rosenqvist, I. Th. 1978 Alternative sources for acidification of river water in Norway. *Sci. tot. Environ.* **10**, 39–49.

Rosenqvist, I. Th. 1981 Importance of acid precipitation and acid soil in freshwater lake chemistry. *Vann.* **4**, 402–409.

Stevenson, A. C., Patrick, S. T., Kreiser, A. & Battarbee, R. W. 1987 Palaeoecological evaluation of the recent acidification of susceptible lakes: methods utilized under DoE contract PECD 7/7/139 and the Royal Society SWAP project. Palaeoecology Research Unit, University College London. Research Paper no. 26.

Timberlid, J. A. 1980 Have changes in use of land influenced the regional lake acidification? In *Ecological impact of acidic precipitation* (ed. D. Drabløs & A. Tollan), pp. 352–353. SNSF Project Report, Oslo.

Timberlid, J. A. 1990 Driftsendringar i jordbruket som årsak til forsuring av norske vassdrag? Ein samanliknande studie av utmarksbruket på Vest – og Sørlandet i perioden 1850–1980. *Økoforsk* no. 14.

Phil. Trans. R. Soc. Lond. B **327**, 369–370 (1990)
Printed in Great Britain

A test of the land-use hypothesis for recent lake acidification by using hill-top lakes in southwest Norway: an extended summary

By H. J. B. Birks, F. Berge and J. F. Boyle

Botanical Institute, University of Bergen, Allégaten 41, *N*-5007 *Bergen, Norway*

Introduction

Three hypotheses have been proposed to explain recent lake acidification in northwest Europe; the acid-deposition, the land-use and the long-term hypotheses. The hypothesis of natural, long-term soil acidification is not relevant for explaining recent, rapid lake acidification. A critical requirement in testing the first two hypotheses is to distinguish unambiguously between lake acidification due to atmospheric deposition and lake acidification following land-use and associated soil changes, such as the accumulation of raw humus.

Hill-top lakes are small, deep basins perched on tops of cliffs and hills. They have very small catchments, often consisting of bare rock. The chemistry of these lakes is primarily influenced by the chemical composition of precipitation and by the underlying bedrock. Because of their very small catchments, their chemistry cannot be influenced by changes in catchment land-use. Hill-top lakes are thus ideal situations in which to test the two hypotheses, because any acidification in these lakes cannot be a result of changes in land-use, but only of acid precipitation. Thus if hill-top lakes have acidified recently, the land-use hypothesis would be falsified for these sites. On the other hand, the acid-deposition hypothesis would clearly be supported.

The sites

Two small hill-top lakes (Holetjørn, Ljosvatn) in the Moi-Flekkefjord-Kvinesdal area of Vest-Agder, southwest Norway were selected for palaeoecological studies, involving diatoms, pollen, microscopic charcoal, geochemistry, and carbonaceous particles (produced by industrial fossil fuel burning). Standard SWAP procedures were followed. Chronology was provided by ^{210}Pb dating at one site, and by statistical correlation with the carbonaceous particle stratigraphy at the other site. Both lakes lie on acid granitic migmatite at elevations of 485 and 385 m. They are small (0.016–0.11 km^2), deep (17–25 m), clear and oligotrophic, with pH values of 4.4–4.6 at present. They are in the area with a weighted yearly precipitation mean pH of 4.4 and an annual deposition of excess SO_4^{2-} of 3.5 g m^{-2}. They have catchment: lake ratios of 2–3.

Conclusions

The following conclusions can be drawn from the results of our palaeoecological studies.

1. Both lakes were naturally acid prior to *ca.* 1880. The reconstructed pH values were 4.8 and 5.1, as inferred from weighted averaging calibration of the diatom assemblages preserved in the sediments.

2. Both acidified to pH 4.5–4.6 beginning at *ca.* 1930–1940.

3. Vegetational change (as shown by pollen analysis) in the last century has been almost non-existent. What vegetational change has occurred is the opposite of predictions from the land-use hypothesis, namely Ericaceae have decreased as the lakes became more acid.

4. The reconstructed drop in pH, of *ca.* 0.5 units, is similar in magnitude to estimates from other palaeolimnological studies in southern Norway.

5. Increased concentrations of trace metals (Cu, Zn, Cr, Pb) occur in the last 100 years. Carbonaceous particles appear about 1880. All peak in the 1930s or later, the same time as lake pH began to drop. These increases reflect atmospheric input into the lake following emission into the atmosphere by fossil fuel combustion.

6. The first major Pb increase, representing the earliest record of atmospheric contamination, pre-dates the onset of lake acidification by 50–100 years. At no site in Norway or Britain is there any convincing evidence for recent lake acidification before the first increase in trace-metal concentrations or the first occurrence of carbonaceous particles.

7. The demonstration of recent lake acidification in these hill-top lakes falsifies the land-use hypothesis.

8. The temporal relations in the hill-top lakes between lake acidification, carbonaceous particles, and trace-metal concentrations support the acid-deposition hypothesis. We conclude that acid deposition is the most likely cause of recent acidification in these two hill-top lakes.

9. In the absence of any critical palaeoecological evidence to support the land-use hypothesis as a mechanism causing recent lake acidification in northwest Europe, and in the face of several independent refutations, we propose that it is perhaps time to put the land-use hypothesis to rest.

This is an extended summary of a paper entitled 'A palaeoecological test of the land-use hypothesis for recent lake acidification in southwest Norway by using hill-top lakes' submitted to the *Journal of Paleolimnology*.

Phil. Trans. R. Soc. Lond. B **327**, 371–372 (1990)
Printed in Great Britain

Spruce and surface water acidification: an extended summary

By I. Renberg, T. Korsman and N. J. Anderson
Department of Ecological Botany, University of Umeå, S-901 87 Umeå, Sweden

Introduction

It has been proposed that vegetation and soil changes resulting from changes in land use cause surface-water acidification. The expansion of spruce forest, from natural colonization and from afforestation, has been one of the major changes that has taken place in the vegetation of South Sweden during this century. Spruce has been favoured at the expense of broad-leafed trees by forest management and has been planted on open land, abandoned farm land and in forests. Since the 1920s, the area covered by spruce forest has increased by 2.3 million ha† in Götaland and Svealand, and the frequency of spruce trees in the forests has increased from 11.5 to 33.5% (data from Department of Forest Survey, Swedish University of Agricultural Science, Umeå). Götaland and Svealand comprise the southernmost third of Sweden, the area that suffers most from lake acidification.

Spruce colonization alters soil conditions. In several investigations, in which conditions in spruce and birch stands have been compared, significantly lower pH values have been recorded in spruce forest soils. It has been suggested that spruce expansion also leads to lake-water acidification, but this has not been confirmed. Unfortunately, it is difficult to design an investigation aimed at studying the acidification effects of spruce forest under prevailing levels of atmospheric pollution because there are problems in distinguishing between true vegetation–soil effects, effects of air pollution, and combined effects.

To assess whether spruce forest *per se* causes lake-water acidification, we have studied the effects of the natural immigration of spruce that reached northern Sweden from the northeast about 3000 years ago, before there was any acid precipitation from fossil-fuel combustion. Palaeoecological studies indicate that spruce colonized land that was occupied by birch, alder and pine.

Methods and study sites

Lakes in areas with poor soil conditions, and thus sensitive to acidification, were selected for the investigation. A further criterion was that the lake catchments should have no, or very small amounts, of peatland, as peat growth and peatland expansion may alter lake-water pH. Eight lakes were studied, six are acidic today (pH 4.5–5.2). In two of them the recent pH trends have also been reconstructed by diatom analysis. These studies verify that the lakes were acidified during the last few decades.

Pollen analysis was used to determine the level of spruce immigration in each sediment core and to reconstruct the vegetation history. Diatom analyses were done on sediment samples taken both below and above the spruce immigration level, to reconstruct pH history before, during and after the spruce immigration; pH was reconstructed by weighted averaging. Diatoms were also classified into Hustedt's pH preference groups.

† 1 ha = 10^4 m^2.

Results and conclusions

Although the diatom assemblages changed slightly in some of the lakes during the periods studied, there was no increase in the relative frequencies of acidophilous and acidobiontic taxa. There were no signs of acidification of the lakes at, or within a few hundred years after the spruce immigration as indicated by diatom-inferred pH. The present investigation does not, therefore, indicate that spruce expansion *per se* causes lake acidification. It is important, however, to point out that spruce canopies are effective filters for aerosols, and that a combination of spruce and air pollutants may contribute to surface-water acidification.

This is an extended summary of a paper to be published elsewhere.

Phil. Trans. R. Soc. Lond. B **327**, 373–376 (1990)
Printed in Great Britain

Land-use change and lake acidification: Iron Age de-settlement in northern Sweden as a pre-industrial analogue

By N. J. Anderson and T. Korsman

Department of Ecological Botany, University of Umeå, S-901 87 Umeå, Sweden

Iron Age de-settlement in Hälsingland, Northern Sweden, can be regarded as a good analogue for the possible effects of land-use and vegetational changes on lake acidification without the effect of contemporary atmospheric pollution. Pollen analyses were used to identify vegetational change associated with a de-settlement period *ca.* 500 A.D. and diatom analyses to assess if there was any associated change in lake-water pH. A clear settlement horizon was found in the two lakes studied, indicating catchment disturbance associated with Iron Age agriculture. There was no change, however, in diatom reconstructed pH after de-settlement, during vegetation regeneration, when it has been postulated that the build up of raw humus and change of ion-exchange conditions would result in acidification. Importantly, one of the lakes began to acidify, before liming, under contemporary levels of acid deposition.

1. Introduction

Rosenqvist (1977, 1978) has postulated the possible importance of soil-generated acidity, by ion-exchange mechanisms, to surface-water acidification. He has argued that the demise of the Norwegian outfield system, where cows were grazed in the forest and hills during the summer, resulted in the replacement of 'grasslands' with coniferous forest and heathlands (Rosenqvist 1978, p. 48). He further suggests (Rosenqvist 1978, 1979) that the timescales of forest regeneration, humus accumulation and soil podsolization after land has been abandoned are precisely those over which the streams and lakes of Norway have acidified. Finding suitable modern analogues to evaluate Rosenqvist's hypothesis has proved difficult because of currently high levels of atmospheric pollution. Palaeolimnological approaches, however, provide a means of assessing the possible effects of land-use change in the absence of anthropogenically derived acidity, by using lake sediments that record the effects of past land-use changes, before industrial effects.

A suitable historical analogue for modern land-use changes is provided by the archaeologically well documented depopulation of Iron Age farms and villages in Hälsingland, Northern Sweden, during the Migration Period (Liedgren 1984, 1989). Iron Age settlements were systematically abandoned in the area from *ca.* 500 A.D. and re-settlement did not occur before the Middle Ages (*ca.* 1100 A.D.). Numbers of farms and settlements were high, between 750 and 1000 in Northern Hälsingland (Liedgren 1989). The area immediately east of Sjösjön has over 100 identified farms in an area of *ca.* 30 km^2. Even if all farms were not occupied simultaneously, human and cattle population levels would have been substantial. It has been estimated that some farms had up to 15 head of cattle.

2. Methods and study site

The lakes (Sjösjön and Lill Målsjön; for details see table 1 in Battarbee & Renberg, this symposium) lie inland of Hudiksvall, N. Sweden, less than 2 km from extensive documented Iron Age remains (figure 1; Liedgren 1989). Both sites have been recently limed but before liming they were of low alkalinity and susceptible to acid deposition. The lake sediments were sampled with a Russian corer in March 1987 from the ice surface. Cores were subsampled at contiguous 1 cm intervals through the period known to include the Iron Age settlement horizon. Preparation of samples for pollen and diatom analyses followed standard methodologies (Moore & Webb 1978; Battarbee 1986); pH was reconstructed by using weighted averaging (Birks *et al.*, this symposium).

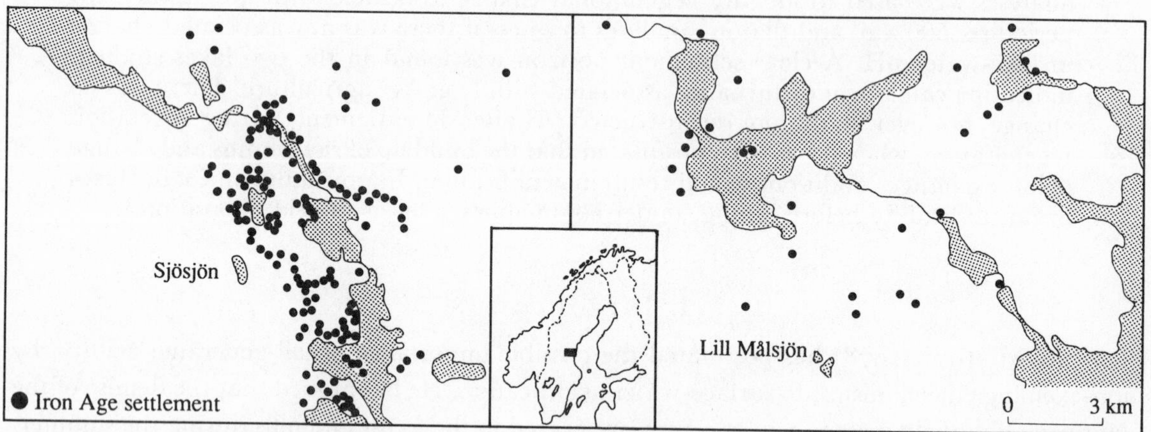

Figure 1. Location of study lakes, showing their proximity to known Iron Age farms (Liedgren 1989). Farms shown are minimum numbers; many sites will have been lost from the record by, for example, modern farming practices; the Lill Målsjön area is also currently under-researched.

3. Results and discussion

Pollen profiles (figure 2) are similar for both lakes, with a clear dominance of *Pinus*. *Picea* values increased *ca.* 500 cm depth in Lill Målsjön and at 1615 cm in Sjösjön, as a result of immigration into the area (*ca.* 2800 BP in Hälsingland). *Betula* and *Alnus* form a subsidiary component of the assemblage. The diversity of pollen types is low at both sites, with low frequencies of shrubs and herbs.

Cultural pollen indicators at Sjösjön increased above background levels at *ca.* 1600 cm, and although cereal grains are not present, the Iron Age settlement period is clear. At Lill Målsjön, there are small but significant increases in shrubs, herbs, graminids and apophytes at the same time as *Betula* increases, and *Picea* and *Pinus* decrease (450 cm depth).

At Sjösjön diatom pH preference groups show no change over the sampled period (figure 2*a*). Diatoms are dominated by pH indifferent (= circumneutral), planktonic taxa, notably *Cyclotella kuetzingiana* and *Aulacoseira subarctica* type 2, and reconstructed pH is uniform at *ca.* 6. At Lill Målsjön, acidophilous diatoms increase from the base of the core, and indifferent taxa vary around 30%. The species assemblage in Lill Målsjön reflects the shallower depth of the lake compared to Sjösjön, with benthic taxa dominant, especially a number of *Fragilaria* spp. (e.g. *Fragilaria virescens*, *F. lata*) and *Aulacoseira perglabra* var. *floriniae*. The planktonic species

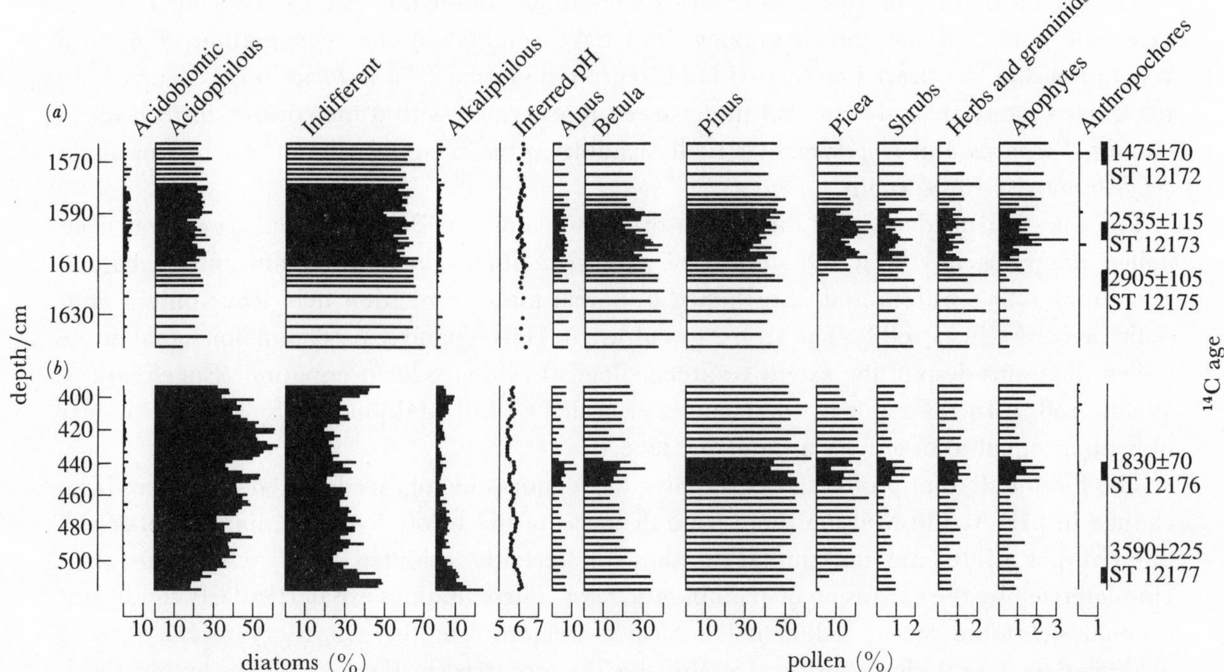

FIGURE 2. Summary diatom and pollen diagrams for (*a*) Sjösjön and (*b*) Lill Målsjön. Depths are centimetres below lake surface. Placement of diatom taxa into pH categories follows the SWAP classification. The pollen sum used for Sjösjön was 500 arboreal grains, but for Lill Målsjön *ca.* 2000 grains were counted to identify the cultural horizon. Grouping of pollen taxa into apophytes and anthropochores follows Engelmark & Wallin (1985). Note scale change for non-tree taxa. Dating: the *Picea* increase in coastal Hälsingland has been dated to *ca.* 2800 BP in varved lake sediments and peat-bogs. The ^{14}C dates, although progressively younger upcore for Sjösjön, are slightly old for both lakes, given contemporary knowledge of the dates of the late Iron Age settlement in this area, and its decline in the Migration period. Similarly, the date for the *Picea* increase at both sites is too old, compared with other sites. The sediments may be contaminated with older carbon from the catchment or ground water.

generally occur at low values (e.g. *A. distans* var. *tenella*, *Asterionella formosa*) although percentages are variable upcore, occasionally >20%; pH reconstructs to 5.4–5.5.

The number of Iron Age archaeological sites in Hälsingland (see, for example, figure 1) indicates substantial populations, sedentary agriculture, and presumably significant effects on the landscape in terms of forest perturbation (Engelmark & Wallin 1985; Liedgren 1989). Animal husbandry was based on the outfield system as the lower-level fields (the home farms) were utilized for arable cultivation and winter-fodder production. The catchments of Sjösjön and Lill Målsjön would have been used for outfield grazing by sheep or goats and cattle, as they lie just outside the homestead areas (Engelmark & Wallin 1985; Liedgren 1989; cf. Hicks 1988). The effect of this grazing on the understorey, and on the regeneration of *Pinus* and *Picea*, would have been substantial (Steen 1958).

Phytosociological studies of the effects of cattle grazing in boreal forest systems in the immediate post-World War II period have been done by Steen (1958). The effects are probably analogous to those resulting from Iron Age agriculture, and importantly, are similar to changes discussed by Rosenqvist (1978, 1979). Grazing of coniferous forest results in the enhancement of grasses, and the appearance of new herbs, whereas shrubs, lichens and certain mosses are reduced and the forest as a whole becomes thinner. It can also result in a transformation of the forest podsols into brown-earth soils (Steen 1958).

The decline of the Iron Age culture and abandonment of the homesteads, associated neglect of arable land and the end of grazing, will have resulted in the regeneration of natural vegetation. On the cleared cultivated land, regrowth of mixed *Picea–Pinus* forest occurred. In the grazed forest areas the natural understorey regenerated with a mixed low shrub layer of *Calluna*, *Vaccinium* and *Empetrum*, eventually leading to the accumulation of raw humus again (cf. Rosenqvist 1978, 1979).

The question of identifying the effects of early people on Scandinavian vegetation from pollen diagrams has been the subject of extensive discussion and remains problematical (Berglund 1985). Substantial disturbance to boreal forest vegetation may leave only a faint pollen record (Hicks 1988). The Iron Age culture in Hälsingland leaves no major signal in the pollen diagrams despite the extensive archaeological evidence for occupation (Engelmark & Wallin 1985). In this context, the changes recorded at Lill Målsjön and Sjösjön are a clear indication of cultural activity around the lake.

The Sjösjön diatom profile shows stability throughout the analysed period and there is no change in pH. At Lill Målsjön there is no decrease of pH below 5.4. The diatom floras and inferred pH values are not similar to those of recently acidified lakes, which are often characterized by the expansion of acidobiontic taxa. These findings are particularly significant as analysis of the recent sediments of Sjösjön demonstrate the sensitivity of the lake to acidification since a characteristic *Cyclotella* decline occurred in the lake before liming (N. J. Anderson, unpublished results).

Human impact on catchment vegetation can undoubtedly cause perturbations to lake ecosystems (Fritz 1989; Renberg, this symposium), but it appears unlikely that changed land-use is itself sufficient to cause lake acidification. Palaeolimnological results do not support the hypothesis that catchment-generated acidity has the ability to acidify surface waters to the extent observed over recent decades in the absence of atmospheric inputs derived from fossil-fuel combustion. In Hälsingland, there is no fossil diatom record of early acidification at the study sites, after the cessation of Iron Age agriculture.

References

Battarbee, R. W. 1986 Diatom analysis. In *Handbook of Holocene palaeoecology and palaeohydrology* (ed. B. E. Berglund), pp. 527–570. Chichester: John Wiley.

Berglund, B. E. 1985 Early agriculture in Scandinavia: research problems related to pollen-analytical studies. *Norwegian Archaeol. Rev.* **18**, 77–105.

Engelmark, R. & Wallin, J.-E. 1985 Pollen analytical evidence for Iron Age agriculture in Hälsingland, Central Sweden. *Archaeol. Envir.* **4**, 353–366.

Fritz, S. C. 1989 Lake development and limnological response to prehistoric and historic land-use in Diss, Norfolk, U.K. *J. Ecol.* **77**, 182–202.

Hicks, S. 1988 The representation of different farming practices in pollen diagrams from Northern Finland. In *The cultural landscape. Past, present and future* (ed. H. H. Birks, H. J. B. Birks, P. E. Kaland & D. Moe), pp. 189–207. Cambridge University Press.

Moore, P. D. & Webb, J. A. 1978 *An illustrated guide to pollen analysis*. London: Hodder & Stoughton.

Liedgren, L. 1984 Iron Age settlements in Hälsingland, Northern Sweden. *Archaeol. Envir.* **2**, 93–112.

Liedgren, L. 1989 Bebyggelseutvecklingen i Forsa, Hälsingland, under den äldre järnåldern. *Arkeologi i norr* **2**, 45–94.

Rosenqvist, I. Th. 1977 *Sur Jord – Surt Vann*. Oslo: Ingeniörforslaget A/S.

Rosenqvist, I. Th. 1978 Alternative sources for acidification of river water in Norway. *Sci. tot. Envir.* **10**, 39–49.

Rosenqvist, I. Th. 1979 Influence of forest vegetation and agriculture on the acidity of freshwater. In *Advances in environmental science and engineering* (ed. J. R. Pfafflin & E. N. Ziegler), vol. 3, pp. 56–79. London: Gordon Breach Science Publ.

Steen, E. 1958 Betesinflytelser i svensk vegetation. *Statens Jordbruksförsök Meddelande* Nr. **89**. Uppsala.

Phil. Trans. R. Soc. Lond. B **327**, 377–383 (1990)
Printed in Great Britain

Afforestation and lake acidification: a comparison of four sites in Scotland

By A. M. Kreiser[1], P. G. Appleby[2], J. Natkanski[1], B. Rippey[3] and R. W. Battarbee[1]

[1] *Palaeoecology Research Unit, Department of Geography, University College London, 26 Bedford Way, London WC1H 0AP, U.K.*

[2] *Department of Applied Mathematics and Theoretical Physics, The University of Liverpool, Liverpool L69 3BX, U.K.*

[3] *University of Ulster Freshwater Laboratory, Traad Point, Ballyronan BT45 6LR, Northern Ireland, U.K.*

Palaeolimnological techniques including diatom analysis were used to examine the acidification and atmospheric contamination histories of four lakes in Scotland. Results from an afforested and a moorland (control) site in a region of high acid deposition are compared with results from two similar sites in an area receiving lower acid deposition levels. Results show that afforestation of a catchment in the higher acid deposition area has increased the rate of lake acidification. There is no evidence for acidification as a result of forest growth alone in the area of lower acid deposition.

Introduction

There has been a considerable increase in coniferous afforestation in the U.K. during the twentieth century, particularly in upland areas previously covered by heath or moorland. Many of these afforested upland regions are inherently vulnerable to surface water acidification because of their slow weathering, base-poor bedrock and high rainfall (Kinniburgh & Edmunds 1986). In addition, afforestation itself might promote acidification through processes associated with tree growth (Nilsson *et al.* 1984), ground preparation techniques (especially drainage (Hornung & Newson 1986)), and the combined effects of acid deposition and forestry, such as the enhanced capture of dry deposition by the canopy and the foliar uptake of sulphur dioxide and subsequent leaching of sulphate (Lindberg & Garten 1988). Forests in upland locations are also efficient collectors of fine acid mist droplets from low cloud (Unsworth 1984).

Evidence exists that afforestation can lead to increased acidification of streams. In Wales and Scotland studies show that streams draining forests have lower pH and higher aluminium and sulphate concentrations than streams with moorland catchments (Harriman & Morrison 1982; Stoner *et al.* 1984), an effect that appears to increase with the age of the plantation. However, although palaeolimnological techniques have been successfully used to show that lakes in the U.K. have acidifed as a result of acid deposition (Battarbee *et al.* 1988), similar studies of afforested sites have so far failed to show any conclusive evidence to link afforestation with lake acidification (Flower *et al.* 1987) as most had acidified before afforestation.

This study was specifically designed to ascertain whether afforestation could lead to lake acidification. Two regions of Scotland known to be geologically sensitive to acidification were selected, one receiving high levels of acid deposition and the other significantly lower levels. In each region a lake with an afforested catchment was chosen along with an adjacent undisturbed moorland site as a control.

The sites

The Trossachs region of central Scotland was chosen as the area of high deposition with two study sites in the Loch Ard forest area; Loch Chon (forested) and Loch Tinker (moorland control site). These lakes are compared with Loch Doilet (forested catchment) and Lochan Dubh (moorland control) in the Loch Sheil area on the west coast of Scotland, an area receiving moderate to low levels of acid deposition. Conifer planting began in 1920 at Loch Doilet and in 1952 at Loch Chon. No other major changes in the catchments have taken place within the last 150 years (Patrick *et al.*, this symposium). Table 1 provides a summary of the

Table 1. Summary of site characteristics and water chemistry

	Loch Chon	Loch Tinker	Loch Doilet	Lochan Dubh
S deposition/($g\ m^{-2}\ a^{-1}$)	1.2	1.2	0.8	0.8
altitude/m	100	420	10	230
forested area (%)	51	0	41	0
mean measured pH	5.2	6.0	5.9	5.6
Ca^{2+}/($\mu eq\ l^{-1}$)	79	78	47	33
SO_4^{2-}/($\mu eq\ l^{-1}$)	85	62	68	40

physical and chemical characteristics of the four sites. The analytical techniques used are outlined in Stevenson *et al.* (1987) and the pH was reconstructed by using weighted averaging (Birks *et al.*, this symposium).

Loch Chon and Loch Tinker

The first sign of acidification in Loch Chon is indicated by the loss of the planktonic taxon *Cyclotella kuetzingiana* in the early nineteenth century (figure 1*a*). Continued but gradual acidification is indicated by the decline in other circumneutral taxa from 1850 onwards. An acceleration in acidification follows catchment afforestation in the 1950s and is marked by the increase in the more acid-tolerant taxa *Navicula leptostriata* and *Eunotia incisa* above 2 cm depth; pH reconstruction from the diatom data suggests a decline from pH 6.5, starting in the early nineteenth century, but the most rapid rate of change occurs from 1960 onwards when pH decreases from pH 5.8 to pH 5.2 at the surface (1985), a value that agrees well with the recent mean measured pH. Additionally, cladoceran analysis of this core shows clear evidence of pH decline in the range pH 6–5. (Nilssen & Sandøy, this symposium).

Loch Tinker also shows an early decline in *Cyclotella* before 1850 (figure 1*b*). Following this, a shift to more acidic conditions is indicated by an increase in *Tabellaria flocculosa* after 1850 and an increase in *Frustulia rhomboides* var. *saxonica* at 12 cm depth (1900). Some further acidification is indicated by the reduction in *Achnanthes minutissima* but there is no overall change in species composition above 8 cm depth (1930). The rapid expansion of acid-tolerant taxa seen in Loch Chon has not occurred in Loch Tinker. The reconstruction of pH from the diatom data suggests a steady decline of pH throughout the nineteenth century and early

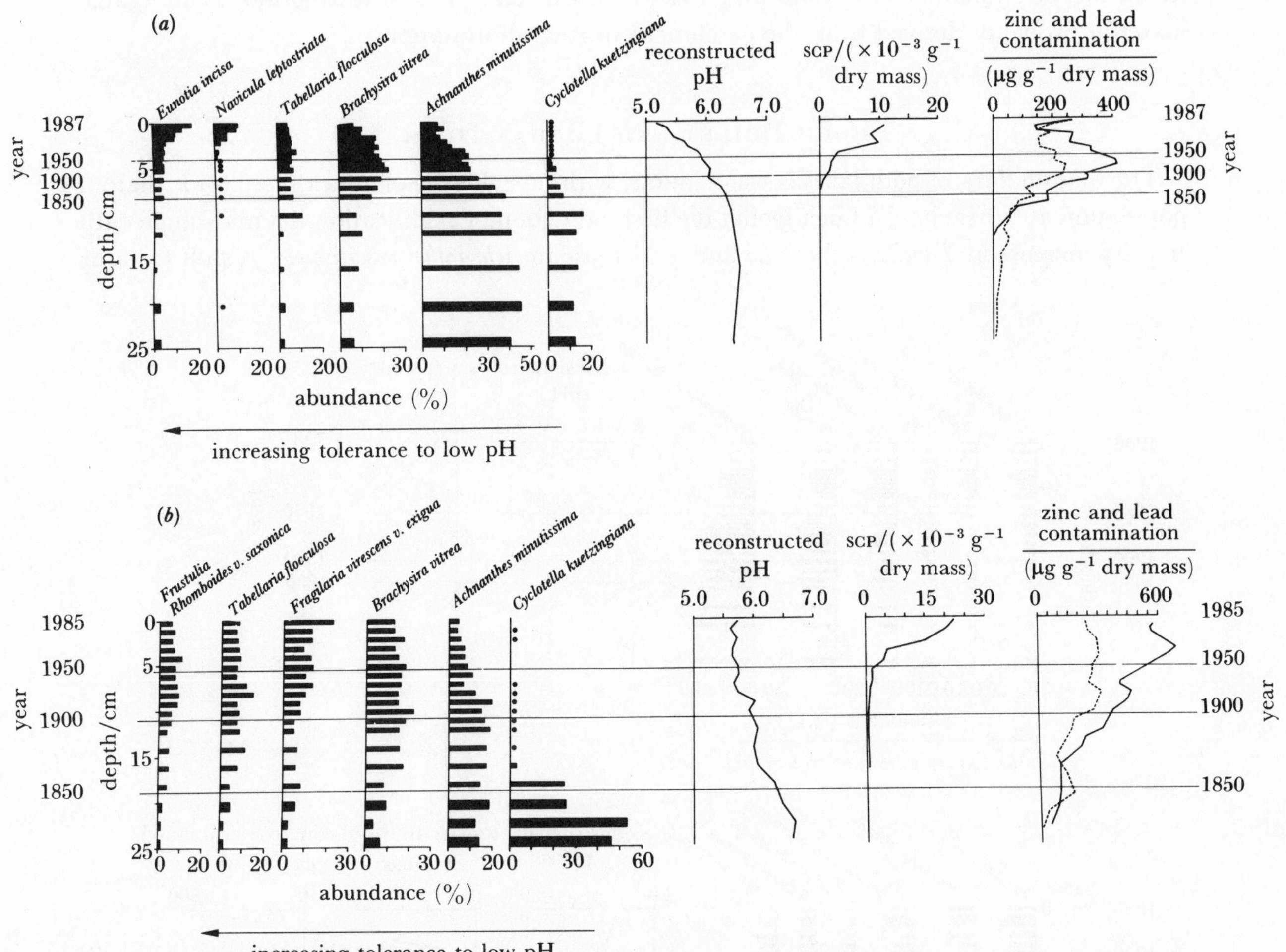

FIGURE 1. Summary diagrams showing the diatom taxa with greater than 10% abundance, reconstructed pH, spheroidal carbonaceous particle (SCP) concentrations and atmospheric zinc (solid line) and lead (dotted line) contamination profiles for (*a*) Loch Chon and (*b*) Loch Tinker. Background trace metal values were calculated by using a regression of zinc and lead concentrations against concentrations of a major cation in pre-nineteenth century sediment. The background values were then subtracted from the total concentrations of lead (dotted line) and zinc (solid line) to give the contamination component in the recent sediment.

twentieth centuries from pH 6.6 to pH 5.7 by 1930, after which pH has fluctuated between pH 5.6–5.7 until the present. The mean measured pH (pH 6.0) is slightly higher than that reconstructed at the surface. The cladoceran data from this core also suggest that pH has not declined over the past fifty years (J. P. Nilssen, personal communication).

Profiles of spheroidal carbonaceous particle concentration and atmospheric zinc and lead contamination (with catchment-derived zinc and lead removed) for Loch Chon and Loch Tinker are shown in figure 1*a*, *b*. Both lochs record an increase in carbonaceous particle deposition from the late 1940s in accordance with the trends found at sites receiving high levels of acid deposition in southwest Scotland (Battarbee *et al.* 1988). Deposition of zinc and lead from the atmosphere begins in the sediments at depths below the limit of ^{210}Pb dating and reflects contamination from early industrial sources. In both lakes the concentrations of lead and zinc increase throughout the nineteenth and twentieth centuries. The decline in zinc and lead concentrations between 1950 and 1970 in Loch Chon is due to dilution by inorganic material probably derived from the catchment during afforestation.

Loch Doilet and Lochan Dubh

The diatom flora of both lakes is very similar, with no evidence of a past planktonic diatom population at either site. In Loch Doilet the first indication of acidification is a mid-nineteenth century increase in *Tabellaria flocculosa* and a decrease in *Achnanthes minutissima*. A shift towards

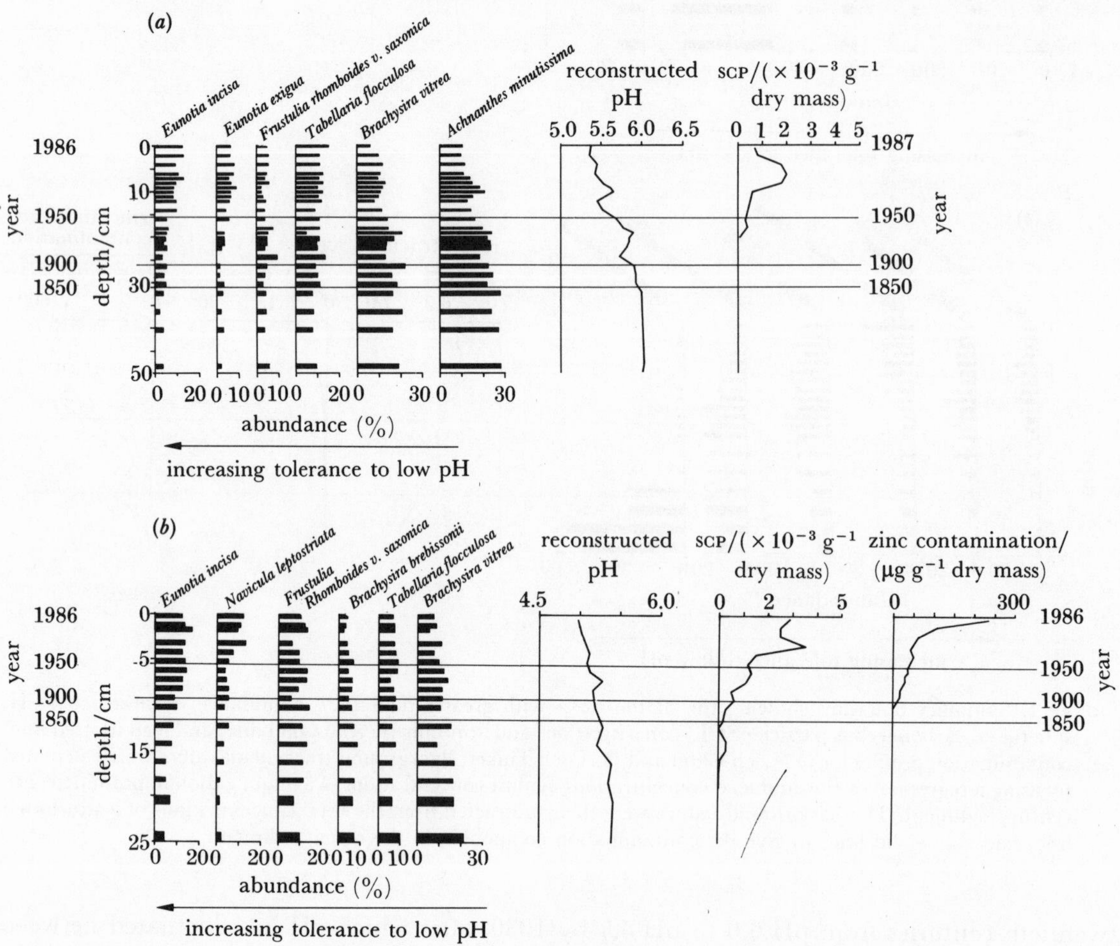

Figure 2. Summary diagrams showing the diatom taxa with greater than 10% abundance, reconstructed pH and spheroidal carbonaceous particle (SCP) concentrations for (*a*) Loch Doilet and (*b*) Lochan Dubh. Trace metal contamination was calculated as for figure 1. Zinc contamination is shown for Lochan Dubh but there is no detectable atmospheric trace metal contamination in Loch Doilet.

slightly more acidic conditions from 1930 onwards is indicated by a further decrease in *Achnanthes minutissima* plus increases in the more acid tolerant taxa *Eunotia incisa* and *Eunotia exigua* (figure 2*a*). Reconstruction of pH for this lake shows a slight acidification from pH 6.0 in the mid-nineteenth century to pH 5.8–5.9 in the 1930s. From this point, pH declines further to a reconstructed pH of 5.4 at the surface, an overall change of 0.6 pH units.

In the case of Lochan Dubh the proportions of acid-tolerant taxa are generally greater throughout the core. The sedimentary diatom record for this lake is described in Jones *et al.* (this symposium). The main floristic changes occur between 18 cm and 14 cm when *Navicula leptostriata* and *Eunotia incisa* begin to increase accompanied by a decline in the circumneutral taxa (figure 2*b*) and this trend continues up to the sediment surface. The time of the point of change cannot be dated as it lies below the limit of the unsupported ^{210}Pb record at 11.5 cm. Reconstruction of pH suggests a pH decline from a pre-1850 value of pH 5.4 to pH 5.0 at present. Evidence for long-term acidic conditions below pH 5.5 is also provided by the cladoceran data for this site (Nilssen & Sandøy, this symposium).

The reconstructed pH for the surface sediments of Loch Doilet and Lochan Dubh are both 0.6 pH units lower than the mean measured pH values. The reason for this is not clear but as there are no problematic diatom taxa and the ecological ranges of the taxa are well described, the diatom-inferred pH may be a better indication of water quality than the mean pH calculated from a small number of water samples.

The carbonaceous particle record for Loch Doilet shows a small increase in particle concentration at 18 cm (about 1940) but the main increase occurs above 10 cm (1966). The decrease in particles above 4 cm (1980) is due to both an increased sediment accumulation rate and a reduced flux of particles to the sediment. In Lochan Dubh the concentration of carbonaceous particles increases throughout the twentieth century until 1970 when both the concentration and flux of particles begin to decrease. In both these lakes the concentrations of carbonaceous particles in the sediments (less than 5×10^3 particles per gram dry mass) are very low compared with the sites in the Trossachs where concentrations exceed 20×10^3 particles per gram dry mass.

There is no measurable contamination by zinc or lead in the sediments of Loch Doilet. The high sedimentation rate may have obscured any small atmospheric flux. In Lochan Dubh, where the sediment accumulation rate is slower, there is a record of zinc contamination starting in the later nineteenth century but no evidence of lead contamination.

Discussion

All four of the lakes studied have acidified since the mid-nineteenth century, although the initial changes in Loch Doilet and Lochan Dubh are very slight. The records of industrially derived atmospheric contamination in the sediments suggest that both regions have been subject to acid deposition from industrial sources, with contamination beginning earlier in the Trossachs region. In the absence of any additional nineteenth century sources of acidity from the catchments, it is reasonable to conclude that, with the exception of Lochan Dubh, the onset of acidification was caused by acid deposition. The reason for the much earlier acidification at Lochan Dubh is less clear as evidence for atmospheric contamination cannot be detected in the sediments before the late nineteenth century.

The pattern of pH decline throughout the twentieth century varies considerably between the four lakes (figure 3). In the region of high acid deposition, the pH of Loch Tinker does not appear to have altered substantially after 1930, whereas at the afforested site, Loch Chon, the greatest pH change occurs after 1960 (figure 3*a*). Because there has been no major change in the catchment of Loch Tinker over this period and the trends in atmospheric input have been broadly similar for both lakes it would appear that the acceleration in acidification in Loch Chon is linked to the planting of conifers in the catchment area in the 1950s.

In the region of lower acid deposition, the afforested site, Loch Doilet, is the less acid of the two sites (figure 3*b*). From the mid-nineteenth century onwards, the pH of Loch Doilet appears to have declined only 0.2 pH units until after 1930 when the rate of acidification increased. By comparison Lochan Dubh has acidified gradually over two centuries. The post-1930 pH change in Loch Doilet occurs at a similar rate over the same period as the continued

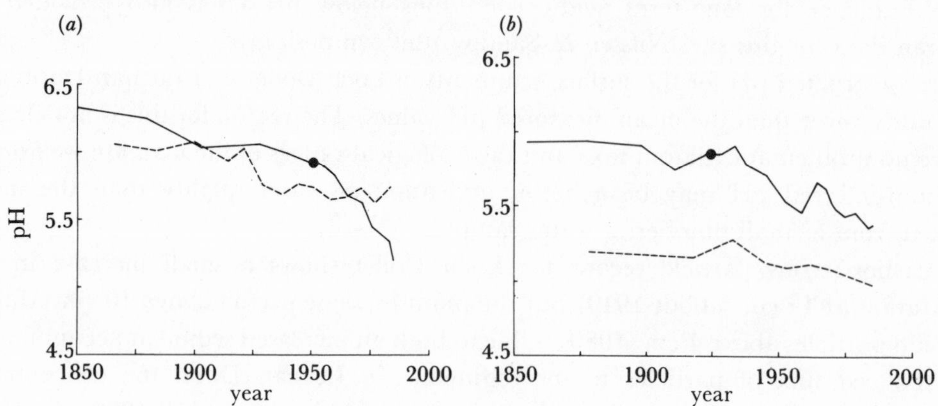

FIGURE 3. Reconstructed pH against time for (*a*) Loch Chon (solid line) and Loch Tinker (dotted line) and (*b*) Loch Doilet (solid line) and Lochan Dubh (dotted line); (●), afforestation.

acidification of Lochan Dubh (in terms of changes in hydrogen ion concentration), suggesting acid deposition could be the cause in both cases. The timing of the acceleration in acidification in Loch Doilet a decade after afforestation is similar to that found in Loch Chon. However, the post-afforestation acidification at Loch Chon was far greater despite being the less sensitive of the two afforested sites to acidification. It can therefore be concluded that the rapid acidification of Loch Chon was largely due to the forest increasing the flux of atmospherically derived acidity to the lake as the presence of forestry at Loch Doilet (where acid deposition is lower) has not resulted in a similar degree of acidification. These results suggest that at the afforested sites discussed here, any acidification caused by forest growth itself has been minimal, compared with the combined effects of forestry and acid deposition.

References

Battarbee, R. W., Anderson, N. J., Appleby, P. G., Flower, R. J., Fritz, S. C., Haworth, E. Y., Higgitt, S., Jones, V. J., Kreiser, A., Munro, M. A. R., Natkanski, J., Oldfield, F., Patrick, S. T., Richardson, N. G., Rippey, B. & Stevenson, A. C. 1988 *Lake acidification in the United Kingdom, 1800–1986*. Palaeoecology Research Unit, University College London, U.K.

Flower, R. J., Battarbee, R. W. & Appleby, P. G. 1987 The recent palaeolimnology of acid lakes in Galloway, south-west Scotland: diatom analysis, pH trends and the role of afforestation. *J. Ecol.* **75**, 797–824.

Harriman, R. & Morrison, B. R. S. 1982 The ecology of streams draining forested and non-forested catchments in an area of Scotland subject to acid precipitation. *Hydrobiologia* **88**, 251–263.

Hornung, M. & Newson, M. D. 1986 Upland afforestation: influences on stream hydrology and chemistry. *Soil Use Mgmnt* **2**, 61–65.

Kinniburgh, D. G. & Edmunds, W. M. 1986 *The susceptibility of U.K. groundwaters to acid deposition*. Hydrological report, British Geological Survey no. 86/3, Wallingford, Oxfordshire.

Lindberg, S. E. & Garten, Jr C. T. 1988 Sources of sulphur in forest canopy throughfall. *Nature, Lond.* **336**, 148–151.

Nilsson, S. I., Miller, H. G. & Miller, J. D. 1982 Forest growth as a possible cause of soil and water acidification: an examination of the concepts. *Oikos* **39**, 40–49.

Stevenson, A. C., Patrick, S. T., Kreiser, A. & Battarbee, R. W. 1987 Palaeoecological evaluation of the recent acidification of susceptible lakes. Methods utilised under DoE contract PECD 7/7/139 and the Royal Society SWAP project. Palaeoecological Research Unit, University College London. Research Paper no. 26.

Stoner, J. H., Gee, A. S. & Wade, K. R. 1984 The effects of acidification on the ecology of streams in the upper Tywi catchment in west Wales. *Environ. Pollut.* **35**, 125–157.

Unsworth, M. H. 1984 Evaporation from forests in cloud enhances the effect of acid deposition. *Nature, Lond.* **312**, 262–264.

Phil. Trans. R. Soc. Lond. B **327**, 385–389 (1990)
Printed in Great Britain

Palaeolimnological changes related to acid deposition and land-use in the catchments of two Norwegian soft-water lakes

By F. Berge[1], Y-W. Brodin[2], G. Cronberg[3], F. El-Daoushy[4], H. I. Høeg[5], J. P. Nilssen[6], I. Renberg[7], B. Rippey[8], S. Sandøy[9], A. Timberlid[10] and M. Wik[7]

[1] *N-2920 Leira, Valdres, Norway*

[2] *National Swedish Environmental Protection Board, Box* 1302, *S-*171 25 *Solna, Sweden*

[3] *Institute of Ecology/Limnology, University of Lund, Box* 65, *S-*221 00 *Lund, Sweden*

[4] *Department of Physics, University of Uppsala, P.O. Box* 530, *S-*751 21 *Uppsala, Sweden*

[5] *Institute of Geology, University of Oslo, P.O. Box* 1050, *Blindern, Oslo* 3, *Norway*

[6] *Institute of Biology, University of Oslo, P.O. Box* 1047, *Blindern, Oslo* 3, *Norway*

[7] *Department of Ecological Botany, University of Umeå, S-*901 87 *Umeå, Sweden*

[8] *Freshwater Laboratory, University of Ulster, Traad Point, Ballyronan, Northern Ireland BT*45 6*LR, U.K.*

[9] *Directorate for Nature Management, Tungasletta* 2, *N-*7004 *Trondheim, Norway*

[10] *O. Hjetlands veg* 4, *N-*5900 *Høyanger, Norway*

This is a palaeolimnological study of two Norwegian soft-water lakes, one receiving high, the other low, deposition of sulphur and nitrogen compounds. At the site with low acid deposition inferred pH has oscillated between 5.6 and 5.9 and there is little evidence of atmospheric contamination. At the site with high acid deposition, many centuries of stability are followed by a rapid acidification from pH around 5 in 1900 to the present (1986) level of pH 4.4. In this lake, the sedimentary record indicates a close connection between acid deposition and recent lake acidification.

Introduction

The objective of this study was to reconstruct the recent pH history of two lakes with similar catchments, one (Verevatn) subjected to high and the other (Röyrtjörna) to low deposition of sulphur and nitrogen compounds and to compare their histories in relation to acid deposition and land-use. Sedimentary concentrations of carbonaceous particles, trace metals, polycyclic aromatic hydrocarbons (PAH) and sulphur were recorded to assess the timing and magnitude of the deposition of airborne pollutants. Pollen analysis and documentary research were employed to study shifts in land-use. Analyses of sedimentary remains of chironomids, cladocerans, chrysophytes, and diatoms were used to document changes in lake acidity and lake history.

Both lakes have similar granitic, forested (*Picea abies* and *Pinus sylvestris*) catchments susceptible to acidification. However, Röyrtjörna is somewhat less sensitive to acid deposition as indicated by its higher calcium content. The distance between the lakes is *ca.* 730 km in a NNE–SSW direction. Verevatn (Aust-Agder) is located near Birkenes, an SNSF Experimental Catchment (established by the Norwegian research project 'Acid precipitation – effects on forest and fish'), and Röyrtjörna (Nord-Trøndelag) near a Surface Water Acidification Project (SWAP) experimental catchment. Further details about lake locations and other characteristics are given in Battarbee & Renberg (this symposium).

Methods

Both lakes were cored at the point of maximum lake depth by using freezing techniques (Renberg 1981) to retrieve the top *ca.* 30 cm of sediment; a Russian sampler was used for the deeper sediments. Details of analytical procedures are given in Stevenson *et al.* (1987). The sediment chronology is based on radiocarbon (Laboratoriet för isotopgeologi, Stockholm) and on ^{210}Pb dating (El-Daoushy, this symposium). Reconstructions of past lake pH from the fossil diatom assemblages were based on weighted averaging (Birks *et al.*, this symposium).

Results

(*a*) *Röyrtjörna*

Concentrations of spheroidal carbonaceous particles (SCP) can be used to detect geographical and temporal differences in deposition and to study deposition history (Wik & Natkanski, this symposium). In Röyrtjörna, particle concentrations are extremely low. No particles were detected below 6 cm in the sediment core. The maximum concentration of 1.6×10^3 particles gds^{-1} occurred at 1.5 cm from the sediment surface, corresponding to the early 1970s.

The concentration–depth profiles show that there is very little contamination by trace metals and no change in sulphur concentrations. Overall, the chemical results confirm that this site has received very little deposition of atmospheric contaminants.

Betula pollen and charcoal suggest the start of some human influence in the catchment of Röyrtjörna already at *ca.* 45 cm (H. I. Høeg, unpublished results). From 29 cm up to 5 cm there are definite pollen indications of land-use (*Rumex*, *Artemisia*, *Hordeum*, *Plantago lanceolata*, *Secale*, *Centaurea cyanus*). No primary land-use indicators were recorded in the top 4 cm of sediment.

The cladoceran remains show a stable community during the whole period. Acid sensitive planktonic *Daphnia* species were common in all samples, but the number of species was low compared with non-acid lakes in southern Norway. This may be related to climatic differences associated with latitude (J. P. Nilssen & S. Sandøy, unpublished results) rather than to differences in water quality.

The profiles of individual diatom taxa and of pH preference groups indicate small oscillations in lake acidity in the 75 cm long core. Diatom-based reconstructions of past pH indicate that the total range of the inferred pH values is 0.3 pH units from 5.6 to 5.9. The lack of recent acidification at this site is confirmed by the result of chrysophyte scale analysis (Cronberg, this symposium), which shows that the indifferent (= circumneutral) taxa *Mallomonas crassisquama* and *M. caudata* dominate the assemblage in the uppermost sediment (cf. Verevatn).

(*b*) *Verevatn*

The carbonaceous-particle profile begins with a 4 cm tail of low values followed by a marked increase at 7 cm. At 3 cm there is a distinct peak value of 59×10^3 particles gds^{-1}, which corresponds to the early 1970s.

The analyses show that this site is strongly contaminated by atmospheric pollutants. Lead contamination started earlier than zinc. Zinc increases around 11 cm depth and, although there is a small increase in lead at 17 cm, the main increase is at 13 cm. The sulphur and PAH profiles are similar to the trace metals, with the increase in concentration around 10 cm (Rippey, this symposium).

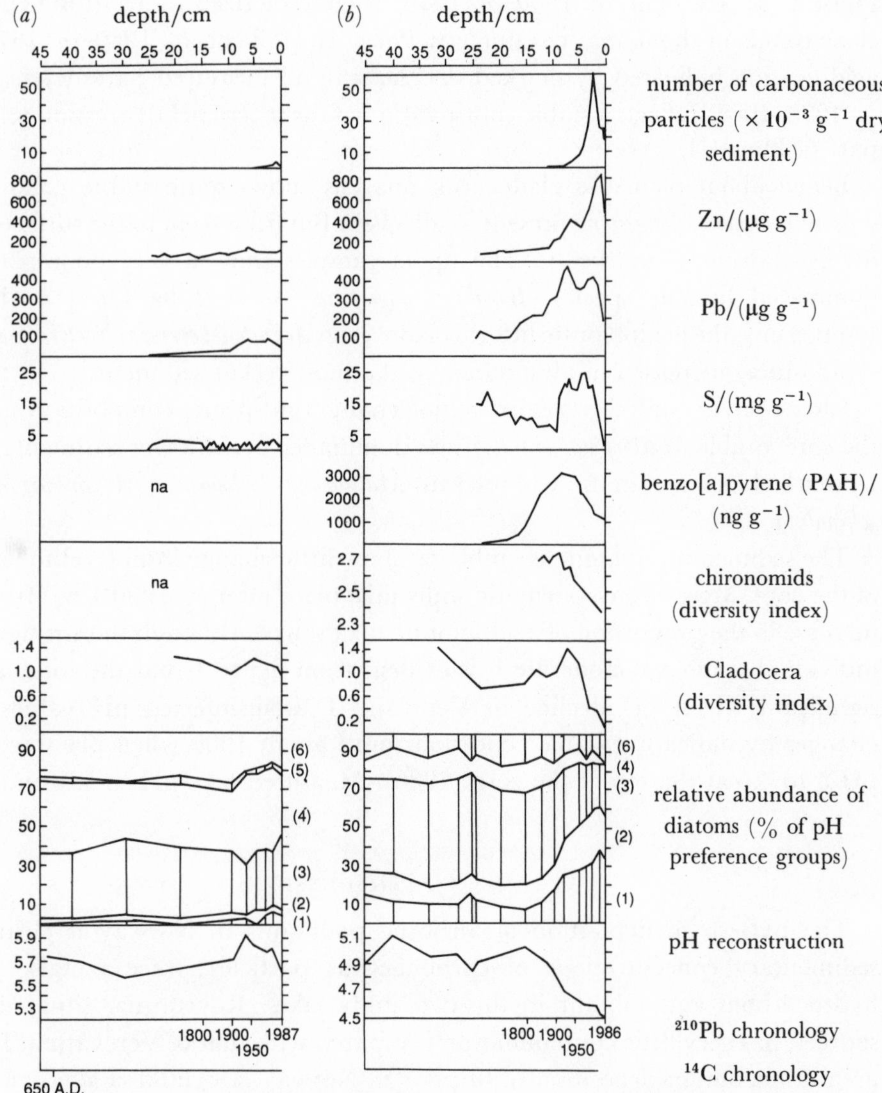

FIGURE 1. Stratigraphy of selected parameters from (*a*) Röyrtjörna and (*b*) Verevatn; na, not available; (1) acidobiontic, (2) acidobiontic/acidophilous, (3) acidophilous, (4) indifferent, (5) alkaliphilous, (6) unknown. Reconstruction of pH is from diatom-based estimates.

Pollen analysis indicates almost continuous agricultural land-use in the vicinity of Verevatn from 175 cm up to the sediment surface (H. I. Høeg, unpublished results). Above 37 cm there are indications of increased agricultural activity but the samples reflect considerable variation in intensity. The profiles of *Hordeum*, *Avena*, *Triticum*, and *Secale* suggest that the most intensive periods were from 21 cm to 15 cm and from 11 cm to 6 cm.

Documentary records show that the catchment contains no farms but certain areas were previously utilized as outlying fields. A study based on statistical records and interviews shows a sharp decline in the utilization of the outlying fields (used for the gathering of fodder and for grazing) during the period 1865–1985 (Timberlid 1990).

The chironomid stratigraphy encompassing the period from *ca.* 1800 to 1986 can be divided into three phases defined by differences in faunal stability, diversity, productivity, survival rate and species composition (Brodin, this symposium). Only the diversity index is shown here.

Phase I (*ca.* 15–7 cm, *ca.* 1800–*ca.* 1940) is characterized by environmental stability with no clear trends in the faunal parameters. Phase II (7–3 cm, *ca.* 1940–*ca.* 1975) represents severe acidification indicated by marked decreases in all measured parameters. Phase III (3–0 cm, *ca.* 1975–1986) reflects a stable continuation of the severe pH depression reached during the last part of Phase II.

Below about 6 cm the cladoceran analysis shows quite stable conditions with the acid sensitive *Daphnia longispina* present at all levels. But from 6 cm to the surface species number and diversity decrease markedly. The upper samples show a very poor planktonic community dominated by one species, *Bosmina longispina*. As in Lilla Öresjön (Renberg *et al.*, this symposium) the acidobiontic littoral cladoceran *Acantholeberis curvirostris* (Sandøy & Nilssen, this symposium) increased in abundance in the most recent sediment.

Chrysophyte analysis revealed major changes in species composition in the top *ca.* 5 cm of the core. Stable *Mallomonas crassisquama* dominance in the lower sediments is abruptly replaced by marked increases in the acid tolerant *Mallomonas lychenensis*, *M. canina*, *M. hamata*, and *Synura echinulata*.

The sedimentary diatom assemblages show little change from level to level in the lower part of the core. Most of the systematic shifts take place after *ca.* 1900 A.D. (10 cm) when a marked increase in the proportion of acidobiontic taxa starts. Although the stratigraphic shifts for each individual taxon are moderate it is evident from figure 1 that the total assemblage reflects a significant recent pH decline in Verevatn. Diatom-inferred pH values reflect the floristic changes by indicating stable conditions until about 1900 when pH started to decrease from pH 5 to 4.5 at the top of the core (1986). Measured lake pH in February 1986 was 4.4.

Discussion

The pattern in deposition of airborne pollutants in Norway is clearly reflected by the sedimentary concentrations of carbonaceous particles, trace metals, polycyclic aromatic hydrocarbons and sulphur in the two study lakes. Röyrtjörna, situated far from polluting sources, has very little contamination compared with that of Verevatn at Birkenes, which is an area of maximum deposition of sulphur in Norway (Dovland *et al.* 1976) and a region with many acidified lakes (Henriksen *et al.* 1988).

For both lakes there is good agreement between the ecological inferences from the sediment stratigraphy of chironomids, cladocerans, chrysophytes and diatoms. There are only minor faunal and floristic shifts within the Röyrtjörna core indicating stable ecological conditions during the period under study. The diatom-based pH reconstructions reveal minor oscillations within a range of 0.3 pH units, but no consistent trend. This pattern in the pH estimates may be related more to pollen-inferred land-use changes than to acid deposition, which is very low at this site. The pH estimates increase during the most intensive land-use period. The succeeding decrease, starting around 1900 A.D., may reflect a trend back to pH conditions that prevailed before the onset of notable land-use.

At Verevatn the biostratigraphy of chironomids, cladocerans, chrysophytes and diatoms indicates stable conditions until shortly after 1900 A.D. Since then, there has been a rapid decrease in the pH of the lake to the present level, which is markedly lower than any estimate of past pH. At Verevatn there is no systematic relation between pollen-inferred shifts in land-use and reconstructed lake pH. In this lake there is a striking similarity between the sediment profiles of air pollutants and biological remains. The pH-related biological changes show a slight time lag relative to the onset of air pollution as recorded in the sediments. The same stratigraphic pattern in air pollution and environmental change has been reported from several other lakes in this geographical region (Berge 1979, 1985; Davis & Berge 1980) including hill-top lakes with virtually no catchments and hence no influence from past or present land-use (Birks *et al.*, this symposium).

The available palaeolimnological evidence thus points to acid deposition as the most likely cause for the recent rapid acidification of Verevatn, a site typical of other acidified soft-water lakes in southernmost Norway.

References

Berge, F. 1979 Diatoms and pH in some lakes in the Agder and Hordaland counties, Norway. IR 42/79. SNSF Project, Oslo, Norway.

Berge, F. 1985 Relationships of diatom taxa to pH and other environmental factors in Norwegian soft-water lakes. Ph.D thesis, University of Maine, U.S.A.

Davis, R. B. & Berge, F. 1980 Diatom stratigraphy and inferred pH. In Ecological impact of acid precipitation (ed. D. Drabløs & A. Tollan), pp. 270–271. *Proceedings of an international conference, Sandefjord, Norway*. Oslo: SNSF report.

Dovland, H., Joranger, E. & Semb, A. 1976 Deposition of air pollutants in Norway, In *Impact of acid precipitation on forest and freshwater ecosystems in Norway* (ed. F. H. Brække), pp. 14–35. SNSF-project, Aas, Norway, research report no. 6/76, pp. 14–35.

Henriksen, A., Lien, L., Traaen, T. S., Sevaldrud, I. S. & Brakke, D. F. 1988 Lake acidification in Norway – present and predicted chemical status. *Ambio* **17**, 259–266.

Renberg, I. 1981 Improved methods for sampling, photographing and varve-counting of varved lake sediments. *Boreas* **10**, 255–258. Oslo. ISSN 0300-9483.

Stevenson, A. C., Patrick, S. T., Kreiser, A. & Battarbee, R. W. 1987 Palaeoecological evaluation of the recent acidification of susceptible lakes. Methods utilised under DoE contract PECD 7/7/139 and the Royal Society SWAP project. Palaeoecology Research Unit, University College London. Research paper no. 26.

Timberlid, J. A. 1990 Driftsendringer i jordbruket som årsak til forsuring av norske vassdrag? Ein samanliknande studie av utmarksjordbruket på Vest- og Sørlandet i perioden 1850–1980. *Økoforsk*. No. 14.

Phil. Trans. R. Soc. Lond. B **327**, 391–396 (1990)
Printed in Great Britain

Recent acidification and biological changes in Lilla Öresjön, southwest Sweden, and the relation to atmospheric pollution and land-use history

By I. Renberg[1], Y.-W. Brodin[2], G. Cronberg[3], F. El-Daoushy[4], F. Oldfield[5], B. Rippey[6], S. Sandøy[7], J.-E. Wallin[1] and M. Wik[1]

[1] *Department of Ecological Botany, University of Umeå, S-901 87 Umeå, Sweden*
[2] *National Swedish Environmental Protection Board, Box 1302, S-171 25 Solna, Sweden*
[3] *Institute of Ecology/Limnology, University of Lund, P.O. Box 65, S-221 00 Lund, Sweden*
[4] *Department of Physics, University of Uppsala, Box 530, S-751 21 Uppsala, Sweden*
[5] *Department of Geography, University of Liverpool, P.O. Box 147, Liverpool L69 3BX, U.K.*
[6] *Freshwater Laboratory, University of Ulster, Traad Point, Ballyronan, Northern Ireland BT45 6LR, U.K.*
[7] *Directorate for Nature Management, Tungasletta 2, N-7004 Trondheim, Norway*

Palaeolimnological techniques were used to study the recent acidification history of Lilla Öresjön in southwest Sweden, and its relation to the deposition of airborne pollutants and land-use. The sediment analyses suggest that water quality began to deteriorate at the beginning of the 20th century and resulted in an acute acidification phase in the 1960s. An indifferent (circumneutral) diatom flora with some planktonic taxa was replaced by a non-planktonic acidophilous and acidobiontic flora; diatom inferred pH decreased from 6.1 in the 19th century to the present value of about 4.6. The history of acidification and of major biological change in the lake is reinforced by the analyses of chrysophyte scales and cladocera and chironomid remains, which show that alterations of species composition and an impoverishment of faunal communities took place. There is close stratigraphic agreement between these biological changes and indicators of the deposition of atmospheric pollutants. The concentration of Pb, Zn, Cu and S increased from the beginning of the 19th century to peak values during the 1960s and 1970s. Spheroidal carbonaceous particles, polycyclic aromatic hydrocarbons (PAH) and 'hard' isothermal remanence, indicative of oil and coal combustion, peaked during the 1970s and 1980s, respectively. The increased deposition of airborne pollutants from fossil fuel combustion and industrial processes is suggested as the main cause of the acidification of the lake, although vegetation changes, such as a recent expansion of spruce–pine forest, have also occurred during the 200–300 year period studied.

Introduction

More than twenty years of monitoring and research in Sweden has contributed to a broad understanding of surface water acidification (Monitor 1986), but palaeolimnological investigations, which provide a longer, retrospective view of acidification in specific lakes, are very few (Charles *et al.* 1989). This project of the Surface Water Acidification Project (SWAP) Palaeolimnology Programme (Battarbee & Renberg, this symposium) was designed to study acidification and biological changes over a 200–300 year perspective; the aim was to contribute answers to the question of whether land-use or acid deposition is the main cause of recent surface water acidification. This question has been debated since Rosenqvist (1977) claimed that changed land-use, vegetation and soil are the key factors for the acidity of freshwater.

Originally, we attempted to find an acidified lake with a catchment with restricted land-use, or one where land-use had not changed significantly during this century, and hence to have the land-use factor constant and to study the temporal relation between atmospheric deposition of air pollutants and the changing chemistry and biology of the lake. Other criteria for lake selection were; (i) minimal influence of extreme local air pollution, which could otherwise distort the signal of more regional pollution from large-scale fossil fuel combustion and industrial processes, (ii) sediments suitable for palaeolimnological investigations and, importantly, (iii) the lake should not be limed. Unfortunately, lakes meeting all these criteria could not be found easily because so many lakes were already limed (about 5000 in Sweden in 1989). Lilla Öresjön, which has some agriculture in the catchment, was chosen as a compromise. It is a reference lake for the Swedish liming programme to allow future studies of, for example, lake response to a reduction in the deposition of sulphur and nitrogen.

Study site and methods

Lilla Öresjön is situated 25 km S.E. of Göteborg in southwest Sweden. Details of the lake and its catchment are given by Battarbee & Renberg (this symposium).

Eight cores of the recent sediment were taken from the deepest part of the 12.3 m deep basin in the N.W. end of the lake in February 1986 from ice by using a freeze corer (Renberg 1981). These cores were carefully correlated by using sediment-colour variations, and contiguous sub-samples were taken (Renberg 1981).

Several palaeolimnological analyses were done by specialists; pollen by Wallin, sediment chemistry by Rippey (this symposium), spheroidal carbonaceous particles by Wik (see Wik & Natkanski, this symposium), 'hard' isothermal remanence ($\text{SIRM}+\text{IRM}_{-300\,\text{mT}}$) by Oldfield & Richardson (this symposium), diatoms by Renberg, chrysophytes by Cronberg (this symposium), cladocerans by Nilssen & Sandøy (this symposium), chironomids by Brodin (1990 and this symposium) and ^{210}Pb dating by El-Daoushy (this symposium). Pollen and diatom analyses were done according to standard methods and about 500 pollen and diatom valves were counted, respectively. Diatom nomenclature follows Williams *et al.* (1988). For other methods see papers by co-authors referred to above.

Results and discussion

(a) *Land use and vegetation*

Pollen analysis and radiocarbon dating suggest agriculture started in the area about 2300 years ago (Renberg, this symposium) and expanded significantly a millenium later (interpolated date). *Calluna* heaths formed gradually, and probably already covered large areas 700–800 years ago; pollen values in the sediment from that time are as high as during the 18th century, when a map shows that large *Calluna* heaths were present. Pine–spruce forest took over during the 20th century, and became more and more closed until the 1980s when large areas were clear cut. Agriculture is still in practice, and no significant area of agricultural land has been abandoned, at least since 1950 according to aerial photos, but forest grazing decreased during the 1930s and ceased during the 1940s. In 1982, coniferous forest covered about 60% of the catchment (15% clear cut), deciduous trees, 10% and arable land, 10%.

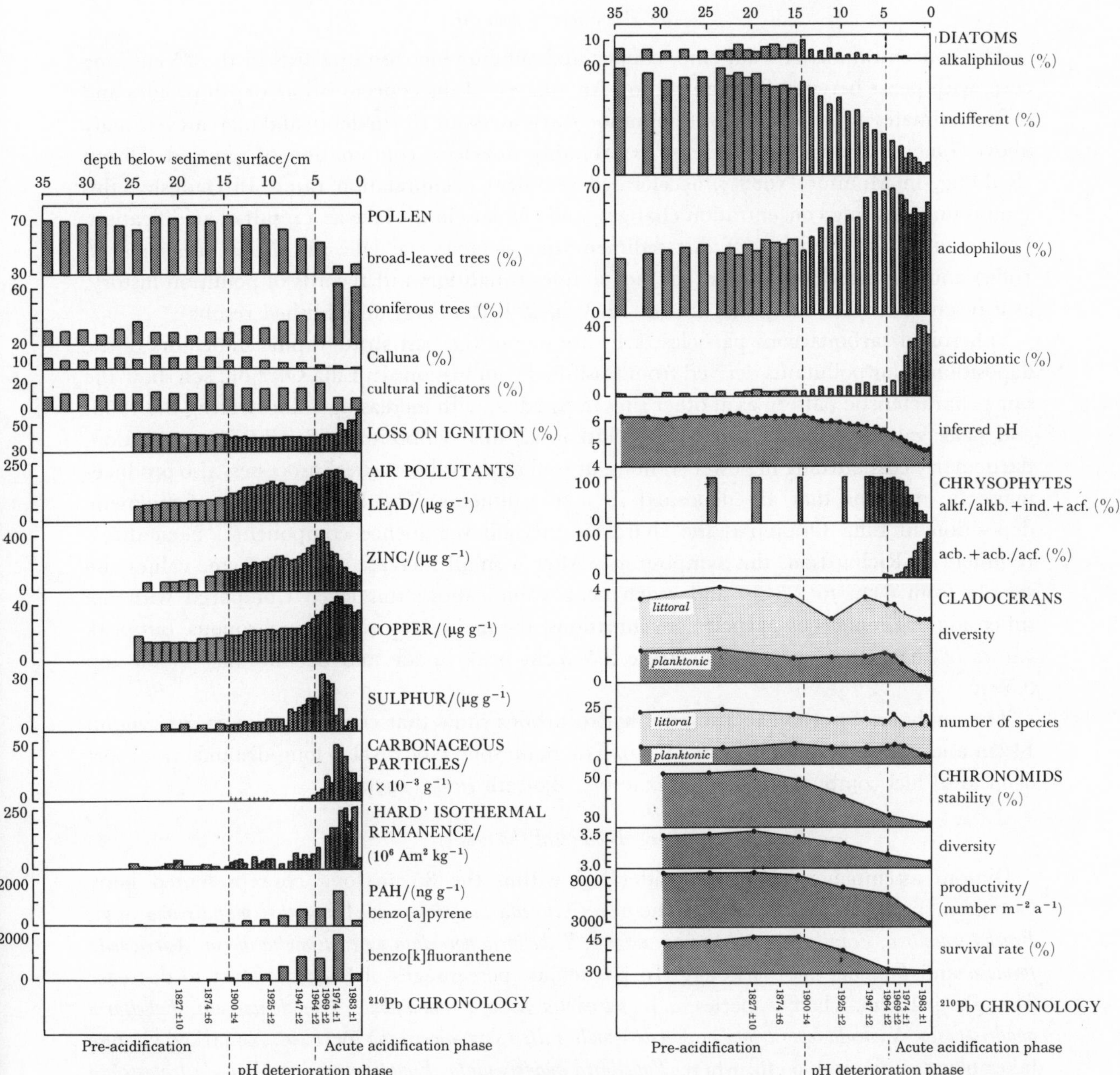

FIGURE 1. Results of analyses of sediment cores from Lilla Öresjön, S.W. Sweden. Left; a schematic pollen diagram, which gives an indication of how vegetation and agriculture have changed during the last 200–300 years (broad-leaved trees are mainly birch, oak and alder; coniferous trees are Norway spruce and Scots pine; cultural indicators are cereals, weeds and plants favoured by cultural activity). Lead, zinc and copper derive from various industrial and combustion processes and give a general indication of increased fall-out of atmospheric pollutants from the 19th century to modern times. Spheroidal carbonaceous particles, 'hard' isothermal remanence ($\mathrm{SIRM}+\mathrm{IRM}_{-300\ \mathrm{mT}}$), polycyclic aromatic hydrocarbons and sulphur, are indicators for deposition of pollutants derived from fossil fuel combustion (all concentrations are per unit dry sediment mass); ^{210}Pb dates were calculated by using the CRS model. Right; results from analyses of algae and animal remains. Diatoms were classified into Hustedt's pH categories and these clearly illustrate the increasing acidity of the lake and agree with the diatom inferred pH trend obtained by using weighted averaging, a method that does not involve this pH classification. Chrysophytes were grouped following Siver & Hamer (1989). The changing communities of cladocerans and chironomids are presented as diversity, number of species recovered, stability, productivity and survival rate, for explanations see Nilssen & Sandøy (this symposium) and Brodin (1990). A pre-acidification, a pH deterioration phase and an acute acidification phase have been distinguished, primarily by using the diatom stratigraphy. Their presence is supported by the chrysophyte and animal records (see also Renberg (this symposium)).

(*b*) *Atmospheric deposition*

The concentrations of lead, zinc, copper and sulphur increase upwards in the 25 cm long core, with peaks between 3 cm and 5 cm. An analysis of the concentration–depth profiles and of flux estimates indicates that contamination starts at about 15 cm depth and increases strongly above 7.5 cm. The surface decrease is probably due to a combination of reduced fall-out (Rühling, in Monitor (1987)), accelerated sediment accumulation rates (El-Daoushy, this symposium) causing concentration changes, and changes in the lake as a result of acidification. For example, the efficiency of zinc sedimentation decreases as lake pH drops (Tessier *et al.* 1989) and sulphur-depth profiles are not simple straightforward records of pollution history, as a recent Swedish survey has shown (M. Wik & I. Renberg, unpublished results).

Spheroidal carbonaceous particles (SCP) are one of the best stratigraphic indicators of the deposition of air pollutants derived from fossil-fuel combustion. In Lilla Öresjön, SCP show the same characteristic pattern as at other sites in Sweden, with increasing values during the 1950s and peak values in the 1970s (Wik & Natkanski, this symposium). Fossil-fuel combustion, particularly coal burning in power stations, as well as several industrial processes, also produces magnetic minerals that are deposited in lake sediments. The best indicator of magnetic deposition in Lilla Öresjön is the 'hard' isothermal remanence component ('haematite') (Oldfield & Richardson, this symposium). After a small increase above 7.5 cm, values rise steeply from 5 cm to 2.5 cm and reach peak values above this level. Compared with the spheroidal carbonaceous particle concentrations, the main steep rise is synchronous, but peak values of 'haematite' persist above the 2.5–3 cm peak in SCP and decline only in the top 0.5 cm.

The analyses of polycyclic aromatic hydrocarbons show that contamination starts around 14 cm and increases strongly above 9 cm. The main source of PAH is long-distance transport from fossil-fuel combustion (see, for example, Bjørseth *et al.* (1979)).

(*c*) *Biological changes*

Diatom assemblages change considerably within the 35 cm long core presented here. Common species in the lower part include *Cyclotella kuetzingiana*, *Achnanthes minutissima* agg., *Brachysira vitrea*, *Fragilaria virescens* var. *exigua*, *Tabellaria flocculosa* agg., *Eunotia incisa*, *Asterionella formosa* and *Frustulia rhomboides* agg. In particular, percentages of *Cyclotella* start to decrease from about 15 cm, whereas species such as *Eunotia incisa*, *Peronia fibula*, *Eunotia naegelii*, *Tabellaria quadriseptata*, *Navicula leptostriata* and *Asterionella ralfsii* var. *americana* increase. A marked change takes place at about 4–5 cm, where *Tabellaria quadriseptata*, *Eunotia naegelii*, *Navicula leptostriata* and *Tabellaria binalis* become dominant.

The results of the diatom analyses are summarized here as Hustedt pH categories. The relative frequency of diatom valves of taxa classified as acidophilous starts to increase at about 15 cm and acidobiontic taxa increase markedly at about 4–5 cm. Reconstruction of pH by using weighted averaging (Birks *et al.*, this symposium) suggests a pH decrease in the lake from about 6.1 before recent acidification, to 4.6–4.7 at the top of the core, and agrees well with measured summer pH values for 1983–1985, which are 4.6, 4.6 and 4.8, respectively. The 15 cm level is dated to *ca.* 1900 and 4 cm to *ca.* 1970 with ^{210}Pb (El-Daoushy, this symposium).

The chrysophyte flora has also changed markedly according to the subfossil scales (Cronberg, this symposium). *Mallomonas crassisquama* and *M. caudata* are abundant below

7.5–10 cm. Between *ca.* 2.5–7.5 cm is a transitionary period, where *M. caudata* peaks, *M. crassisquama* almost disappears and new species such as *Synura sphagnicola*, *M. hamata*, *M. allorgei* and *M. canina* appear, the latter two becoming very abundant in the top 2.5 cm of the core. Acidophilous and acidobiontic taxa increase markedly in the recent sediments.

Cladoceran and chironomid remains reinforce this picture of acidification and biological change. Decreasing diversity and species numbers of Cladocera are found towards the sediment surface, indicating an impoverished community in recent years. A distinct change in community composition takes place at 4–5 cm. *Bosmina longispina* totally dominates the planktonic community in the topmost levels (>96%). *Holopedium gibberum*, *Bosmina longirostris* and the acid-sensitive *Daphnia longispina*, which are quite common further down, are absent above 3–4 cm. Numbers of the acidobiontic macrothricid, *Acantholeberis curvirostris*, increase considerably above 3 cm, strongly indicating recent lake acidification (Nilssen & Sandøy, this symposium).

The chironomid fauna begins to change between levels 10 cm and 15 cm. Major alterations of the species composition occur at about 4–5 cm, when some previously abundant taxa such as *Parakiefferiella bathophila*, *Stempellinella minor* and *Tanytarsus sp.* II disappear completely and new species appear, such as *Ablabesmyia longistyla*, *Macropelopia goetghebueri*, *Psectrocladius* sp. E and *Sergentia longiventris*. Faunal stability, diversity, productivity and survival rate all decrease. Other insect groups such as mayflies, phantom midges, biting midges and caddisflies, as well as water mites, also show decreased stability, diversity and productivity during the present century (Brodin, this symposium). These faunal changes indicate successively more unstable and harsh environmental conditions in the lake.

There are very few fish in the lake; a 'test-fishing' in the early 1980s resulted in only a few perch being caught; according to local people, pike, perch, roach, bream and eel previously lived in the lake. Roach and bream disappeared in the 1960s (Billing *et al.* 1981).

(*d*) *Causes of acidification*

The subfossil remains of diatoms, chrysophytes, cladorerans and chironomids and data about loss of earlier fish populations, clearly show that the lake acidified during the post-war period. The situation became acute during the 1960s with pH values around 4.5 (since monitoring started in 1972 values above 4.7 have been recorded only twice; data from the National Swedish Environmental Protection Board). However, the sediment record also shows that deterioration had started much earlier, at the turn of the century.

Since the 19th century, major changes in vegetation, and probably in soil conditions, have occurred in the catchment. According to the 'land-use hypothesis', this alone could account for the acidification of the lake. This hypothesis, advocated by Rosenqvist in several papers (see, for example, Rosenqvist (1978, 1980)) suggests that: (i) changed land-use, such as the cessation of cattle farming and forest grazing, has caused regeneration of coniferous forest vegetation and the increase of acid raw humus; (ii) ion-exchange reactions in the raw humus layer and the influence of cation uptake by plant growth are the most important factors in determining the pH of runoff water and (iii) the acidic precipitation during the last decades is responsible for only a minor part of the acidity of surface water.

However, at Lilla Öresjön support for the principal role of airborne acidic pollutants comes from several factors.

1. Although vegetation has changed, agricultural activity has not ceased (10% of the

catchment is still cultivated). Other disturbances have been introduced, such as building of roads and houses that have exposed unweathered soils, and clear cutting that increases leaching and runoff of base cations and nutrients (Grip 1982). These new disturbances would counteract possible acidification effects caused by vegetation and soil changes in other areas of the catchment.

2. In addition to the temporal correlation between increased atmospheric deposition and lake-water acidification, as demonstrated in this study, there is a geographic correlation in Sweden between these two parameters, but no such correlation between lake acidification and changed land-use. The latter has taken place all over Sweden, but surface water acidification is mainly restricted to S. Sweden where acid deposition is greatest.

3. The land use hypothesis has been rejected by several palaeolimnological investigations specifically designed for testing it (Battarbee, this symposium).

Although this investigation can neither refute the land-use nor the acid-deposition hypothesis, because changed land-use and increased acidic atmospheric deposition occurred simultaneously, it is most likely that the recent acute acidification at least, is caused by the acid precipitation. The recent acid phase has no similarity in the history of the lake (Renberg, this symposium). Whether the deterioration phase before the recent acute phase also results from deposition of airborne pollutants that consumed alkalinity derived from agricultural and other catchment disturbances, or can be ascribed to the land-use factor *sensu* Rosenqvist, cannot be assessed from this study. The increased pH in Lilla Öresjön about 2300 years ago, at the same time as a cultural expansion (Renberg, this symposium), shows, however, that human land-use and catchment disturbance can be important for lake pH. Significantly, however, the magnitude of this earlier change was smaller than that associated with the recent acidification.

References

Billing, S., Hyltegren, P., Olsson, M., Welander, H. & Årgårdh, C. 1981 *Försurningsläget i Lilla Öresjön i Kungsbacka k:n.* Miljövårdsinst Göteborgs universitet. (Mimeograph).

Bjørseth, A., Lunde, G. & Lindskoog, A. 1979 Long-range transport of polycyclic aromatic hydrocarbons. *Atmos. Environ.* **13**, 45–53.

Brodin, Y.-W. 1990 Non-biting midges (Diptera, Chironomidae) as indicators of past and present trends in lake acidification in northern Europe. *National Swedish Environmental Protection Board, Report.* (In the press.)

Charles, D. F., Battarbee, R. W., Renberg, I., van Dam, H. & Smol, J. P. Paleoecological analysis of lake acidification trends in North America and Europe using diatoms and chrysophytes. In *Acid precipitation vol.* 4. *Soils, aquatic processes and lake acidification* (ed. S. A. Norton, S. E. Lindberg & A. L. Page). New York: Springer-Verlag. (In the press.)

Grip, H. 1982 Water chemistry and runoff in forest streams at Kloten. *UNGI Rapport* **58**, 1–144. Stockholm: Liber.

Monitor 1986 1986 Sura och försurade vatten (Acid and acidified surface waters). *Statens Naturvårdsverk.* Stockholm: Liber. (In Swedish.)

Monitor 1987 1987 Tungmetaller – förekomst och omsättning i naturen (Heavy metals – occurrence and turnover in the environment). *Statens Naturvårdsverk.* Stockholm: Liber. (In Swedish.)

Renberg, I. 1981 Improved methods for sampling, photographing and varve-counting of varved lake sediments. *Boreas* **10**, 255–258.

Rosenqvist, I. Th. 1977 *Sur jord – Surt vann* (Acid soil – Acid water). Oslo: Ingeniørsforlaget A/S. (In Norwegian.)

Rosenqvist, I. Th. 1978 Alternative sources for acidification of river water in Norway. *Sci. tot. Envir.* **10**, 39–49.

Rosenqvist, I. Th. 1980 Influence of forest vegetation and agriculture on the acidity of fresh water. In *Advances in environmental science and engineering* (ed. J. R. Pfafflin & E. N. Ziegler), pp. 56–79. London: Gordon Breach Science Publ.

Siver, P. A. & Hamer, S. 1989 Multivariate statistical analysis of the factors controlling the distribution of scaled chrysophytes. *Limnol. Oceanogr.* **34**, 368–381.

Tessier, A., Carignan, R., Dubreuil, B. & Rapin, F. 1989 Partitioning of zinc between the water column and the oxic sediments in lakes. *Geochim. cosmochim. Acta* **53**, 1511–1522.

Williams, D. M., Hartley, B., Ross, R., Munro, M. A. R., Juggins, S. & Battarbee, R. W. 1988 *A coded checklist of British diatoms.* London: Ensis Publishing.

Phil. Trans. R. Soc. Lond. B **327**, 397–402 (1990)
Printed in Great Britain

The recent palaeolimnology of two sites with contrasting acid-deposition histories

By V. J. Jones[1], A. M. Kreiser[1], P. G. Appleby[2], Y.-W. Brodin[3], J. Dayton[4], J. A. Natkanski[1], N. Richardson[5], B. Rippey[6], S. Sandøy[7] and R. W. Battarbee[1]

[1] *Palaeoecology Research Unit, Department of Geography, University College London, 26 Bedford Way, London WC1H 0AP, U.K.*

[2] *Department of Applied Mathematics and Theoretical Physics, The University of Liverpool, Liverpool L69 3BX, U.K.*

[3] *National Swedish Environmental Protection Board, Box 1302, S-171 25 Solna, Sweden*

[4] *Department of Geological Sciences, University of Birmingham, P.O. Box 363, Birmingham B15 2TT, U.K.*

[5] *Department of Geography, Roxby Building, University of Liverpool, P.O. Box 147, Liverpool L69 3BX, U.K.*

[6] *University of Ulster Freshwater Laboratory, Traad Point, Ballyronan, Northern Ireland, BT45 6LR, U.K.*

[7] *Directorate for Nature Management, Tungasletta 2, N-7004 Trondheim, Norway*

A palaeoecological comparison is made between geologically sensitive sites chosen from an area of low sulphur deposition (Lochan Dubh) and area of high sulphur deposition (Round Loch of Glenhead). Pre-industrial (pre-1800) acidities of the lakes were similar but the pH of the Round Loch of Glenhead has subsequently dropped by over 0.5 of a pH unit whereas the pH of Lochan Dubh has only decreased slightly. The record of atmospheric contamination confirms that the Round Loch of Glenhead is a more heavily polluted site than Lochan Dubh. The increased degree of lake acidification and higher levels of atmospheric contamination at the Round Loch of Glenhead are correlated with the greater sulphur deposition levels at this site.

Introduction

Palaeoecological evidence based principally on diatom analysis (Battarbee 1984) suggests that many lakes in the British Isles have rapidly acidified over about the last 150 years (Flower & Battarbee 1983; Battarbee *et al.* 1988). Possible reasons for lake acidification have been evaluated by using palaeolimnological techniques, which include land-use change (Jones *et al.* 1986; Patrick *et al.*, this symposium), afforestation (Flower *et al.* 1987) and long-term soil acidification (Jones *et al.* 1989). These factors cannot be used to explain present-day acidities at the sites investigated so far, although afforestation may enhance lake acidification at certain sites (Kreiser *et al.*, this symposium). However, there is strong evidence for atmospheric contamination of acidified lakes by trace metals (Rippey, this symposium), spheroidal carbonaceous particles (Wik & Natkanski, this symposium) and magnetic minerals (Oldfield & Richardson, this symposium). This evidence of increasing atmospheric contamination, from the mid-19th century onwards at many sites, is correlated with an increase in national sulphur emissions (Barrett *et al.* 1983) and at sensitive sites (cf. Edmunds & Kinniburgh 1986) with a trend of lake acidification. For the palaeolimnological programme of the Surface Water Acidification Project (SWAP), sites were carefully chosen to evaluate the relation between the history of atmospheric contamination, and the degree of acidification and ecological change.

Site descriptions and methods

Two lakes are examined in this study. The Round Loch of Glenhead is situated in the Galloways Hills, southwest Scotland, an area currently subjected to high levels ($1.24\ g\ S\ m^{-2}\ a^{-1}$) of sulphur deposition. Lochan Dubh forms part of the Loch Doilet catchment in the Sunart area of central western Scotland, and lies about 200 km north of the Round Loch, where levels of atmospheric deposition are considerably lower ($0.78\ g\ S\ m^{-2}\ a^{-1}$).

The two sites have Ca^{2+} levels less than 50 $\mu eq\ l^{-1}$ (see table in Battarbee & Renberg, this symposium) indicating that both are very susceptible to acidification (Battarbee *et al.* 1988). However, the Round Loch of Glenhead has a lower pH, a lower alkalinity and over twice the concentration of excess non-marine SO_4^{2-} compared with Lochan Dubh. This difference in non-marine SO_4^{2-} is likely to be mainly attributable to atmospheric sulphate deposition (cf. Gorham *et al.* 1986). The relatively high Na^+ and Cl^- levels at the sites reflects a substantial marine influence.

The lakes are both of glacial origin situated on granite (Round Loch of Glenhead) and quartzite (Lochan Dubh) bedrock, both of which have a low weathering rate. Catchment vegetation consists of moorland communities dominated by *Molinia caerulea* and *Calluna vulgaris* overlying blanket peat. Neither site shows any pollen or documentary evidence for recent land-use or land-management change (Patrick *et al.*, this symposium).

Piston cores were obtained from the Round Loch of Glenhead (core RLGH3) in 1984 and from Lochan Dubh (core LOD2) in 1986. Analytical techniques and diatom analysis are outlined in Stevenson *et al.* (1987). Diatom nomenclature follows the SWAP protocol (Munro *et al.*, this symposium), and pH reconstruction follows Birks *et al.* (this symposium).

Results

(*a*) *Diatom analysis; floristic changes and* pH *reconstruction*

In the Round Loch of Glenhead core, the diatom flora below 20 cm is dominated by indifferent (= circumneutral) taxa, for example, *Achnanthes minutissima*, and acidophilous taxa, for example, *Eunotia incisa* (figure 1). At about 20 cm (*ca.* 1850) the percentages of indifferent species start to decline, and there is an increase in acidophilous forms. At 9 cm (*ca.* 1900) the acidobiontic taxa, for example, *Tabellaria quadriseptata* increase and the values of the indifferent species *Achnanthes minutissima*, *Brachysira vitrea* and *Cymbella lunata* fall sharply. At 5 cm (*ca.* 1953) the acidobiontic species *Tabellaria binalis* becomes important for the first time, and the sum of acidobiontic taxa makes up more than 20 % of the diatom assemblage. Results of diatom-based pH reconstruction suggest that the lake was acid (pH 5.4–5.6) before 1850. A decline of about 0.3 pH units occurred between 1850 and 1900, and there was a further decrease in pH from 1900 to the present day (from pH 5.0 to 4.7). The reconstructed pH is 4.9 at 0–0.5 cm, giving a relatively good agreement with the present pH of the lake water (pH 4.7).

Results of diatom analysis from levels below 80 cm in core RLGH3 indicate that the Round Loch of Glenhead was acid during the entire post-glacial period (Jones *et al.* 1989; Birks *et al.*,

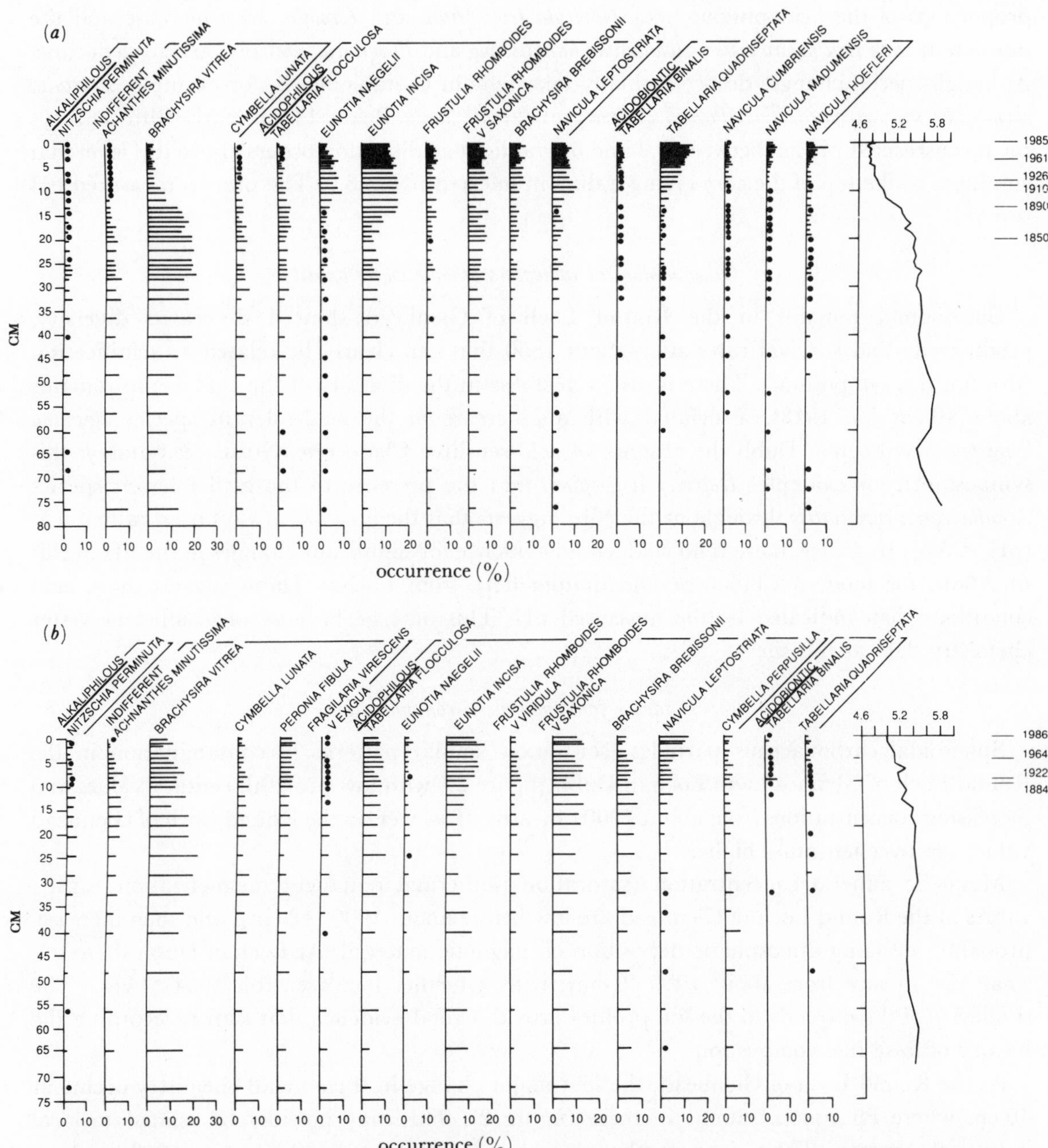

FIGURE 1. Diatom frequency diagrams of selected species (expressed as percentage of total diatoms) from (*a*) the Round Loch of Glenhead and (*b*) Lochan Dubh. The order of species left to right represents a gradient of increasing tolerance to low pH; pH reconstruction is calculated by using a weighted averaging technique. The standard error of prediction is based on bootstrap estimation (see Birks *et al.*, this symposium) and is between 0.31–0.32 of a pH unit for both of these sites. Dates are calculated from ^{210}Pb dating.

this symposium). There is little evidence of acidification from 10000 BP to the mid-19th century despite the effects of extensive catchment paludification and long-term soil leaching. Indeed, reconstructed pH never fell below 5.0 until after 1900. Birks *et al.* (this symposium) have also shown that the rate of pH change from 1874–1931 is significantly different from the rate of change over the rest of the post-glacial period.

At Lochan Dubh, the major floristic changes occur between 18 cm and 14 cm, where the proportions of the acidophilous taxa *Navicula leptostriata* and *Eunotia incisa* increase and the indifferent taxa *Brachysira vitrea*, *Achnanthes minutissima* and *Fragilaria virescens* var. *exigua* decline. Although species changes do occur, many taxa remain at stable levels, for example, *Frustulia rhomboides* var. *saxonica*, *Tabellaria flocculosa* and *Peronia fibula*. Below 14 cm (early 19th century) the reconstructed pH lies between 5.3 and 5.4; a slight acidification occurs above this level that continues to the top of the core giving a diatom inferred pH of 5.0. The present measured pH is 5.55.

(*b*) *Other biological indicators of lake water quality*

Chironomid remains in the Round Loch of Glenhead showed decreased diversity, productivity and survival rates after about 1850 that can clearly be related to acidification (Brodin, this symposium). There is also a decrease in the diversity of the cladoceran remains above 10 cm (*ca.* 1913), associated with an increase in the acid-tolerant species *Bosmina longispina*. At Lochan Dubh the absence of acid-sensitive Cladocera (Nilssen & Sandøy, this symposium), for example, *Daphnia longispina*, and the presence of the acid tolerant species *Acantholeberis curvirostris* throughout the core suggests that the lake has always been rather acid (pH < 5.5). However, there is no cladoceran evidence for significant changes in the pH at this site. Both the modern Cladocera and diatom flora from Lochan Dubh suggest more acid conditions than indicated by the measured pH. This may be because of insufficient water chemistry data at this site.

(*c*) *Evidence for atmospheric contamination*

Spheroidal carbonaceous particles (SCP) show similar patterns of contamination in the Round Loch of Glenhead and Lochan Dubh (figure 2), with low pre-20th century values and increasing concentrations from about 1900 onwards. However, in the Round Loch of Glenhead values are over ten-times higher.

Magnetic mineral concentration (saturation isothermal remanent magnetization (SIRM)) values at the Round Loch of Glenhead are low before about 1900 (12 cm), and then increase, probably reflecting atmospheric deposition of magnetic material. At Lochan Dubh there is a small rise in SIRM from about 1900 (9 cm), with a further increase after 1964 (4 cm). The similarity of these trends to the SCP profiles provides good evidence that SIRM is recording the history of fossil-fuel combustion.

At the Round Loch of Glenhead, the first major change in trace metal chemistry occurs at 40 cm where Pb concentrations increase (figure 2). This may possibly be related to local industrial sources. There is a further increase in Pb above 20 cm (*ca.* 1850), where concentrations of Zn also rise. These recent changes in the total concentrations of Pb and Zn cannot be explained in terms of catchment changes and are due to increased atmospheric inputs. The recent (*ca.* 1950) drop in Zn and Pb at the Round Loch of Glenhead is partly due to a decreased contamination flux from the atmosphere, together with the additional effect of a decrease in Zn sedimentary efficiency with falling pH. At Lochan Dubh there is little evidence of any atmospheric contamination by Pb. However, Zn concentrations rise above background levels at about 10 cm (1884), but maximum concentrations are much lower than those found at the Round Loch of Glenhead.

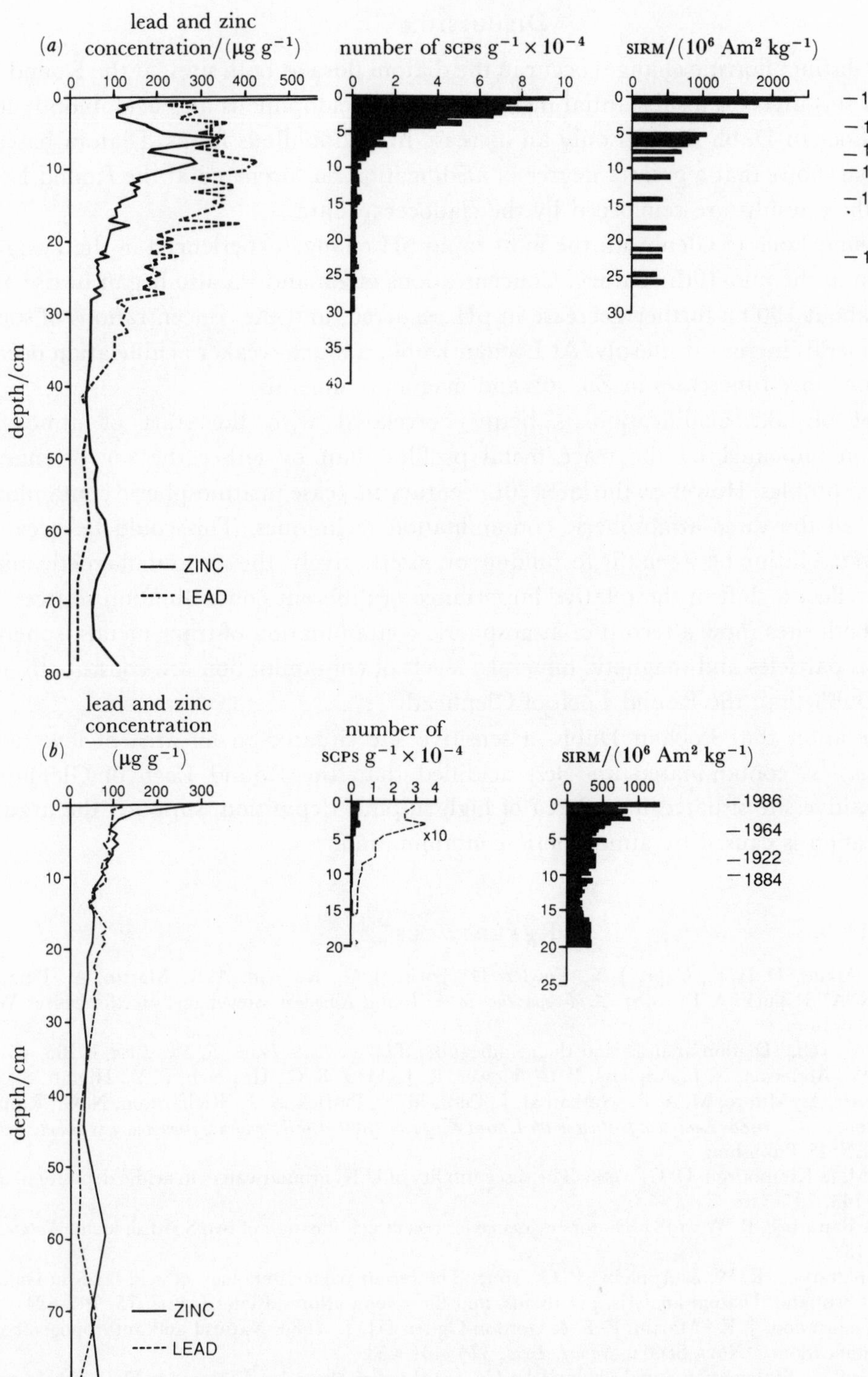

FIGURE 2. Degree of atmospheric contamination. Trace metal, spheroidal carbonaceous particle (SCP) and saturation isothermal remanent magnetisation (SIRM) profiles from (*a*) the Round Loch of Glenhead and (*b*) Lochan Dubh, plotted against depth. Dates are calculated from ^{210}Pb dating.

Discussion

Although distinct floristic changes occur in the diatom flora at both sites, at the Round Loch of Glenhead this involves a substantial increase in both acidophilous and acidobiontic forms, whereas at Lochan Dubh there is only an increase in acidophilous forms. Diatom based pH reconstruction shows that a greater degree of acidification has occurred at the Round Loch of Glenhead; these results are reinforced by the cladoceran data.

At the Round Loch of Glenhead, the most rapid pH change experienced in the Postglacial period began in the mid-19th century. Concentrations of Zn and Pb also began to rise at this time. After about 1900 a further decrease in pH occurred, and the concentrations of SCP and magnetic minerals increased sharply. At Lochan Dubh, a much weaker acidification occurred with less pronounced increases in Zn, SCP and magnetic minerals.

The onset of lake acidification is better correlated with the start of atmospheric contamination indicated by the trace metal profiles than by either the SCP or magnetic concentration profiles. However, the later 20th century increase in atmospheric contamination is shown by all the three atmospheric contamination techniques. This could be because of differences in resolution between the techniques or, alternatively, the SCP and magnetic mineral trends may reflect a shift in the relative importance of different contamination sources.

Whereas both sites show a record of atmospheric contamination of trace metals, spheroidal carbonaceous particles and magnetic minerals, levels of contamination are consistently lower at Lochan Dubh than the Round Loch of Glenhead.

The observation that Lochan Dubh, a sensitive site situated in an area of low sulphur deposition, is less contaminated and less acidified than the Round Loch of Glenhead, a similarly sensitive site situated in an area of high sulphur deposition, supports the argument that acidification is caused by atmospheric contamination.

References

Barrett, C. F., Atkins, D. H. F., Cape, J. N., Fowler, D., Irwin, J. G., Kallend, A. S., Martin, A., Pitman, J., Scriven, R. A. & Tuck, A. F. 1983 *Acid deposition in the United Kingdom.* Stevenage, Hertfordshire: Warren Spring Laboratory.

Battarbee, R. W. 1984 Diatom analysis and the acidification of lakes. *Phil. Trans. R. Soc. Lond.* B **305**, 451–477.

Battarbee, R. W., Anderson, N. J., Appleby, P. G., Flower, R. J., Fritz, S. C., Haworth, E. Y., Higgitt, S., Jones, V. J., Kreiser, A., Munro, M. A. R., Natkanski, J., Oldfield, F., Patrick, S. T., Richardson, N. G., Rippey, B. & Stevenson, A. C. 1988 *Lake acidification in the United Kingdom 1800–1986: evidence from analysis of lake sediments.* London: ENSIS Publishing.

Edmunds, W. M. & Kinniburgh, D. G. 1986 The susceptibility of U.K. groundwaters to acidic deposition. *J. geol. Soc. Lond.* **143**, 707–720.

Flower, R. J. & Battarbee, R. W. 1983 Diatom evidence for recent acidification of two Scottish lochs. *Nature, Lond.* **305**, 130–133.

Flower, R. J., Battarbee, R. W. & Appleby, P. G. 1987 The recent palaeolimnology of acid lakes in Galloway, south-west Scotland. Diatom analysis, pH trends, and the role of afforestation. *J. Ecol.* **75**, 797–824.

Gorham, E., Underwood, J. K., Martin, F. B. & Gordon-Ogden III, J. 1986 Natural and anthropogenic causes of lake acidification in Nova Scotia. *Nature, Lond.* **324**, 451–453.

Hustedt, F. 1937–39 Systematische und ökologische Untersuchungen über den Diatomeen-Flora von Java, Bali, Sumatra. *Arch. Hydrobiol.* Supplements **15** and **16**.

Jones, V. J., Stevenson, A. C. & Battarbee, R. W. 1986 Lake acidification and the land-use hypothesis: a mid-post-glacial analogue. *Nature, Lond.* **322**, 157–158.

Jones, V. J., Stevenson, A. C. & Battarbee, R. W. 1989 Acidification of lakes in Galloway, south west Scotland: a diatom and pollen study of the post-glacial history of the Round Loch of Glenhead. *J. Ecol.* **77**, 1–23.

Stevenson, A. C., Patrick, S. T., Kreiser, A. & Battarbee, R. W. 1987 Palaeoecological evaluation of the recent acidification of susceptible lakes. Methods utilised under DoE contract PECD 7/7/139 and the Royal Society SWAP Project. Palaeoecology Research Unit, University College London, U.K. Research Paper no. 26.

Phil. Trans. R. Soc. Lond. B **327**, 403–412 (1990)
Printed in Great Britain

Effects of acidic deposition on North American lakes: palaeolimnological evidence from diatoms and chrysophytes

By D. F. Charles†

Department of Biology, Indiana University, Bloomington, Indiana 47405, *U.S.A.*

Analysis of sediment diatom and chrysophyte assemblages is the best technique currently available for inferring past lake water pH trends. Use of this approach for assessing the ecological effects of acidic deposition is increasing rapidly. As of August 1989, sediment core inferred pH data existed for at least 150 lakes in North America and cores from about 100 more lakes are being analysed. Equations for inferring past pH are based on at least 15–20 calibration data-sets involving about 700 lakes.

Palaeolimnological studies indicate that recent acidification has been caused by acidic deposition in the Adirondack Mountains (New York), northern New England, Ontario, Quebec and the Canadian Atlantic provinces. Inferred pH decreases are commonly as much as 0.5–1.0 pH units. With the exception of one lake, no acidification trends were observed in regions currently receiving low deposition of strong acids (e.g. Rocky Mountains and Sierra Nevada in the western United States). Slight or no trends towards decreasing pH were observed in study lakes receiving moderately acidic deposition (upper Mid-west and northern Florida). The amount of inferred acidification (increase in H^+ concentration) correlates with the amount of S and N loading and the ability of watersheds and lakes to neutralize acid inputs, and is generally consistent with current lake-acidification theory.

In most cases, the primary cause of recent acidification (post-1850) is acidic deposition, as opposed to land-use changes or natural processes, though these may be contributing factors. Acid loading has decreased in some regions since 1970 (e.g., northeastern United States). Some lakes have become less acidic in response, but others continue to lose acid neutralizing capacity. Many currently acidic lakes were naturally acidic (pH < 5.5) before the onset of anthropogenic acidification. These lakes are typically small (less than 10 ha‡) are located at moderately high elevations, have thin or peaty soils, or are located in outwash deposits. Many of these have acidified further recently.

Introduction

Acidification of lakes by atmospheric deposition of strong acids is a major environmental issue in North America and causes and effects have been studied intensively. Several research projects have been implemented to determine the acidity status of lakes before the onset of acidic deposition, and to estimate their response to strong acid inputs. Information from these studies is necessary to fully assess the effects of acidic deposition on aquatic resources and to accurately predict the nature and extent of response to future changes in deposition. Historical changes have been assessed by (i) comparison of recent and historical water chemistry, fish and diatom data, (ii) use of empirical and dynamic models and (iii) analysis of palaeoecological data (National Research Council 1986). Other than the sparse historical chemistry and fisheries

† Present address: U.S. Environmental Protection Agency, Environmental Research Laboratory, 200 S.W. 35th Street, Corvallis, Oregon 97333, U.S.A.

‡ 1 ha $= 10^4$ m^2.

information, which is usually difficult to interpret, palaeoecological studies have provided the most direct indication of trends in past lake pH and acid neutralizing capacity (ANC), the rate and magnitude of the change and possible causes of the change (Battarbee 1984; Charles & Norton 1986; Smol *et al.* 1986; Battarbee & Charles 1986, 1987; Davis 1987; Charles *et al.* 1989; Battarbee, this symposium).

The purpose of this paper is to summarize what we have learned in North America from palaeolimnological studies about the nature and extent of recent acidification in different regions, and the role of acidic deposition and other factors as causes of observed changes.

Methods for inferring past pH and assessing acidification causes

Before 1989, most pH reconstructions used Index α (Nygaard 1956; Meriläinen 1967), index B (Renberg & Hellberg 1982) and multiple regression approaches (see, for example, Charles (1985)). The standard error for the pH inference equations based on these indices ranges between 0.25 and 0.4 pH units (Battarbee 1984; Charles & Norton, 1986; Smol *et al.*, 1986; Charles *et al.* 1989). A multiple regression technique, similar to that for pH, has been developed to infer alkalinity (Charles *et al.* 1990). New techniques have been developed to infer pH by using both diatoms and scaled chrysophytes (Charles & Smol 1988). These are particularly useful in acidic lakes (pH < 5.0), because chrysophytes appear more sensitive to pH changes in these ranges than do diatoms (Smol 1986, 1987). Also, methods based on canonical correspondence analysis (ter Braak 1986; ter Braak & Van Dam 1988) and weighted averaging (Birks *et al.* and Kingston & Birks, this symposium) are now being used to reconstruct pH, ANC, DOC, and Al for lakes in the Adirondacks (Charles & Smol 1990) and New England (Davis *et al.*, this symposium).

Diatom and chrysophyte data are being used not only to infer the past pH trend of a lake but also, in many cases, to suggest the causes of the changes. There are three major possible causes of regional acidification of low-alkalinity lakes in North America: (i) long-term natural acidification, (ii) catchment disturbances, such as fires, blowdown, logging, and ensuing responses of vegetation and soils and (iii) atmospheric deposition of strong acids. These possible causes, and the use of palaeolimnological techniques to determine their importance, are discussed in detail in Charles *et al.* (1989) and Battarbee (this symposium).

Recent lake acidification trends in regions of North America

Diatom data-sets from several regions (figure 1; table 1) have been assembled and reviewed for the purpose of evaluating recent acidification trends in North America (see Charles & Norton (1986) and Charles *et al.* (1989) for locations of lakes and for tables of diatom inferred (DI) pH data and lake characteristics; results from some completed studies are as yet unpublished and are not included in table 1). Data were selected for lakes having: (i) current alkalinity less than 200 $\mu eq\ l^{-1}$; (ii) minimal or, if not minimal, well-known watershed disturbance of influence from local emission sources and (iii) adequate quality and quantity of diatom or chrysophyte data. Inferred pH values were based on calibration sets developed for regions in which the study lakes are located.

In general, the study lakes represent the most acidic lakes in each region. Most of the lakes in the Adirondacks (12), upper Mid-west (9), and northern Florida (6), and some in New

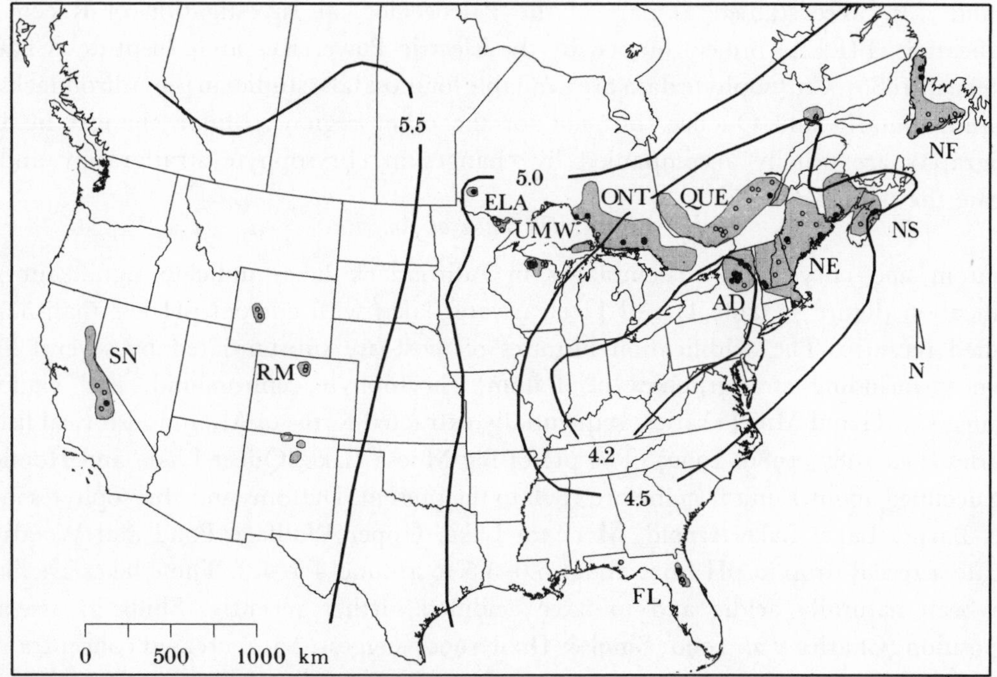

FIGURE 1. Locations in North America of palaeolimnological studies using diatom and chrysophyte assemblages to infer recent trends in lake acidity status. Shaded regions indicate areas covered by calibration data sets. Solid symbols represent sites where recent acidification is indicated. Open symbols represent sites where no change or an increase in pH has been inferred. See text for further explanation. See Charles *et al.* (1989) for tables of measured and inferred pH for the study lakes. Isopleths of precipitation pH are from Barrie (1984). Lakes in New Mexico are not included in Charles *et al.* (1989). Data available (Lynch *et al.* 1988) do not indicate any significant recent acidification. (AD, Adirondack Park, New York; ELA, Experimental Lakes Area, Ontario, Canada; FL, northern Florida; NE, New England; NF, Newfoundland, Canada; NS, Nova Scotia and New Brunswick, Canada; ONT, Ontario, Canada; QUE, Quebec, Canada; RM, Rocky Mountains; SN, Sierra Nevada.)

TABLE 1. ACIDIFICATION TRENDS FOR NORTH AMERICAN LAKES BASED ON DIFFERENCE IN DI pH BETWEEN SURFACE (MODERN) AND PRE-1850 SEDIMENT CORE ASSEMBLAGES. LAKES WERE DETERMINED TO HAVE BECOME MORE ACIDIC IF DI pH DECREASED BY 0.2 pH UNITS OR MORE. REGIONS ARE LISTED IN DECREASING ORDER OF CURRENT ACID DEPOSITION LOADING. ACIDIFICATION CATEGORIES ARE DIVIDED ACCORDING TO PRE-1850 DI pH (ABOVE OR BELOW pH 5.5)

(See text for explanation. Data on which this table is based are presented in Charles *et al.* (1989).)

		no acidification		acidification	
region	pre-1850 pH:	< 5.5	⩾ 5.5	< 5.5	⩾ 5.5
Adirondacks		1	6	6	6
Northern New England		7	1	5	1
Ontario		0	1	1	5
Quebec		1	11	0	1
New Brunswick/Nova Scotia		0	5	2	7
Newfoundland		0	2	0	1
Upper Midwest		3	6	1	4
Northern Florida		3	1	1	1
Rockies		0	7	0	0
Sierra Nevada		0	4	0	1
total		15	44	16	26

England, (3), were studied as part of the Paleoecological Investigation of Recent Lake Acidification (PIRLA) project funded by the Electric Power Research Institute (Charles & Whitehead 1986). Chrysophyte data are available for most lake studies in the Adirondacks, New England, Ontario and Quebec, but not for the other regions. Major changes in diatom stratigraphy are usually accompanied by changes in chrysophyte stratigraphy and they indicate the same pH trend.

(*a*) *United States of America*

Diatom and chrysophyte assemblages in Adirondack lakes indicate significant recent acidification (figure 1, table 1). All 11 clearwater lakes with current pH less than 5.5 have acidified recently. The acidification histories of most are substantiated by several lines of evidence, including stratigraphies of diatom, chrysophyte, chironomid, and cladoceran remains; Ca:Ti and Mn:Ti ratios; sequentially extracted forms of Al; and historical fish data (Charles *et al.* 1987, 1989, 1990). The pH of Big Moose Lake, Queer Lake, and Honnedaga Lake declined about 1 unit from before 1800 to the present. Diatoms and chrysophytes in Deep Lake, Barnes Lake, Lake Arnold, Merriam Lake, Upper Wallface Pond and Woods Lake indicate a recent drop in pH from about 5.0–5.5 to around 4.7–4.9. These lakes are likely to have been naturally acidic and to have acidified further recently. Shifts in assemblage composition (Charles *et al.* 1990; Smol & Dixit 1990) suggest that increased concentrations of Al or other metals, and decreased organic matter (Davis *et al.* 1985; Davis 1987) may have accompanied the pH decline. Acidification trends appear to be continuing in some lakes, despite recent reductions in atmospheric sulphur loading.

All clearwater lakes with current pH greater than 6.0 have acidified only slightly or not at all, reflecting the ability of the lake–catchment systems to neutralize acid inputs. Diatoms and chrysophytes in high DOC lakes and bogs suggest a relatively small pH change, as would be expected in highly coloured acidic waters buffered by organic acids.

The primary cause of recent acidification is clearly the increased atmospheric deposition of strong acids derived from combustion of fossil fuels, though other factors may play a role. Natural processes and catchment disturbances cannot account for the rapid changes in water chemistry that have occurred (see, for example, Whitehead *et al.* (1986)). For many of the lakes, sediment core profiles of Pb, Ca, V, Zn, S, polycyclic aromatic hydrocarbons (PAH) and carbonaceous particles provide a record of deposition of materials associated with fossil fuel combustion beginning in the late 1800s and early 1900s. The onset of acidification began after that time (Charles *et al.* 1990).

As part of the recently initiated PIRLA II project (Charles & Smol 1990), funded by the U.S. Environmental Protection Agency (EPA), recent (0–1 cm) and pre-1850 (> 30 cm) sediment core intervals of 37 lakes statistically selected as part of EPA's Eastern Lake Survey (Landers *et al.* 1988) were analysed to determine historical pH and ANC trends. All of the 17 lakes with current pH less than 5.8 declined in pH and ANC (J. P. Smol, personal communication). This further corroborates findings based on palaeolimnological and other studies indicating that acidic deposition has caused widespread acidification of Adirondack lakes.

In New England, changes in sediment diatom assemblage composition indicate recent acidification of some lakes. However, most of the pH trend data indicate no change or only a slight decrease in pH from pre-1800 to be present (Norton *et al.* 1985; Charles *et al.* 1989; Davis *et al.* 1990; Ford 1986, 1990). Fluctuations in some of the profiles appear to be related to watershed events (Davis *et al.* 1983). Sediment chemistry data for Mud Pond, Haystack Pond, and Little Long Pond indicate post-1900 increases in materials associated with the combustion of fossil fuels (e.g. total Pb and V) (Davis *et al.* 1990). The DI pH of Duck Pond, a kettle pond on Cape Cod, Massachusetts, suggests a slight recent acidification trend (pH 5.2–5.0), though this pond has been naturally acidic for thousands of years, with a mean DI pH for its entire history (about 12000 years) of 5.2 ± 0.3 pH units (Winkler 1988).

Lakes in the Upper Mid-west differ as a group from those in the northeast in that most are seepage lakes and are very dilute (conductivities as low as 9 $\mu S\ cm^{-1}$). There is no indication of acidification in Minnesota lakes (three lakes studied); and there is evidence of post-1900 pH declines in four of nine Wisconsin lakes; one of two lakes studied in Michigan has become slightly more acidic (Charles *et al.* 1989; Kingston *et al.*, this symposium). These results are generally consistent with the strong gradient of decreasing precipitation pH from west to east (see, for example, figure 1). McNearney Lake in Michigan is a naturally acidic lake (pre-1800 DI pH = 4.9); its pH has not declined, but current Al concentrations are high. Concentrations of S, Pb, Cu, V and polycyclic aromatic hydrocarbons increase towards the surface of the cores, but they are not as great as concentrations in the northeastern United States (Kingston *et al.* 1990).

Northern Florida has the largest percentage of lakes with pH less than 5.0 (12%) of all regions in the United States (Landers *et al.* 1988). Analysis of pre-1850 sediment core diatom assemblages indicates that four of six PIRLA lakes had low pH values due to natural causes (Sweets *et al.* 1990). Low base cation concentrations are probably attributable to the low cation exchange capacity and low base saturation of the deep coarse sands in which the lakes are situated, and to isolation from the local groundwater table (Floridan aquifer) by the clay-rich Hawthorne formation. The high SO_4^{2-} concentrations, which contribute most to the acidity, apparently result from high evapoconcentration rates (Pollman & Canfield 1990). Lake Barco and Lake Suggs have become more acidic recently, with DI pH decreases of about 0.5 pH units. There are two possible causes: acidic deposition and a decrease in the regional groundwater table (Sweets *et al.* 1990; Pollman & Canfield 1990).

The Rocky Mountain and Sierra Nevada lakes may be considered control or reference lakes. They all have low alkalinity (most with alkalinity $< 60\ \mu eq\ l^{-1}$) and are therefore sensitive to increased input of strong acids, but do not currently receive precipitation with an annual average pH lower than about 5.0 (see, for example, Barrie (1984)). Current SO_4^{2-} concentrations are typically less than 20 $\mu eq\ l^{-1}$. Changes in the diatom stratigraphy of most Rocky Mountain lakes are relatively minor, occur gradually and do not indicate recent acidification (Baron *et al.* 1986). The same is true for Sierra Nevada lakes (see, for example, Holmes *et al.* (1989), but there is evidence of trends of both increasing and decreasing pH, particularly based on analysis of floristic changes (M. Whiting, personal communication). Some of the trends began well before 1900. Causes are not clear, but may include effects of volcanic eruptions during the past few thousand years, land-use changes in nearby valleys that have caused changes in dry deposition of particulates containing base cations, and increased episodic acidification events following summer rainstorms (M. Whiting & D. Whitehead, personal communication).

(*b*) *Eastern Canada*

In contrast to studies in the United States, in which the goal has been to assess the effects of acidic substances transported long distances, a large percentage of the Canadian studies have focused on lakes that are near large point sources of sulphurous oxide (SO_x) and metal emissions (e.g. Sudbury, Wawa), near mining effluents, or on lakes that have been manipulated (e.g. limed or acidified). Several studies deal with lakes that are strongly influenced by organically rich soils and bogs. Nevertheless, in all lake regions studied thus far where acidic precipitation occurs, diatoms and chrysophytes have indicated a recent pH decrease in at least some lakes. The floristic changes are similar to those recorded in the northern United States and some areas of Europe.

In Ontario, Dickman *et al.* (1984) and Dixit & Dickman (1986) studied acidification of lakes in the Wawa area, northeast of Lake Superior and downwind of a major smelting operation. They inferred that the pH in Lake CS and Lake B had markedly declined. During the past 200 years, other lakes had been rather acidic, one lake had relatively stable pH, and one had fluctuating pH (Fortescue 1984). The acidification of Lake CS and Lake B in the past 30–50 years is apparently attributable to emission of S from Wawa, Ontario, in the 1940's and 1950's (Dickman *et al.* 1984). Forest fires and logging may also have affected diatom stratigraphy and lakewater pH.

Dixit *et al.* (1987, 1988) used diatoms and chrysophytes to infer the pH history of two lakes (Hannah and Clearwater) near Sudbury, an area of major smelting operations. In Hannah Lake, acidification started soon after the roasting of ore began at Copper Cliff in the 1880s. Between about 1800 and 1975, the DI pH declined from about 6.0 to 4.6. After liming in 1975, the DI pH increased. In Clearwater Lake, the diatom assemblages indicated that acidification occurred after the installation of tall stacks at Copper Cliff in the 1920s. The pH declined from about 6.0 in *ca.* 1930 to about 4.2 by *ca.* 1970. Acidification appears to have stopped after that time.

Chrysophyte scales from a variety of Ontario lakes are being used to infer pH change (K. Nicholls (Ontario Ministry of the Environment) and J. P. Smol, unpublished data). Chrysophytes indicate a decrease in lakewater pH in Algonquin Park, in the Parry Sound region, and in Pukaskwa National Park. Davidson (1984) and Dickman *et al.* (1988) studied the artificially acidified Lake 223 in the Experimental Lakes Area by using a variety of techniques and found that the diatom flora in a core from the lake showed good agreement with the known plankton history.

Cores from Key Lake and Lake C-22 in the Matamek Watershed in northeastern Quebec were studied by Hudon *et al.* (1986). In the recent sediments of Key Lake, there was a decrease in the number of circumneutral diatom taxa and an increase in acidobiontic forms; however, no statistical increase in acidity could be inferred. Similarly, in Lake C-22 there has been a slight tendency toward greater acidification in the past 20 years, but the trend was less distinct than that shown in Key Lake.

In a study of several lakes in Quebec located in a strip 150 km wide north of the St Lawrence River, Dixit and others found either a small change or no change in inferred pH (Dixit 1988; Charles *et al.* 1989). Analysis of four of the lakes suggested a recent minor pH reduction. Chrysophytes changed much more strikingly than diatoms in recent sediments of several lakes, but again suggesting only minor acidification.

Delorme *et al.* (1983) inferred pH trends for Kejimkujik Lake (central Nova Scotia), a presently acidic (pH = 4.8) site in a drainage basin of organic rich soils and bogs. Since those results were published, the core has been reanalysed by using more recent taxonomic information. Instead of a significant increase in DI pH, only a slight increase is now inferred

(H. Duthie, personal communication). The present low pH of the lake cannot be attributed entirely to atmospheric loading; acid conditions have persisted for at least the last 1000 years, probably because of organic acids.

A study of three Nova Scotia lakes and four New Brunswick lakes showed that DI pH declines in the unbuffered lakes (e.g. a decline from 6.1 to 5.3 for Big Indian Lake), but not in the higher alkalinity lakes (Elner & Ray 1987). The changes occurred over about the past 70 years, coincident with assumed increases in acidic precipitation.

Diatom inferred pH profiles for seven lakes in Newfoundland indicate declines of about 0.2–0.3 pH unit in three of the lakes (Scruton *et al.* 1987*a*, *b*). The pH changes were probably caused by atmospheric sources, as well as by possible watershed disturbances (e.g. forest fire) and natural processes. These small changes in inferred pH are consistent with the relatively low level of acidic deposition in Newfoundland.

Assessment of trend data and possible acidification causes

Considerable high-quality data now exist with which to make assessments of acidification trends in North America. As of August 1989, sediment core DI pH data existed for about 150 lakes. Reports on studies of about another 100 lakes will probably appear within the next two years. The pH inference equations on which the DI pH data were calculated are based on 15–20 calibration data sets for North America involving a total of about 700 lakes (Charles *et al.* 1989). The predictive equations based on these data sets have a good ability to infer pH. With few exceptions, the surface sediment DI pH values agree with current measured pH within about 0.1–0.4 units (Charles *et al.* 1989).

Palaeoecological data now available are sufficient to conclude that lake acidification has occurred in the Adirondack Mountains (New York), New England, Ontario, Quebec, the Atlantic provinces, the Upper Mid-west, and Florida (figure 1, table 1; Charles *et al.* 1989).

Based on palaeolimnological and other data, the primary cause of recent lake acidification in most of the above regions is acidic deposition derived from combustion of fossil fuels, although catchment changes and natural long-term processes may play a minor role. Data for the Upper Mid-west and Florida strongly suggest that acid deposition may be the cause for acidification of some lakes, but the evidence is not sufficiently strong to suggest that acidic deposition has caused significant acidification of many lakes within those regions. The relative importance of these possible causes was evaluated by using the hypothesis testing criteria described by Charles *et al.* (1989). It is clear that pH declines in most areas cannot be accounted for by natural long-term processes (the rates of change are too fast) or by catchment changes, although these probably contributed to the process in some areas. In the majority of cases, DI pH declines occurred after the onset of acidic deposition (post-1850–1960), as palaeoecological evidence (e.g. Pb, V, PAH, carbonaceous particles) demonstrates. All regions where pH declines have been inferred receive relatively high levels of acidic deposition.

Taken together, the DI pH profiles exhibit a continuum of acidification trends that have been classified arbitrarily into four basic patterns (Charles & Norton 1986; Charles *et al.* 1989; table 1). Two represent trends and two represent no trend. The patterns are: (i) background pH greater than about 6.0 and no overall change in pH; (ii) relatively rapid decline in pH from the range of 5.7–6.0 to less than 5.0 (some pH declines start in pH ranges above 6.0); (iii) pH about 4.8–5.2 throughout the entire profile, and no overall trend and (iv) decline from the range of pH 4.8–5.3 to as low as about 4.3.

The most rapid changes in DI pH and sediment core diatom composition occur when DI pH decreases from a value above approximately 5.7–6.0 to below 5.0 (pattern 2). A smaller pH drop is observed for lakes with pre-1850 DI pH values of less than 5.5 (pattern 4). These patterns are consistent with the logarithmic nature of the pH scale and the response of sample lake-water pH to titration with strong acid in the laboratory. The pre-1850 water chemistry of lakes with patterns 1 and 2 and patterns 3 and 4 represent the dominant pre-1850 buffering systems in the studied regions: bicarbonate in the higher pH lakes, organic acids and Al species in the lower-pH lakes. Declines in pH in the latter group (pattern 4) should be interpreted carefully. Though pH may have decreased only slightly, increases in Al may have been substantial, because the change in Al per pH unit is greater in the pH range 4.5–5.0 than in the range 5.5–6.0 (Driscoll *et al.* 1984; Sullivan *et al.* 1989).

Lakes with pre-1850 DI pH less than 5.5 deserve special attention. First, they represent what have been considered 'naturally' acidic lakes, and second, it is difficult to explain their past chemistry and how it may have changed during the process of acidification (Charles *et al.* 1989). Many lakes of this type have been studied. In the Adirondacks, northern New England, and northern Florida (table 1), at least 40% of the lakes have pre-1850 DI pH less than 5.5. There are two probable reasons for this high percentage. First, a region may have a high proportion of naturally acidic lakes due to its geologic setting (e.g. Florida), or second, because of conscious site-selection criteria, only the more acidic lakes in a region may have been chosen for study, many of which were found to be naturally acidic (e.g. New England). It seems probable that organic acids were an important cause of acidic conditions in many lakes in acid sensitive areas before 1850 (Patrick *et al.* 1981; Davis *et al.* 1985). Also, if the pH was about 5.0, Al concentrations may have been moderate at that time, although much of the Al would have been complexed with organic compounds (Driscoll *et al.* 1984).

As low pH (5.0–5.5) lakes have become more acidic, changes in Al and organic-acid concentrations have probably been important factors affecting pH and alkalinity (see, for example, Sullivan *et al.* (1989)). The output of dissolved Al from the watersheds of these lakes should have increased with increased inputs of strong acids (Driscoll *et al.* 1984), except perhaps for seepage lakes in outwash deposits. This is consistent with the fact that most of the lakes examined that have current pH less than 5.5 have concentrations of total Al greater than 100–200 $\mu g\ l^{-1}$; the concentration in some lakes is as high as 600–700 $\mu g\ l^{-1}$ (see, for example, National Research Council (1986), appendix table E.3).

Preparation of this paper has been funded partially by the U.S. Environmental Protection Agency through Contract no. 68-C8-0006 with NSI Technology Services at the Environmental Research Laboratory in Corvallis, Oregon and through cooperative agreement CR-813933-01-1 with Indiana University. I especially thank John Smol for his efforts in helping to assemble and interpret data from Canadian studies. Tony Selle prepared figure 1. Larry Baker, Timothy Sullivan and Susan Christie made several helpful comments on the manuscript.

References

Baron, J., Norton, S. A., Beeson, D. R. & Herrmann, R. 1986 Sediment diatom and metal stratigraphy from Rocky Mountain lakes with special reference to atmospheric deposition. *Can. J. Fish. aq. Sci.* **43**, 1350–1362.

Barrie, L. A. 1984 The spatial distributions of precipitation acidity and major ion wet deposition in North America during 1980. *Tellus* **36B**, 333–355.

Battarbee, R. W. 1984 Diatom analysis and the acidification of lakes. *Phil. Trans. R. Soc. Lond.* B **305**, 451–477.

Battarbee, R. W. & Charles, D. F. 1986 Diatom-based pH reconstruction studies of acid lakes in Europe and North America: a synthesis. *Wat. Air Soil Pollut.* **30**, 347–354.

Battarbee, R. W. & Charles, D. F. 1987 The use of diatom assemblages in lake sediments as a means of assessing the timing, trends, and causes of lake acidification. *Prog. phys. Geog.* **11**, 552–580.

Charles, D. F. 1985 Relationships between surface sediment diatom assemblages and lakewater characteristics in Adirondack lakes. *Ecology* **66**, 994–1011.

Charles, D. F. & Norton, S. A. 1986 Palaeolimnological evidence for trends in atmospheric deposition of acids and metals. In *Acid deposition: long-term trends*, pp. 335–435. Washington, D.C.: National Academy Press.

Charles, D. F. & Smol, J. P. 1988 New methods for using diatoms and chrysophytes to infer past pH of low-alkalinity lakes. *Limnol. Oceanogr.* **33**, 1451–1462.

Charles, D. F. & Smol, J. P. 1990 The PIRLA II project: regional assessment of lake acidification trends. *Verh. int. Verein. Limnol.* (in the press).

Charles, D. F. & Whitehead, D. R. 1986 The PIRLA project: paleoecological investigations of recent lake acidification. *Hydrobiologia* **143**, 13–20.

Charles, D. F., Whitehead, D. R., Engstrom, D. R., Fry, B. D., Hites, R. A., Norton, S. A., Owen, J. S., Roll, L. A., Schindler, S. C., Smol, J. P., Uutala, A. J., White, J. R. & Wise, R. J. 1987 Paleolimnological evidence for recent acidification of Big Moose Lake, Adirondack Mountains, NY (U.S.A.). *Biogeochemistry* **3**, 267–296.

Charles, D. F., Battarbee, R. W., Renberg, I., van Dam, H. & Smol, J. P. 1989 Paleoecological analysis of lake acidification trends in North America and Europe using diatoms and chrysophytes. In *Acid precipitation*, vol 4 (ed. S. A. Norton, S. E. Lindberg & A. L. Page). New York: Springer-Verlag. (In the press).

Charles, D. F., Battarbee, R. W., Renberg, I., van Dam, H. & Smol, J. P. 1989 Paleoecological analysis of lake acidification trends in North America and Europe using diatoms and chrysophytes. In *Acid precipitation, vol. 4. Soils, aquatic processes, and lake acidification* (ed. S. A. Norton, S. E. Lindberg & A. L. Page). New York: Springer-Verlag.

Davidson, G. A. 1984 Palaeolimnological reconstruction of the acidification history of an experimentally acidified lake. M.Sc., thesis, University of Manitoba.

Davis, R. B. 1987 Palaeolimnological diatom studies of acidification of lakes by acid rain: an application of quaternary science. *Q. Sci. Rev.* **6**, 147–163.

Davis, R. B., Norton, S. A., Hess, C. T. & Brakke, D. F. 1983 Paleolimnological reconstruction of the effects of atmospheric deposition of acids and heavy metals on the chemistry and biology of lakes in New England and Norway. *Hydrobiologia* **103**, 113–123.

Davis, R. B., Anderson, D. S. & Berge, F. 1985 Palaeolimnological evidence that lake acidification is accompanied by loss of organic matter. *Nature, Lond.* **316**, 436–438.

Davis, R. B., Norton, S. A., Kahl, J. S., Whiting, M. C., Ford, J. & Smol, J. P. 1990 Paleoecological investigation of recent lake acidification in Northern New England. *J. Paleolimnol.* (In preparation.)

Delorme, L. D., Esterby, S. R. & Duthie, H. 1983 Prehistoric pH trends in Kejimkujik Lake, Nova Scotia. *Int. Rev. gesamten Hydrobiol.* **69**, 41–55.

Dickman, M. D., Dixit, S. S., Fortescue, J., Barlow, B. & Terasmae, J. 1984 Diatoms as indicators of the rate of acidification. *Wat. Air Soil Pollut.* **21**, 375–386.

Dickman, M. D., Thode, H. G., Rao, S. & Anderson, R. 1988 Downcore sulphur isotope ratios and diatom inferred pH in an artificially acidified Canadian Shield lake. *Environ. Pollut.* **49**, 265–288.

Dixit, S. S. 1988 Chrysophyte scales in lake sediments provide evidence of recent acidification in two Quebec (Canada) lakes. *Wat. Air Soil Pollut.* **38**, 97–104.

Dixit, S. S. & Dickman, M. D. 1986 Correlation of surface sediment diatoms with the present lake water pH in 28 Algoma lakes, Ontario, Canada. *Hydrobiologia* **131**, 133–143.

Dixit, S. S., Dixit, A. S. & Evans, R. D. 1987 Paleolimnological evidence of recent acidification in two Sudbury (Canada) lakes. *Sci. tot. Environ.* **67**, 53–67.

Dixit, S. S., Dixit, A. S. & Evans, R. D. 1988 Scaled chrysophytes (Chrysophyceae) as indicators of pH in Sudbury, Ontario lakes. *Can. J. Fish. aq. Sci.* **45**, 1411–1421.

Driscoll, C. T., Baker, J. P., Bisogni, J. J. & Schofield, C. L. 1984 Aluminum speciation and equilibria in dilute acidic surface waters of the Adirondack region of New York State. In *Geological aspects of acid deposition* (ed. O. P. Bricker), pp. 55–75. Boston, Massachusetts: Butterworth.

Elner, J. K. & Ray, S. 1987 pH profiles from diatom stratigraphies in sediment cores of selected lakes of New Brunswick and Nova Scotia, Canada, *Wat. Air Soil Pollut.* **32**, 17–29.

Ford, J. 1986 The recent history of a naturally acidic lake (Cone Pond, N.H.). In *Diatoms and lake acidity* (ed. J. P. Smol, R. W. Battarbee, R. B. Davis & J. Meriläinen), pp. 131–148. Dordrecht: Dr W. Junk.

Ford, M. S. (J.) 1990 A 10000-year history of natural ecosystem acidification. *Ecol. Monogr.* (In the press).

Fortescue, J. A. C. 1984 Interdisciplinary research for an environmental component (acid rain) in regional geochemical surveys (Wawa area). Algoma District, Ontario Geological Survey Map 80713. Compiled 1983. Geochemical Series.

Holmes, R. W., Whiting, M. C. & Stoddard, J. L. 1989 Changes in diatom inferred pH and acid neutralizing capacity in a dilute, high elevation, Sierra Nevada lake since A.D. 1825. *Freshwater Biol.* **21**, 295–310.

Hudon, C., Duthie, H. C., Smith, S. M. & Ditner, S. A. 1986 Relationships between lakewater pH and sedimentary diatoms in the Matamek Watershed, northeastern Quebec, Canada. *Hydrobiologia* **140**, 49–65.

Kingston, J. C., Cook, R. B., Kreis, R. G., Jr., Camburn, K. E., Norton, S. A., Sweets, P. R., Binford, M. W., Mitchell, M. J., Shane, L. C. & King, G. A. 1990 Palaeoecological investigation of recent lake acidification in the Northern Great Lakes States. *J. Palaeolimnol.* (In the press).

Landers, D. H., Overton, W. S., Linthurst, R. A. & Brakke, D. F. 1988 Eastern Lake Survey: regional estimates of lake chemistry. *Environ. Sci. Technol.* **22**, 128–135.

Lynch, T. R., Popp, C. J., Jacobi, G. Z. & Robertson, J. 1988 Assessing the sensitivity of high altitude New Mexican wilderness lakes to acidic precipitation and trace metal contamination. Technical Completion Report, Project no. 1423697, New Mexico Water Research Institute, New Mexico State University, Las Cruces, New Mexico.

Meriläinen, J. 1967 The diatom flora and the hydrogen-ion concentration of the water. *Annls bot. fenn.* **4**, 51–58.

National Research Council 1986 *Acid deposition: long-term trends.* Washington, D.C.: National Academy Press.

Norton, S. A., Davis, R. B. & Anderson, D. S. 1985 The distribution and extent of acid and metal precipitation in Northern New England. Final Report. Grant no. 14-16-0009-75-040.: U.S. Fish and Wildlife Service.

Nygaard, G. 1956 Ancient and recent flora of diatoms and chrysophyceae in Lake Gribsø. In *Studies on the humic, acid Lake Gribsø.* (ed. K. Berg & I. C. Petersen), pp. 39–94. Scandinavia: Folia Limnol.

Patrick, R., Binetti, V. P. & Halterman, S. G. 1981 Acid lakes from natural and anthropogenic causes. *Science, Wash.* **211**, 446–448.

Pollman, C. D. & Canfield, D. E., Jr. 1990 Florida. In *Acid deposition and aquatic ecosystems: regional case studies* (ed. D. F. Charles). New York: Springer-Verlag. (In the press.)

Renberg, I. & Hellberg, T. 1982 The pH history of lakes in southwestern Sweden, as calculated from the subfossil diatom flora of the sediments. *Ambio* **11**, 30–33.

Scruton, D. A., Elner, J. K. & Howell, G. D. 1987*a* Palaeolimnological investigation of freshwater lake sediments in insular Newfoundland, part 2: downcore diatom stratigraphies and historical pH profiles for seven lakes. Canadian Technical Report of Fisheries and Aquatic Sciences. no. 1521. St Johns, Newfoundland: Department of Fisheries and Oceans, Science Branch.

Scruton, D. A., Elner, J. K. & Rybak, M. 1987*b* Regional calibration of fossil diatom – contemporary pH relationships for insular Newfoundland, Canada, including historical pH reconstruction for five lakes and assessment of paleo-inferred productivity changes in one lake. In *Acid rain: scientific and technical advances* (ed. R. Perry, R. M. Harrison, J. B. N. Bell & J. N. Lester), pp. 457–464. London, Selper Ltd.

Smol, J. P. 1986 Chrysophycean microfossils as indicators of lakewater pH. In *Diatoms and lake acidity* (ed. J. P. Smol, R. W. Battarbee, R. B. Davis & J. Meriläinen), pp. 275–287. Dordrecht: Dr W. Junk.

Smol, J. P. 1987 Chrysophycean microfossils in paleolimnological studies. *Palaeogeog. Palaeoclimatol, Palaeoecol.* **62**, 287–297.

Smol, J. P. & Dixit, S. S. 1990 Patterns of pH change inferred from chrysophycean microfossils in Adirondack and New England lakes. *J. Paleolimnol.* (In the press).

Smol, J. P., Battarbee, R. W., Davis, R. B. & Meriläinen, J. (eds). 1986 *Diatoms and lake acidity.* Dordrecht: Dr W. Junk.

Sullivan, T. J., Driscoll, C. T., Cook, R. B., Gherini, S. A., Charles, D. F. & Yatsko, C. P. 1989 The influence of organic acid anions and aqueous aluminum on measurements of acid neutralizing capacity in surface waters. *Nature, Lond.* **338**, 408–410.

Sweets, P. R., Bienert, R. W., Jr., Crisman, T. L. & Binford, M. W. 1990 Paleoecological investigation of recent lake acidification in northern Florida. *J. Paleolimnol.* (In the press.)

ter Braak, C. J. F. 1986 Canonical correspondence analysis: a new eigenvector technique for multivariate direct gradient analysis. *Ecology* **67**, 1167–1179.

ter Braak, C. J. F. & van Dam, H. 1988 Inferring pH from diatoms: a comparison of old and new calibration methods. *Hydrobiologia* **178**, 209–223.

Whitehead, D. R., Charles, D. F., Reed, S. E., Jackson, S. T. & Sheehan, M. C. 1986 Late-glacial and holocene acidity changes in Adirondack (NY) lakes. In *Diatoms and lake acidity* (ed. J. P. Smol, R. W. Battarbee, R. B. Davis & J. Meriläinen), pp. 251–274. Dordrecht: Dr W. Junk.

Winkler, M. G. 1988 Paleolimnology of a Cape Cod Kettle Pond: diatoms and reconstructed pH. *Ecol. Monogr.* **58**, 197–214.

Phil. Trans. R. Soc. Lond. B **327**, 413–421 (1990)
Printed in Great Britain

Alkalinity and pH of three lakes in northern New England, U.S.A., over the past 300 years

By R. B. Davis[1], D. S. Anderson[1], M. C. Whiting[1], J. P. Smol[2] and S. S. Dixit[2]

[1] *Department of Botany and Plant Pathology and Institute for Quaternary Studies, University of Maine, Orono, Maine* 04469, *U.S.A.*

[2] *Department of Biology, Queen's University, Kingston, Ontario K7L 3N6, Canada*

Three-hundred-year histories of pH and total alkalinity (alk) have been inferred from diatom and chrysophyte remains in deep-water sediment cores from Mud Pond (pH 4.6, alk -23 μeq l^{-1}) and Little Long Pond (pH 5.7, alk 4 μeq l^{-1}), Maine and Haystack Pond (pH 4.8, alk -18 μeq l^{-1}), Vermont. Three replicate cores were studied from each Mud Pond and Haystack Pond; one core from Little Long Pond; pH and alk inferences from diatoms were based on three different calibration equations: CLUSTER, DECORANA and CCA (CANOCO) (only CCA for chrysophytes). Replication of pH and alk inferences between cores was excellent. Different calibration approaches led to the same conclusions with minor exceptions. There were minor differences between chrysophyte- and diatom-based inferences, but both led to similar conclusions regarding acidification. These were: Mud Pond, *ca.* 1700–1925, pH 5.2–5.3, alk 0 to -15 μeq l^{-1}; 1925–1970, acidification to pH $\simeq$ 4.8 and alk -20 to -30 μeq l^{-1}. Little Long Pond *ca.* 1700–1950, pH $\simeq$ 5.9, alk 20–50 μeq l^{-1}; 1950 ff., possible slight acidification to pH 5.7–5.8. Haystack Pond, *ca.* 1700–1925, pH 5.2–5.3, alk 0 to -10 μeq l^{-1}; 1925–1970, acidification to pH $\simeq$ 4.9 and alk -10 to -30 μeq l^{-1}. Correlation of lake acidification with great increases in sedimentary indicators of air pollution (carbonaceous particles, Pb, polycyclic aromatic hydrocarbons) and absence of correlated catchment disturbance point to anthropogenic acid deposition as the cause of lake acidification. Extreme acid sensitive lakes like these three are atypical for northern New England.

Introduction

The palaeolimnological approach has proven useful for understanding the effects of anthropogenic acid deposition on lakes. The approach has relied heavily on inferences of past pH and total alkalinity (alk) from the remains of diatoms and chrysophytes in sediment cores. This area of palaeolimnology, or major parts of it, have been reviewed by Battarbee *et al.* (1986), Charles & Norton (1986), Davis (1987) and Charles *et al.* (1989). Summary results from northern New England (Vermont, New Hampshire and Maine) were given by Davis *et al.* (1983), Norton *et al.* (1985) and Davis (1987), but much of the information on the study lakes in the region has not been published. This paper aims to partially rectify that situation by giving more complete results for three lakes (figure 1). Additional results are given by Davis *et al.* (1990). This work was part of the Paleolimnological Investigation of Recent Lake Acidification Project (PIRLA) (Charles & Whitehead 1986*a*).

The specific objectives of this project were: (i) methodological (*a*) compare reconstructions of pH and alk from replicate cores from the same lake (can conclusions regarding lake acidification be based on a single core?), (*b*) compare pH and alk reconstructions based on different calibration equations (does the particular calibration equation affect conclusions on

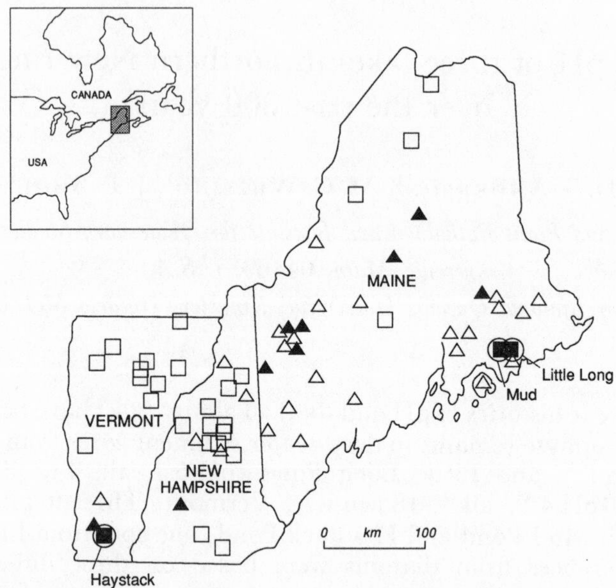

FIGURE 1. Locations of Haystock Pond (1), Mud Pond(2) and Little Long Pond (3), and the additional 60 lakes used for pH and alkalinity calibrations. Squares indicate sites studied as part of the PIRLA Project; triangles as part of earlier projects. Solid symbols indicate lakes where cores were subjected to diatom and chemical stratigraphic analyses, and where pH and alk reconstructions have been made (Davis *et al.* 1990).

lake acidification?) and (*c*) compare pH and alk reconstructions based on diatom against chrysophyte remains from the same core (do the different remains lead to different conclusions regarding lake acidification?). (ii) Interpret pH and alk reconstructions in terms of (*a*) pre-pollution pH and alk conditions of the lakes, (*b*) any changes in conditions during the period of anthropogenic acid deposition, and the timing of such changes and (*c*) correlations between changes and the sedimentary record of air pollutants associated with fossil fuel combustion and acid deposition (carbonaceous particles (CarbP); Pb; polycyclic aromatic hydrocarbons (PAH)).

STUDY LAKES

The study lakes are Haystack Pond in southern Vermont and Little Long Pond and Mud Pond in eastern Maine (figure 1). Water from Mud Pond flows into Little Long Pond via a 200 m long stream. The three water bodies have heavily forested catchments that have been undisturbed since selective logging around 1900. The thin, coarse-grained soils are derived from granite. Haystack Pond and Mud Pond had (1983 and 1984) negative alk and, respectively, mean pH values of 4.8 and 4.6. Little Long Pond had mean alk of about 4 μeq l^{-1} and mean pH 5.7. The lakes are oligotrophic and low in dissolved organic matter (table 1).

SUMMARY OF METHODS

Detailed field and laboratory methods for all aspects of the PIRLA Project were given by Charles & Whitehead (1986*b*). Undisturbed cores of sediment approx. 2 m apart were obtained from the deepest part of each lake by using a 10 cm diameter improved version of a

TABLE 1. CHARACTERISTICS OF THE THREE STUDY LAKES

(Each value is a mean of depth-integrated samples taken on six to eight dates from the mid-lake mixed stratum in 1983 and 1984 ice-free seasons. See Charles & Whitehead (1986*b*) and Davis *et al.* (1990) for methods.)

	Haystack Pond	Mud Pond	Little Long Pond
catchment			
area/ha[a]	52	50	205
total relief/m	132	246	285
mean slope (%)	36	12	10
lake			
surface elevation a.s.l./m	910	110	72
surface area/ha[a]	11	1	22
maximum depth/m	11.6	15.0	24.5
transparency/m	9.5	7.3	10.7
conductance/(μS cm^{-1})	19	31	24
dissolved organic carbon/(mg l^{-1})	1.5	3.7	1.0
chlorophyll *a*/(μg l^{-1})	0.2	0.5	0.7
total phosphorus/(μg l^{-1})	4.7	4.2	2.4
silicon/(mg l^{-1})	0.3	1.5	1.4
total aluminium/(μg l^{-1})	129.8	330.3	40.9
labile aluminium/(μg l^{-1})	85.5	219.7	31.0
calcium/(μeq l^{-1})	41.0	23.4	43.9
nitrate/(μeq l^{-1})	5.7	0.7	1.1
non-marine sulphate/(μeq l^{-1})	72.3	89.6	70.6
total alkalinity/(μeq l^{-1})	−18.3	−23.0	3.7
pH	4.83	4.57	5.70

[a] 1 ha = 10^4 m^2.

corer described by Davis & Doyle (1969). Three cores were studied from Haystack Pond, three from Mud Pond and one from Little Long Pond.

Cores were analysed for a wide range of chemical variables (Davis *et al.* 1990) but only Pb and PAH are reported here. Diatoms and chrysophyte scales were determined microscopically on the same slides, from a series of depths in each core. Diatom taxonomy in the PIRLA Project was standardized (Camburn *et al.* 1984–1986). ^{210}Pb dating was supplemented by dates based on pollen chronostratigraphic markers (Davis *et al.* 1990; Charles & Whitehead 1986*b*). Carbonaceous particles, determined on pollen slides, consisted of coal and oil combustion spherules as well as other soot particles, but as much as possible did not include carbonized remains of plants (e.g., charcoal). A collection of slides and photomicrographs of emission particles from fossil-fuel combustion facilities and carbonized plant parts including crushed charcoal of several tree species was used for reference.

A data-set for pH and alk calibration of sedimentary remains of diatoms and chrysophytes, comprising 63 lakes in Vermont, New Hampshire and Maine (figure 1) was established (partially reported by Davis & Anderson (1985)). Three different calibration equations were developed for diatom-inferred pH (DIpH) and three for diatom-inferred alk (DIalk). These equations consisted of regressions of pH and alk of: (i) groups of diatoms as determined by a cluster analysis; (ii) diatom scores on the first DECORANA axis; and (iii) diatom scores from a canonical correspondence analysis (CCA) (CANOCO of ter Braak (1987)). Only CCA equations were used for chrysophyte inferred pH (CIpH) and CIalk. Low sedimentary concentrations of chrysophyte remains in five of the lakes led to a reduced number of lakes in the chrysophyte calibration set ($n = 58$). Statistics for the calibration equations are given in table 2. See Battarbee & Charles (1987) for a general explanation of the calibration approach.

Table 2. Statistics for calibration equations

(Chrysophyte statistics from Dixit *et al.* (1990).)

	method	Ho[a]	r^2	*Se*
diatoms ($n = 63$)				
pH	clusters	< 0.001	0.86	0.29
	DECORANA	< 0.001	0.84	0.29
	CCA (CANOCO)	< 0.001	0.93	0.29
alkalinity	clusters	< 0.001	0.79	27
	DECORANA	< 0.001	0.75	27
	CCA (CANOCO)	< 0.001	0.88	29
chrysophytes ($n = 58$)				
pH	CCA (CANOCO)	< 0.001	0.74	0.35
alkalinity	CCA (CANOCO)	< 0.001	0.62	138

[a] Probability that null hypothesis (Ho) is true.

Microfossil stratigraphies

In the following text, a pH value in parentheses following a diatom taxon is its abundance weighted mean pH in the calibration data set. Major shifts in diatom assemblages in the Mud Pond cores occur around and above 8 cm (figure 2). Minor peaks at 7 cm (*ca.* 1900) of *Melosira distans* var. *distans* (5.75) and *Fragilaria virescens* (6.00) may be responses to lake enrichment from

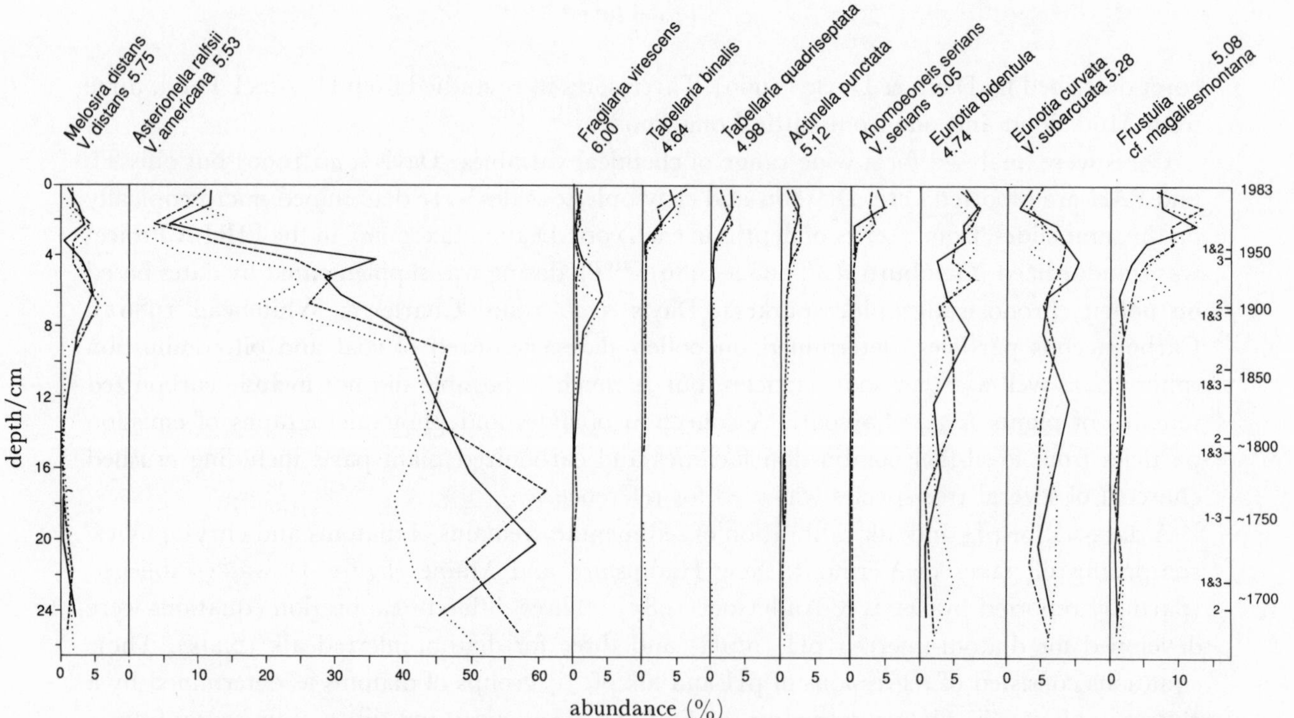

Figure 2. Percent abundance of common and informative diatom taxa in Mud Pond core 2 (master core) (——) and in cores 1 (-----) and 3 (· · · ·) (three replicate cores). The abundance weighted mean pH in the calibration data set is given for each taxon. Stratigraphy is presented on a scale of equal increments of depth (cm). Dates (1983, 1950, 1900, etc.) along that depth scale for each numbered core are given by tick marks on the right. Dates are based on ^{210}Pb (to *ca.* 1850) and pollen chronostratigraphic markers (to *ca.* 1800), and for older–deeper sediment on down-core linear extrapolation of the slope of the 1850–1800 part of the date–depth curve (Davis *et al.* 1990).

selective logging of the catchment at that time. Above 6 cm (*ca.* 1920) the changes indicate an acidification. Taxa associated with water pH of *ca.* 4.5 to 5.0 increase, and taxa associated with water pH of *ca.* 5.3 to 6.0 decrease. For example, the benthic *Tabellaria binalis* (4.64) and *T. quadriseptata* (4.98) increase and the planktonic *Asterionella ralfsii* var. *americana* (5.53) decrease. Chrysophyte shifts (Smol & Dixit 1990) support the diatom indications of a recent acidification. Most notable are the replacements of *Mallomonas crassisquama* and *M. allorgei* by *M. acaroides* var. *muskokana*, *M. hamata* and *M. punctifera*.

Microfossil stratigraphies for Haystack Pond also suggest a recent acidification (Davis *et al.* 1990). At that lake, *Tabellaria flocculosa* strain 3 (5.73) (Koppen 1975) is largely replaced by *T. quadriseptata* (4.98) and *Eunotia pectinalis* var. *minor* (5.00). Chrysophyte counts are overwhelmingly dominated (more than 90%) by one taxon (*M. crassisquama*) and are not useful for pH and alk inference. Microfossil assemblages at Little Long Pond exhibit little change above 40 cm (since *ca.* 1700) except that in the top few centimetres, *Cyclotella stelligera* (6.6) and *Tabellaria flocculosa* strain 3P (6.30) are partially replaced by more acidophilic forms including *Melosira perglabra* (5.6).

Different cores from the same lake

The diatom stratigraphies of Mud Pond cores 1, 2 and 3 are very similar to each other (figure 2). As for diatoms, stratigraphic replication of Mud Pond chrysophytes is very good (Smol & Dixit 1990). At Haystack Pond, stratigraphic replication for diatoms and chrysophytes is not as precise as at Mud Pond but is still quite good (Davis *et al.* 1990; Smol & Dixit 1990).

Replication of DIpH based on the same equation applied to multiple cores from the same lake is excellent for both absolute pH and chronology of change (figure 3). For Haystack Pond and Mud Pond, pre-1900 inferences for the same date generally agree to within 0.1–0.2 IpH units. For post-1900 at Haystack Pond, IpH ranges more widely (to about 0.3 unit), but acidification is indicated in all cases. Replication of CIpH at Mud Pond is about as precise as for DIpH.

Core replication for DIalk appears to be less precise than for DIpH (figure 3). Nevertheless, replicate Ialk values for the same date generally have small differences (less than or about 15 μeq l^{-1}); post-1900 trends are in good agreement, with certain exceptions, for example, slopes for CCA at Haystack Pond and variance for cluster at Mud Pond. Core replication of CIalk at Mud Pond is also very good.

Different equations applied at the same lake

For pre-1900, DIpH based on the three equations at the same lake ranges only about 0.1 units, except for Little Long Pond where the CCA equation gives values about 0.2 units higher than the other two equations (figure 3). Post-1900 inferences range slightly more widely. Trends are similar to each other but are dampened for DECORANA IpH (especially at Haystack Pond). The three equations for DIalk give results for pre-1900 at Haystack Pond that vary little (less than or about 10 μeq l^{-1}). At Mud Pond, DECORANA DIalk is about 20 μeq l^{-1} higher than cluster DIalk. Pre-1900 DIalk at Little Long Pond ranges a little more widely: about 20–30 μeq l^{-1}. Post-1900 trends in DIalk at each lake are similar for the three equations, except

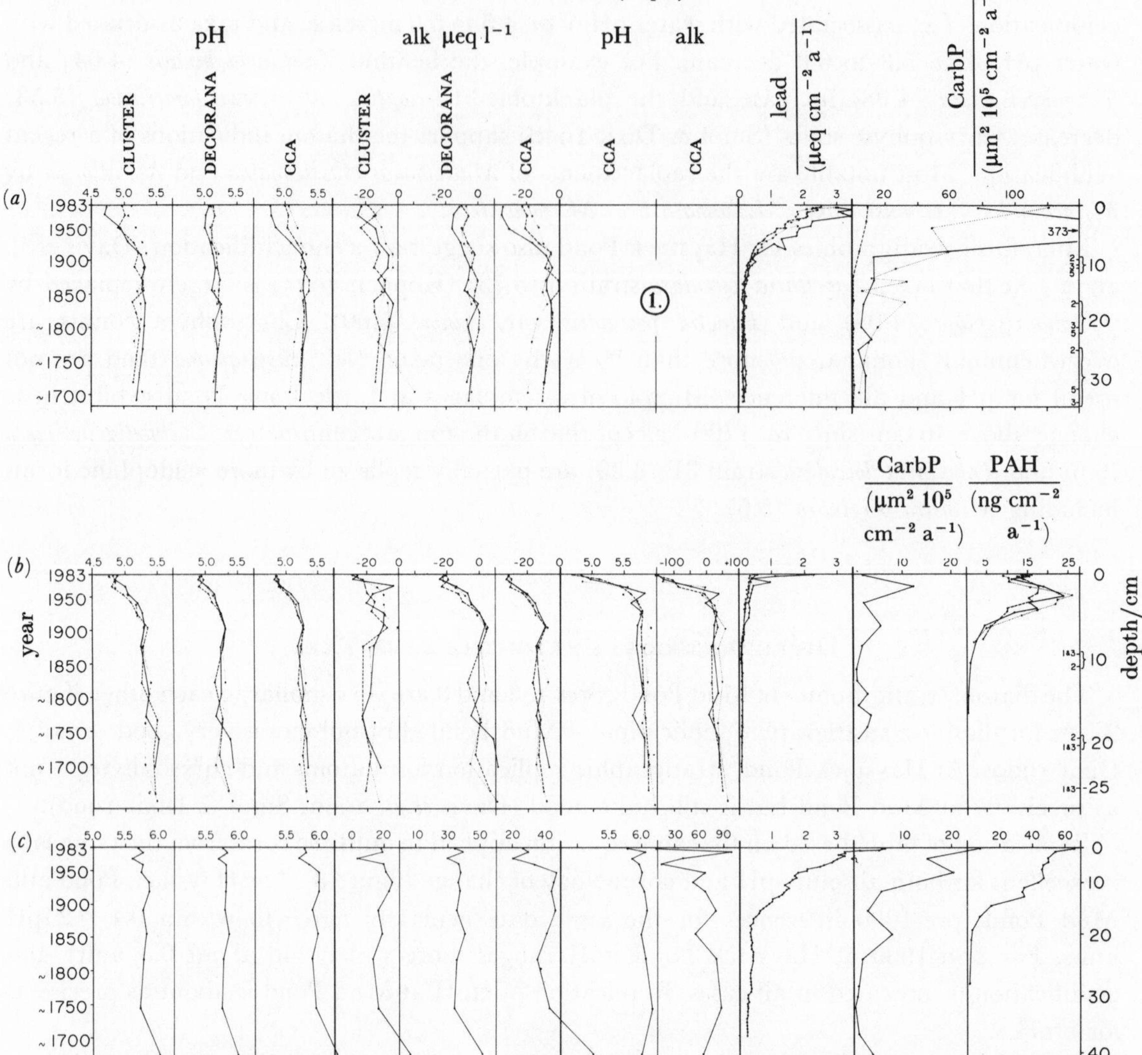

FIGURE 3. Replicate core pH and alkalinity reconstructions for (*a*) Haystack Pond and (*b*) Mud Pond, and single core reconstructions for (*c*) Little Long Pond based on diatoms and scaled chrysophytes and on three calibration approaches (CLUSTER, DECORANA and CCA). Sedimentary indicators of fossil fuel combustion: lead, carbonaceous particles (CarbP) and polycyclic aromatic hydrocarbons (PAH) are given for comparison. Stratigraphy is presented on a scale of equal increments of time (year date) (see legend of figure 2 for dating techniques). Depths (10 cm, 20 cm, etc.) along that time scale for each numbered core are indicated by tick marks on the right. ((*a*), (——) core 5, (----) core 3, (····) core 2; (*b*), (——) core 2, (----) core 1, (····) core 3; (*c*) core 2 only; (1.), overwhelming dominance by *Mallomonas crassisquama* (unsuitable for pH and alk inferences).)

are most invariable for DECORANA at Haystack Pond, most variable for CLUSTER at Mud Pond, and most pronounced for CCA at Little Long Pond.

DIATOMS VERSUS CHRYSOPHYTES

At Mud Pond, diatom analysis leads to slightly different conclusions than chrysophyte analysis (figure 3). Pre-1900 DIpH and DIalk values are lower than CI values; and post-1960 DIalk is much higher than CIalk. The CIalk of about -150 μeq l^{-1} derived from the surface sediment sample is inconsistent with the mean measured alk of -23 μeq l^{-1}, whereas diatom IALK based on surface sediment is in good agreement with the measured value (table 1). Statistics for CIalk CCA equations are poorer than for the diatom alk equations (table 2). Although the direction and timing of change of CIpH and CIalk are the same as for the diatom inferences, the amount of change is greater for chrysophytes. At Little Long Pond, CIpH is in fair agreement with DIpH, but Ialk values are somewhat higher when based on chrysophytes. At Little Long Pond, CIalk displays more extreme responses (than DIalk) to shifts in individual taxa.

pH AND ALKALINITY OF THE LAKES DURING THE PAST 300 YEARS

These three lakes had low pH and alk in the 18th and 19th centuries, before any suggestion of anthropogenic acidification (figure 3). The pre-1900 DIpH is about 5.2–5.3 and DIalk about 0 to -20 μeq l^{-1} for Haystack Pond and Mud Pond and, respectively, about 5.7–6.0 and about +20 to 70 for Little Long Pond. A rapid acidification started between 1920 and 1930 in Haystack Pond and in Mud Pond. Little Long Pond changed little in the three centuries covered by the core, although there is some suggestion of slight acidification starting about 1950.

The aforementioned recent acidifications of Haystack Pond and Mud Pond are correlated with steep increases in sedimentary indicators of fossil fuel combustion (Pb, CarbP, PAH; see figure 3).

Discussion

These results are encouraging in regard to the use of single cores from the deep part of lakes. In Mud Pond and in Haystack Pond, microfossil stratigraphies and environmental inferences from different cores are very similar. These results say nothing about differences that would arise from coring over wide ranges of water depths in the same lake. That consideration is somewhat peripheral here because for both the calibrations and the palaeolimnological reconstructions only deepest-water sediments were used. It has not been our intention to reconstruct whole lake communities of siliceous algae. If one wished to do so, the study of cores from a wide range of water depths would be necessary. See Frey (1988) regarding differential representation of littoral versus pelagial remains in sediments.

These results demonstrate the comparability of different well-established calibration approaches for pH and alk inference. Although only three different approaches (equations) for each parameter were used, the results do suggest that conclusions would only occasionally be misleading because of the use of different calibration approaches. Comparisons of results from different lakes where different calibration approaches were used, both within and between regions, have been extensively and effectively made in the review papers cited in the Introduction. However, in the present study a few differences between inferences from different equations did arise. Those differences do point to the desirability in comparative studies of using the same calibration approach as much as possible.

Some differences arose at Mud Pond between the diatom and chrysophyte reconstructions. Although the timing and direction of inferred change (acidification) in the 20th century were the same regardless of the algal group used, the absolute IpH and Ialk differed. Given the greater amounts of variance explained (r^2) and smaller standard errors of the diatom equations (table 2), we place more confidence in them at this time. Apart from any statistical or methodological considerations, however, we would expect to encounter real differences between inferences based on the two groups. In lakes, diatom taxa characteristic of both planktonic–pelagial and benthic–littoral communities occur. However, in most strongly acidic (pH less than or about 5.0) lakes, planktonic diatom taxa are virtually absent. On the other hand, scaled chrysophytes occur only in the planktonic community and may be abundant in strongly acidic lakes. The seasonality of these groups also differs. Although the use of combined diatom–chrysophyte calibrations can be more appropriate for some inferences (Charles & Smol 1988), it may also be desirable to carry out separate diatom and chrysophyte reconstructions for the different habitat information they may reveal.

Haystack Pond and Mud Pond started to acidify rapidly around 1920–1930 during the period of maximum sulphur emission in northeastern United States (Husar 1986). Close correlation of the acidifications with sedimentary indicators of fallout of pollutants from fossil fuel combustion, and the usual association of these pollutants with acid deposition, suggest that the acidifications are due to acid deposition. Absence of correlated changes in land-use and any substantial changes in vegetation and soils in the catchments largely eliminate such possible causes of acidification.

The catchment of Little Long Pond includes that of Mud Pond. The land-use history of the combined catchment has been approximately uniform. However, Little Long Pond has not undergone a major anthropogenic acidification. The Mud Pond catchment (24% of Little Long's) has steeper slopes and thinner soils. Water residence time in Mud Pond is about a tenth of that in Little Long Pond. For these reasons, Mud Pond responds more directly to rain-water chemistry and acid deposition than Little Long Pond.

Haystack Pond and Mud Pond had inferred pH values of less than 5.5 and lacked alk before anthropogenic acidification. Little Long Pond has not had quite as low a pH, and has had positive, but very low, alk values during the period of the reconstruction. These water chemistries, and the characteristics of the catchments, have made these lakes very sensitive to acidification by acid deposition (Little Long Pond least so). More than 50% of the lakes that have been shown by palaeolimnological study to have undergone a recent rapid acidification were in this extremely acid-sensitive condition before acidification (Charles *et al.* 1989).

The three lakes studied here are far more sensitive to acid deposition than is typical for lakes in northern New England. Although many hundreds of lakes (and catchments) in the region have low acid neutralizing capacity (Brakke *et al.* 1988), only a very small percentage (probably less than 1%) of these have the extreme characteristics of these three lakes and their catchments. This is not to say that fallout of air pollutants is not having detrimental effects on the larger population of lakes.

We thank D. F. Charles for expediting many aspects of this study, S. A. Norton and J. S. Kahl for providing data on lead and for ^{210}Pb dating, and R. Hites for PAH data. S. A. Norton, R. W. Battarbee and I. Renberg provided helpful suggestions for the manuscript. The work was part of the PIRLA Project supported by the Electric Power Research Institute (U.S.A.).

References

Battarbee, R. W. & Charles, D. F. 1987 The use of diatom assemblages in lake sediments as a means of assessing the timing, trends, and causes of lake acidification. *Prog. phys. Geog.* **11**, 552–580.

Battarbee, R. W., Smol, J. P. & Meriläinen, J. 1986 Diatoms as indicators of pH: an historical review. In *Diatoms and lake acidity* (ed. J. P. Smol, R. W. Battarbee, R. B. Davis & J. Meriläinen), pp. 5–16. Dordrecht: Dr W. Junk.

Brakke, D. F., Landers, D. H. & Eilers, J. M. 1988 Chemical and physical characteristics of lakes in the northeastern United States. *Environ. Sci. Tech.* **22**, 155–163.

Camburn, K. E., Kingston, J. C. & Charles, D. F. (eds.) 1984–1986 PIRLA diatom iconograph. Rep. 3, PIRLA unpublished report series. Bloomington, Indiana: Department of Biology, University of Indiana.

Charles, D. F. & Norton, S. A. 1986 Paleolimnological evidence for trends in atmospheric deposition of acids and metals. In *Acid deposition: long-term trends* (ed. U.S. National Research Council), pp. 335–505. Washington, D.C.: National Academy Press.

Charles, D. F. & Smol, J. P. 1988 New methods for using diatoms and chrysophytes to infer lake water pH in low alkalinity lakes. *Limnol. Oceanogr.* **33**, 1457–1462.

Charles, D. F. & Whitehead, D. R. 1986*a* The PIRLA project: paleolimnological investigation of recent lake acidification. *Hydrobiologia* **143**, 13–20.

Charles, D. F. & Whitehead, D. R. (eds.). 1986*b* Paleoecological investigation of recent lake acidification: methods and project description: interim report. *EPRI Research Project* 2174–10. Palo Alto, California: Electric Power Research Institute.

Charles, D. F., Battarbee, R. W., Renberg, I., van Dam, H. & Smol, J. P. 1989 Paleoecological analysis of lake acidification trends in North America and Europe using diatoms and chrysophytes. In *Advances in environmental Sciences vol.* 4. *Soils, aquatic processes, and lake acidification* (ed. S. A. Norton, S. E. Lindberg & A. L. Page), pp. 207–276. New York: Springer-Verlag.

Davis, R. B. 1987 Paleolimnological diatom studies of acidification of lakes by acid rain: an application of quaternary science. *Quat. Sci. Rev.* **6**, 147–163.

Davis, R. B. & Anderson, D. S. 1985 Methods of pH calibration of sedimentary diatom remains for reconstructing history of pH in lakes. *Hydrobiologia* **120**, 69–87.

Davis, R. B. & Doyle, R. W. 1969 A piston corer for upper sediment in lakes. *Limnol. Oceanogr.* **14**, 643–648.

Davis, R. B., Anderson, D. S., Norton, S. A., Kahl, J. S., Whiting, M. C., Ford, M., Dixit, S. S. & Smol, J. P. 1990 Acidification of northern New England lakes. *J. Paleolimnol.* (In the press.)

Davis, R. B., Norton, S. A. & Hess, C. T. 1983 Paleolimnological reconstruction of the effects of atmospheric deposition of acids and heavy metals on the chemistry and biology of lakes in New England and Norway. *Hydrobiologia* **107**, 113–123.

Dixit, S. S., Smol, J. P., Davis, R. B. & Anderson, D. S. 1990 The utility of sedimentary chrysophyte remains for inferring lake water acidity in northern New England lakes. *J. Paleolimnol.* (In the press.)

Frey, D. G. 1988 Littoral and offshore communities of diatoms, cladocerans and dipterous larvae, and their interpretation in paleolimnology. *J. Paleolimnol.* **1**, 179–191.

Husar, R. 1986 Emissions of sulfur dioxide and nitrogen oxides and trends for eastern North America. In *Acid deposition: long-term trends* (ed. U.S. National Research Council), pp. 48–92. Washington, D.C.: National Academy Press.

Koppen, J. D. 1975 A morphological and taxonomic consideration of *Tabellaria* (Bacillariophyceae) for the north-central United States. *J. Phycol.* **11**, 236–244.

Norton, S. A., Davis, R. B. & Anderson, D. S. 1985 Distribution and extent of acid and metal precipitation in northern New England. *Final report, U.S. fish & wildlife service grant no.* 14-16-0009-79-040 Washington, D.C.: U.S. Department of the Interior.

Smol, J. P. & Dixit, S. S. 1990 Patterns of pH change inferred from chrysophycean microfossils in Adirondack and New England lakes. *J. Paleolimnol.* (In the press.)

ter Braak, C. J. F. 1987 CANOCO – a FORTRAN program for canonical community ordination by [partial]-[detrended] [canonical] correspondence analysis, principal components analysis and redundancy analysis (version 2.1). Wageningen, Netherlands: TNO Institute of Applied Computer Science.

Phil. Trans. R. Soc. Lond. B **327**, 423–425 (1990)
Printed in Great Britain

Lake acidification in Finland

By J. Meriläinen and P. Huttunen
University of Joensuu, P.O. Box 111, *SF*-80101 *Joensuu, Finland*

Although pioneer work on the relation between diatoms and the hydrogen-ion concentration of lakes was done in Finland, recent lake acidification studies did not begin until the 1980s. Now, pH reconstructions for about 50 lakes are available and approximately half of these show clear signs of acidification during the 20th century.

Almost every lake in Finland has been affected by human activity. Agriculture, especially slash-and-burn agriculture, has played an important role since the 16th century, and more recently problems from peatland drainage, fertilization of forest soil, and domestic and industrial waste-waters have occurred. The new threat is the increase in airborne pollution.

The seriousness of lake acidification was recognized in Finland later than in other Nordic countries. The Finnish government started a nationwide research programme on acidification in 1985. The final reports of the project will be published in 1990 but some of the conclusions are presented here.

Finland has not officially participated in international acidification projects, but the results of national investigations have been reported at several international scientific meetings, and the methods and results of earlier Finnish limnological and palaeolimnological projects have influenced the design of acidification projects in other countries. One such project was started in 1978 in eastern Finland on 151 lakes. The lake-water was sampled during the summer stagnation and autumn turnover period and the surface sediments were sampled in winter through the ice. More than 60 physical and chemical variables were measured from the lakes and their catchments. Following an earlier study (Meriläinen 1967) the main focus of this project was the relation between diatom assemblages of surface sediments and water chemistry (Meriläinen & Huttunen 1984; Huttunen & Meriläinen 1986*a*, *b*, *c*). The same chemistry data-set has been used to explore relations between water chemistry and also cladoceran remains (Cotten 1985; Huttunen *et al.* 1988), chrysophyte scales (Christie *et al.* 1988), and phytoplankton (Ilmavirta *et al.* 1984; Ilmavirta 1988; Ilmavirta & Huttunen 1989*a*, *b*, *c*). In addition, several multivariate methods have been adopted and tested (Oksanen *et al.* 1988; Oksanen & Huttunen 1989) to find suitable criteria for the ecological classification of lakes in Finland.

Tolonen & Jaakkola (1983) were the first to describe the recent acidification history of Finnish lakes. They showed that the pH of their three study sites had decreased between 1.1 and 1.5 pH units since about 1960. Later, Tolonen *et al.* (1986) studied 11 small lakes of which four indicated a clear recent acidification, and Simola *et al.* (1985) described the acidification history of three additional sites. Together with the results of the Finnish acidification project (Huttunen *et al.* 1989) the recent history of 50 small or medium-sized head-water lakes in different parts of Finland has been described. Twenty-three of the lakes had clearly acidified during this century, and the remaining sites were naturally acid or indicated some slight acidification (figure 1).

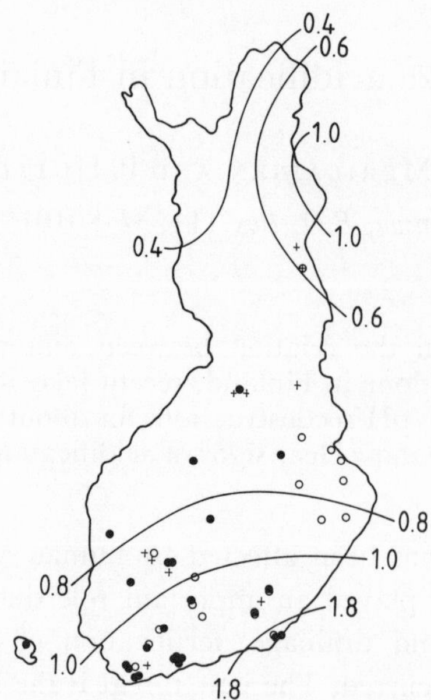

FIGURE 1. The sites studied in palaeolimnological investigations of recent lake acidification in Finland (Tolonen & Jaakkola 1983; Simola *et al.* 1985; Tolonen *et al.* 1986; Huttunen *et al.* 1989). Recently acidified lakes are indicated by (○), naturally acidic lakes (●) and lakes with no clear change (+). The sulphur deposition (in g m^{-2} a^{-1}) in 1985 is shown by isolines.

Unpublished modelling results from the MAGIC model showed the same trends as the diatom assemblages. Kamari (1985) estimated that the general trend of acidification in small, sensitive forest lakes in south Finland ranged from 500 to 100 μeq l^{-1} in alkalinity. Huttunen *et al.* (1989) have recently reported an even greater acidification than that indicated by chemical models, and they stressed the sensitivity of planktonic diatoms to acidification.

For natural reasons, most Finnish lakes are very vulnerable to acid deposition. Almost half of the study sites have lost a substantial portion of their buffering capacity during the last three decades. Though serious, recent acidification in Finland has not yet led to widespread damage, but the threat is real and almost all aquatic systems might be affected if acid deposition increases further.

Despite the clear link between acid deposition and lake acidification described above, future palaeolimnological research in Finland should be more focused on the causes of acidification. Only then can defence strategies against the acidification problem be effectively constructed. Representative reference areas would be needed, and, fortunately, they can still be found in the Komi region of northeast Europe.

REFERENCES

Cotten, C. 1985 Cladoceran assemblages related to lake conditions in eastern Finland. Ph.D. thesis, Biology Department, Indiana University, U.S.A.

Christie, C., Smol, J., Huttunen, P. & Meriläinen, J. 1988 Chrysophyte scales recorded from eastern Finland. *Hydrobiologia* **161**, 237–243.

Huttunen, P. & Meriläinen, J. 1986*a* Applications of multivariate techniques to infer limnological conditions from diatom assemblages. In *Diatoms and lake acidity* (ed. J. Smol, R. Battarbee, R. Davis & J. Meriläinen), pp. 201–211. Dordrecht: Dr W. Junk.

Huttunen, P. & Meriläinen, J. 1986*b* A comparison of different pH indices derived from diatom assemblages. *Univ. Joensuu, Publication of Karelian Institute* **79**, 41–46.

Huttunen, P. & Meriläinen, J. 1986*c* Diatom response to pH and humic matter of the water. *Univ. Joensuu, Publication of Karelian Institute* **79**, 47–54.

Huttunen, P., Meriläinen, J., Cotten, C. & Rönkkö, J. 1988 Attempts to reconstruct lake water pH and colour from sedimentary diatoms and Cladocera. *Verh. int. Verein. Limnol.* **23**, 870–873.

Huttunen, P., Kenttämies, K., Liehu, A., Liukkonen, M., Nuotio, T., Sandman, O. & Turkia, J. 1989 Palaeoecological evaluation of the recent acidification of susceptible lakes in Finland. In *Acidification in Finland* (ed. P. Kauppi, K. Kenttämies & P. Anttila). Berlin: Springer-Verlag. (In the press.)

Ilmavirta, V. 1988 Phytoplankton and their ecology in Finnish brown-water lakes. *Hydrobiologia* **161**, 255–270.

Ilmavirta, V. & Huttunen, P. 1989*a* Phytoplankton communities in 151 small lakes of different trophic status and with different forms of land-use parameters in their catchment areas. In *Conservation and management of lakes* (ed. S. Salanki & S. Herodek), pp. 437–445. Budapest: Akademiai Kiado.

Ilmavirta, V. & Huttunen, P. 1989*b* Water chemistry and phytoplankton communities in acidic clear- and brown-water lakes in eastern Finland. *Wat. Air Soil Pollut.* (In the press.)

Ilmavirta, V. & Huttunen, P. 1989*c* Characterization of 151 small lakes in eastern Finland based on their water chemistry, land-use and phytoplankton communities. *Limnologica* (Berlin). (In the press.)

Ilmavirta, K., Huttunen, P. & Meriläinen, J. 1984 Phytoplankton in 151 eastern Finnish lakes: species composition and its relations to the water chemistry. *Verh. int. Verein. Limnol.* **22**, 822–828.

Kämäri, J. 1985 A quantitative assessment of lake acidification in Finland. *Aqua Fenn.* **15**, 11–20.

Meriläinen, J. 1967 The diatom flora and hydrogen ion concentration of the water. *Ann. Bot. Fenn.* **4**, 77–104.

Meriläinen, J. & Huttunen, P. 1984 Ecological interpretations of diatom assemblages by means of two-way indicator species analysis (Twinspan). In *Proceedings of the seventh international diatom symposium* (ed. D. G. Mann), pp. 385–391. Koenigstein: Otto Keoltz.

Oksanen, J., Läärä, E., Huttunen, P. & Meriläinen, J. 1988 Estimation of pH optima and tolerances of diatoms in lake sediments by the methods of weighted averaging, least squares and maximum likelihood, and their use for the prediction of lake acidity. *J. Paleolimnol.* **1**, 39–49.

Oksanen, J. & Huttunen, P. 1989 Finding a common ordination for several data sets: characterization of lakes by chemical and biological traits. *Vegetatio.* (In the press.)

Simola, H., Kenttämies, K. & Sandman, O. 1985 The recent pH-history of some headwater and seepage lakes, studied by means of diatom analysis of ^{210}Pb dated sediment cores. *Aqua Fenn.* **15**, 245–255.

Tolonen, K. & Jaakkola, T. 1983 History of lake acidification and air pollution studied on sediments in South Finland. *Ann. Bot. Fenn.* **20**, 57–78.

Tolonen, K., Liukkonen, M., Harjula, R. & Pätilä, A. 1986 Acidification of small lakes in Finland by sedimentary diatom and chrysophycean remains. In *Diatoms and lake acidity* (ed. J. Smol, R. Battarbee, R. Davis & J. Meriläinen), pp. 169–199. Dordrecht: Dr. W. Junk.

Phil. Trans. R. Soc. Lond. B **327**, 427–433 (1990)
Printed in Great Britain

Post-1970 water-chemistry changes and palaeolimnology of several acidified upland lakes in the U.K.

By R. J. Flower[1], N. G. Cameron[1], N. Rose[1], S. C. Fritz[2], R. Harriman[3] and A. C. Stevenson[4]

[1] *Palaeoecology Research Unit, Department of Geography, University College, London WC1H 0AP, U.K.*

[2] *Limnological Research Center, University of Minnesota, Minneapolis, Minnesota* 55455. *U.S.A.*

[3] *Freshwater Fisheries Laboratory, Department of Agriculture and Fisheries for Scotland, Pitlochry PH16 5LB, U.K.*

[4] *Department of Geography, University of Newcastle upon Tyne NE1 7RU, U.K.*

Responses of four lakes to post-1970 changes in acid deposition, afforestation and liming are examined by using water quality measurements and palaeolimnological analysis. pH and non-marine sulphate concentrations at an undisturbed site approximately parallel trends in precipitation and indicate that lake water quality has improved since the late-1970s as atmospheric S emissions have declined. Carbonaceous particle contamination of the lake also declines in this period but diatom analysis shows that the ecological response to these changes are as yet small. However, at a similar but recently afforested site, major changes in sedimentary diatoms have occurred and we argue that fertilizer leaching is the cause. At the two limed sites the diatom response is proportional to liming intensity but at neither site has the pre-acidification diatom flora been re-established.

Introduction

Many upland soft-water lakes in the U.K. are now acidified by atmospheric pollution (Battarbee *et al.* 1988*a*). Recent acidification of sensitive sites typically began in the mid-19th century as industrialization and consequent sulphur oxide (SO_x) and nitrogen oxide (NO_x) emissions increased. Since the early 1970s, however, U.K. atmospheric sulphur emission has declined by about 30% (Barrett *et al.* 1987) and has led to reduced acidity in Scottish lakes (Battarbee *et al.* 1988*b*). Nevertheless, any improvement at sites remote from emission sources will be small or unsustained until emissions are further reduced (Cosby *et al.* 1986). Where rapid recovery of lakes is desired, liming has been initiated (see, for example, Underwood *et al.* (1987)) but, despite reducing acidity, further ecosystem disturbance can result (Hultberg & Andersson 1982). Other catchment management changes indirectly influence acidified lakes and afforestation methods can both exacerbate water acidification (Harriman & Morrison 1982) and increase nutrient supply (Gibson 1976).

Here, we examine responses of four acidified U.K. lakes, three in southwest Scotland and one in Mid-Wales, to contrasting post-1970 external changes. The Round Loch of Glenhead (RLGH) is located in an undisturbed peatland catchment where only sulphur deposition has changed significantly in the past two decades. At nearby Loch Grannoch an additional change has been extensive catchment afforestation in the 1960s and 1970s. Palaeolimnological techniques and water quality measurements are used to assess responses of both sites to recent changes in precipitation quality and land-use. At the former site, carbonaceous-particle analysis of sediment was used to infer changes in atmospheric contamination. Loch Fleet and Llyn Hir (Mid-Wales) were treated with 362 tonnes and less than 5 tonnes of limestone in 1986 and 1985, respectively (Brown *et al.* 1988; Underwood *et al.* 1987); the ecological response to liming is assessed by diatom analysis. A further 83 tonnes of limestone were applied to the Loch Fleet catchment in 1987.

Study procedure

Short sediment cores were collected from each of the four lakes between 1986 and 1988; sampling procedures follow Stevenson *et al.* (1987). Cores were dated by comparison with previous ^{210}Pb-dated cores from each site (Fritz *et al.* 1986; Flower *et al.* 1987; Battarbee *et al.* 1988*a*; Anderson *et al.* 1986), either by direct correlation of sediment accumulation rates or at the afforested sites where rates vary, by biostratigraphic correlation. Diatom analysis (Battarbee 1986) was done on all four cores and diatom data are summarized into pH preference groups. Historical pH values and time-tracks of floristic change were produced by numerical analysis by using mainly canonical correspondence analysis (CCA) (ter Braak 1986). Carbonaceous particle analysis of the RLGH core followed Rose (1989). Water-chemistry determinations used standard methods (Harriman *et al.* 1987). Values for pH and non-marine sulphate concentration in precipitation (at Eskdalemuir, 80 km east of the Scottish sites) were supplied by Dr J. G. Irwin.

Table 1. Annual precipitation-weighted mean pH and non-marine sulphate concentrations in precipitation for Eskdalemuir 1973–1987, annual mean of measured pH values and non-marine sulphate concentrations for the Round Loch of Glenhead (unafforested) and Loch Grannoch (afforested), where $n = 5$–12

(Water pH values calculated from sedimentary diatoms by using multiple regression (MR) (Flower 1986) and weighted averaging (WA) (Birks *et al.*, this symposium) methods. Sulphate concentrations (μeq l^{-1}) are in parentheses.)

		Round Loch of Glenhead			Loch Grannoch		
			pH reconstructed			pH reconstructed	
year	pH precipitation	pH measured	MR	WA	pH measured	MR	WA
1988	4.6 (32)	4.92 (66)	—	—	4.73 (92)	4.7	4.66
1987	4.7 (30)	4.95 (68)	—	—	4.84 (97)	—	—
1986	4.7 (33)	4.78 (80)	—	—	4.59 (122)		
1985	4.7 (32)	4.87 (104)	—	—	4.67 (128)	—	—
1984	4.7 (33)	4.77 (95)	4.7	4.73	4.71 (139)	4.6	4.63
1983	4.7 (34)	—	—	—	—	—	—
1982	4.6 (35)	4.70 (—)	—	—	4.47 (143)	—	—
1981	4.4 (43)	—	—	—	4.78 (149)	—	—
1980	4.2 (53)	—	—	—	—	—	—
1979	4.4 (48)	4.69 (111)	—	—	4.64 (152)	—	—
1978	4.5 (54)	4.65 (99)	—	—	4.60 (133)	4.7	4.72
1977	4.4 (—)	—	—	—	—	—	—
1976	4.1 (—)[a]	—	4.7	4.75	—	—	—
1975	4.3 (49)	—	—	—	—	—	—
1974	4.4 (41)	—	—	—	—	5.3	5.28
1973	4.4 (52)	—	—	—	—	—	—
1972	—	—	—	—	—	—	—
1971	—	—	4.8	4.76	—	—	—

[a] Only pH measured in this year and this value is unverified.

Atmospheric deposition

Round Loch of Glenhead

Annual mean weighted pH and non-marine sulphate concentration in precipitation and in lake water at RLGH are given in table 1; pH in precipitation and lake water have both increased by between 0.2 and 0.3 units since the 1970s and sulphate has decreased by 40% and 33%, respectively. Note, the concentration of sulphate in precipitation is about half of that in lake water.

The diatom pH preference diagram (figure 1*a*) constructed from a 1988 core shows a strong shift to acidophilous and acidobiontic forms beginning between 9 and 7 cm depth as the lake acidified. Diatom changes in the post-1970's core section (top 1.5 cm) are small, acidobiontic

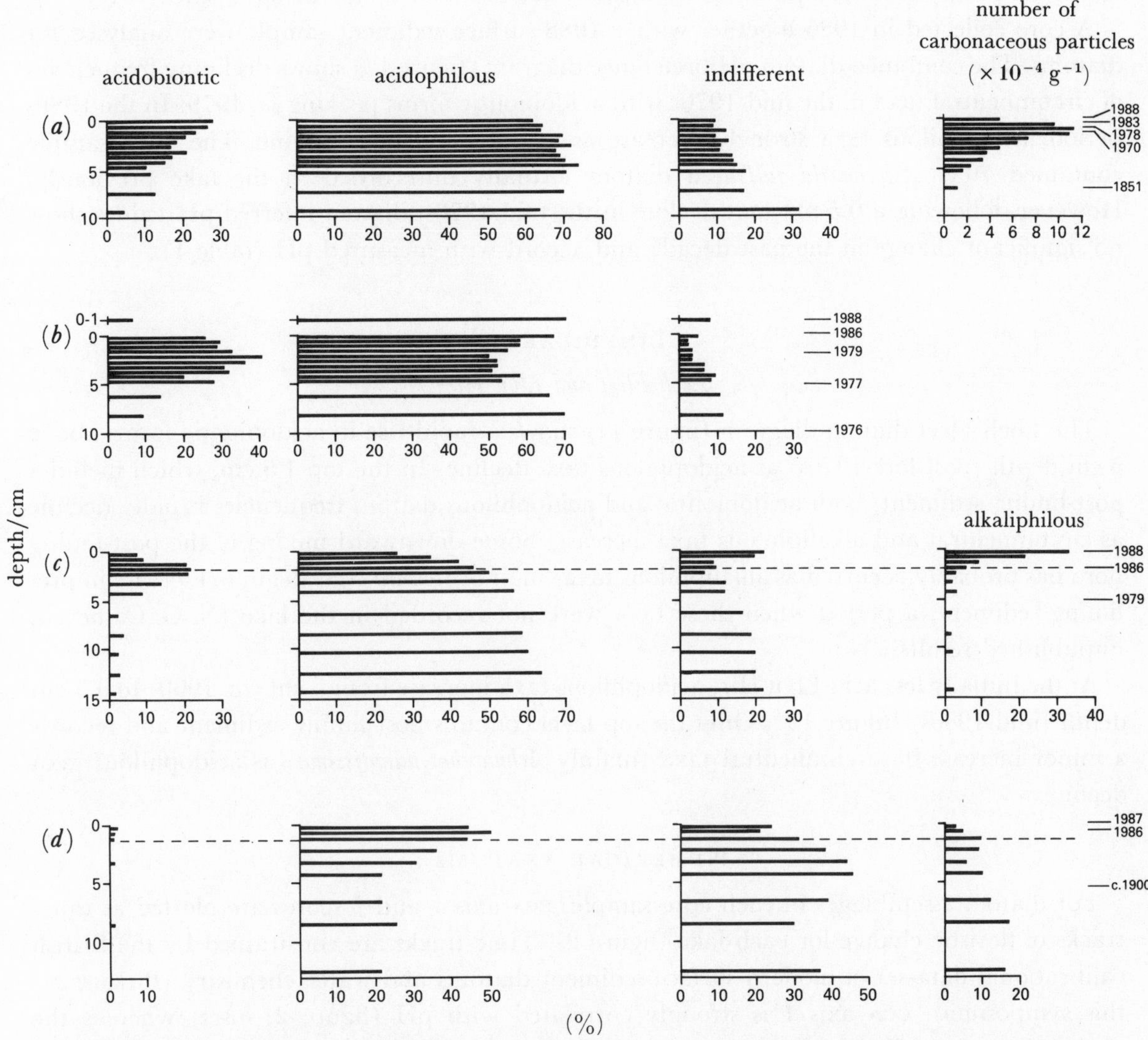

Figure 1. Frequency profiles of diatom pH preference groups in dated short cores from four acidified U.K. lakes. Broken lines on the latter two diagrams indicate time of liming. Note that group frequencies in a 1988 surface sediment sample (0.0–1.0 cm) are added to the top of the Loch Grannoch 1986 core diagram. The carbonaceous particle profile for the Round Loch of Glenhead core is shown upper right; (*a*) Round Loch of Glenhead 1988, (*b*) Loch Grannoch 1986 and 1988, (*c*) Loch Fleet 1988, (*d*) Llyn Hir 1987.

and indifferent (= circumneutral); diatoms slightly increase in abundance as acidophilous taxa decline. The diatom-inferred pH values of 4.7–4.8 for the period are marginally lower than corresponding measured values (table 1).

The carbonaceous particle profile for RLGH (figure 1*a*) shows low concentrations (less than 2×10^4 g^{-1}) in sediment below 5 cm depth (pre-1910). The concentration increases strongly to peak values between 1 and 2 cm depth (1960's period) before declining in the top 1 cm (post late-1970s).

Afforestation

Loch Grannoch

Precipitation data for Loch Grannoch are as for RLGH and measured pH and non-marine sulphate concentrations are shown in table 1. Annual mean pH of lake water has increased by about 0.2 pH units and sulphate concentration has declined by about 30% since 1978.

A core collected in 1986 together with a 1988 surface sediment sample were analysed for diatoms. The combined diatom pH preference diagram (figure 1*b*) shows declining frequencies of circumneutral taxa in the mid-1970s with acidobiontic forms peaking *ca.* 1979. In the 1980s period, acidophilous taxa strongly increase as acidobiontic taxa decline. The 1988 sample contained 70% *Asterionella ralfsii*, a diatom virtually unrecorded in the lake previously. However, following a 0.5 pH unit decline in the mid-1970s, diatom-inferred pH values show no significant change in the past decade and accord with measured pH (table 1).

Limed lakes

Loch Fleet and Llyn Hir

The Loch Fleet diatom diagram (figure 1*c*) shows a rapid rise in acidobiontic forms above 5 cm depth (post late-1970s) as acidophilous taxa decline. In the top 1.5 cm, which includes post-liming sediment, both acidobiontic and acidophilous diatom frequencies rapidly decline as circumneutral and alkaliphilous taxa increase. Some downward mixing of the post-liming flora has probably occurred as alkaliphilous taxa (mainly *Synedra acus*) begin to increase in pre-liming sediment, a period when these taxa were not recorded in the lake (N. G. Cameron, unpublished results).

At the initially less acid Llyn Hir, acidophilous taxa increase from 5 cm (*ca.* 1900) to 0.5 cm depth (mid-1980s) (figure 1*d*). Only the top level contains post-liming sediment and records a minor increase in circumneutral taxa (mainly *Achnanthes minutissima*) as acidophilous taxa decline.

Numerical analysis

For diatom assemblages in each core sample, CCA axis 1 and 2 scores are plotted as time-tracks of floristic change for each lake (figure 2). Time-tracks are constrained by the British calibrational data-set of modern surface-sediment diatoms and water chemistry (Birks *et al.*, this symposium). CCA axis 1 is strongly correlated with pH (figure 2, inset) whereas the environmental gradients of axis 2 are unclear. The RLGH time-track trends across axis 1 reflecting a strong floristic response to acidification since *ca.* 1850 A.D. The analysis indicates several small pH reversals, the most recent of which concerns the top sample, representing 1980–1988. The Loch Grannoch time-track follows a similar trend but, being a core with a

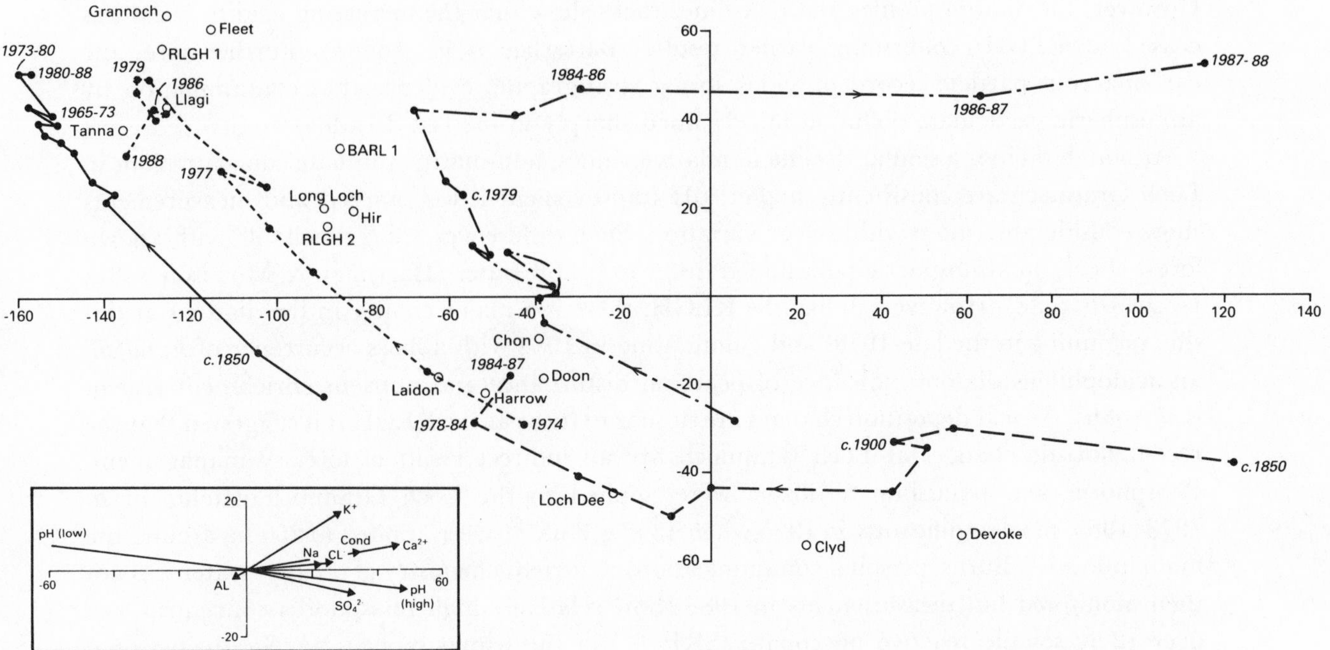

FIGURE 2. Canonical correspondence analysis (CCA) of diatom assemblages in the Round Loch of Glenhead, Loch Grannoch, Loch Fleet and Llyn Hir cores. Time-tracks of floristic change are constructed by using CCA axis 1 and 2 sample scores and are constrained by modern U.K. chemistry (see inset) and diatom samples (o), which approximately defines axis 1 as the pH axis (see text). Note, RLGH axis 1 scores are offset by −30 to improve diagram clarity. Time-tracks for the Loch Grannoch and Loch Fleet cores are constructed by using several lower levels in addition to those indicated in Figure 1; (----), Loch Grannoch; (—–—), Llyn Hir; (—·—) Loch Fleet; (——), Round Loch of Glenhead.

much faster accumulation rate, it spans little more than a decade. There is a single point reversal *ca.* 1977 followed by a clear change in trend direction in 1979 as samples begin tracking down axis 2. Loch Fleet also trends across axis 1 as the lake acidified but circumneutral and alkaliphilous diatoms in the early 1980s sediment cause sample scores to reverse on axis 1, indicating a marked increase in lake pH. The reversal apparently occurs several years before liming and probably reflects down-mixing of circumneutral and alkaliphilous diatoms in the sediment. The Loch Hir time-track shows a clear acidification response from *ca.* 1850 A.D. but here the environmental variables associated with axis 2 have less influence. Although the most recent sample (1984–1987) includes the liming period, the score shows only a minor reverse on axis 1, the floristic response to liming being much less marked than in Loch Fleet.

DISCUSSION

Water-chemistry results for the RLGH clearly demonstrate that the lake has responded to post-1970 changes in precipitation chemistry. Both measured acidity and sulphate concentrations have significantly declined in lake water, and during the summer of 1988 the pH exceeded 5 for the first time since measurements began. The higher annual mean pH values recorded in 1986–1988, compared with 1978–1979, reflect higher winter pH values during the most recent period. This amelioration of pH in the winter, rather than in the diatom growing season, could partially explain the small diatom response to decreased mean acidity.

However, the diatom profiles and CCA time-tracks show that the increasing acidity trend has ceased at RLGH, confirming earlier results (Battarbee *et al.* 1988*b*). Furthermore, the carbonaceous particle record provides strong stratigraphic evidence that contamination by atmospheric particulate pollution has declined sharply in the last decade.

Although there is a similar decline in relative values, non-marine sulphate concentrations in Loch Grannoch are consistently higher, pH improvement is less marked and measurements show considerably more within-year variation. Such differences are reconcilable with known forest effects on atmospheric pollutant transfer to runoff water (Harriman & Morrison 1982; Unsworth 1984). However, unlike the RLGH, there is a major change in the diatoms at this site, beginning in the late-1970s and culminating in 1988 with a mass occurrence of *A. ralfsii*, an acidophilous diatom indicative of peatland disturbance and nutrient enrichment (Liehu *et al.* 1986). As acid deposition changes are similar to those at the RLGH it is suggested that the recent floristic changes at Loch Grannoch are an indirect result of forestry management. Phosphorus and potassium fertilizers were applied to the Loch Grannoch catchment in 1973–1985, most significantly in 1985 when 450 kg P ha^{-1}† were applied to 250 ha around the main inflow (A. Burns, personal communication). Nutrient chemistry of the lake water was not then monitored but measurements in 1988 show relatively high phosphorus concentrations, over 12 μg soluble reactive phosphate (SRP) l^{-1} in the winter months (A. Smith, personal communication). As fertilizer application to acid soils can cause significant SRP increases in surface water (Harriman 1978) it is likely that leached forest fertilizers have had a major effect on the diatom flora of this lake, despite little change in lake water pH.

Diatom changes and resulting CCA axis 1 scores clearly reflect the difference between intervention impacts at the two limed sites. The Loch Fleet catchment was limed disproportionately more heavily than was Llyn Hir and resulted in lake pH values much higher than in the past (cf. Anderson *et al.* 1986). The lake diatom flora is now dominated by taxa that were previously rare or absent. Liming of Llyn Hir was restricted to the open water and has resulted in the re-emergence of several diatoms common in the pre-acidification flora. However, a *Cyclotella* plankton has not been re-established at either limed site. Acidity mitigation measures are therefore only partially effective as pre-acidification diatom floras have not been restored. Despite claims that these lakes have now recovered and can support game fish, the structure of the ecosystem remains perturbed.

All four acidified lakes have responded to post-1970 external changes, but as yet there is no evidence of a strong positive ecological response to reduced sulphur emissions. Significant improvements in annual mean pH and non-marine sulphate concentration in RLGH and, to a lesser extent, in afforested Loch Grannoch parallel changes in precipitation chemistry and are considerably greater than average post-1970 improvements found in acid Norwegian lakes (Henriksen *et al.* 1988). Forestry practice, notably fertilizer additions, has had a greater ecological impact at Loch Grannoch than has any recent change in precipitation chemistry. Adding large quantities of lime to the terrestrial catchment of acidified Loch Fleet caused major changes in diatom communities leading to proliferation of new species rather than to re-establishment of the pre-acidification flora.

We thank Dr A. Smith for discussions concerning recent changes in Loch Grannoch, Dr J. G. Irwin for the precipitation data and Mr A. A. Burns for supplying forest management details. Dr R. W. Battarbee kindly commented upon and improved the manuscript.

† 1 ha = 10^4 m^2.

References

Anderson, N. J., Battarbee, R. W., Appleby, P. G., Stevenson, A. C., Oldfield, F., Darley, J. & Glover, G. 1986 *Palaeolimnological evidence for the acidification of Loch Fleet*. Palaeoecology Research Unit, University College London, Working paper no. 17.

Barret, C. F., Atkins, D. H. F., Cape, J. N., Crabtree, J., Davies, T. D., Derwent, R. G., Fisher, B. E. A., Fowler, D., Kallend, A. S., Martin, A., Scriven, R. A. & Irwin, J. G. 1987 *Acid deposition in the United Kingdom 1981–1985*. A second report of the United Kingdom Review Group on acid rain. Warren Spring Laboratory.

Battarbee, R. W. 1986 Diatom analysis. In *Handbook of Holocene palaeoecology and palaeohydrology* (ed. B. E. Berglund), pp. 527–570. Chichester: John Wiley.

Battarbee, R. W., Anderson, N. J., Appleby, P. G., Flower, R. J., Fritz, S. C., Haworth, E. Y., Higgitt, S., Kreiser, A., Munro, M. A. R., Natkanski, J., Oldfield, F., Patrick, S. T., Raven, P. J., Richardson, N., Rippey, B. & Stevenson, A. C. 1988*a* *Lake acidification in the United Kingdom 1800–1986: evidence from analysis of lake sediments*. London: ENSIS Publishing.

Battarbee, R. W., Flower, R. J., Stevenson, A. C., Jones, V. J., Harriman, R. & Appleby P. G. 1988*b* Diatom and chemical evidence of acidification of Scottish lochs. *Nature, Lond.* **332**, 530–532.

Brown, D. J. A., Howells, G. D., Dalziel, T. R. K. & Stewart, B. R. 1988 Loch Fleet – a research watershed liming project. *Wat. Air Soil Pollut.* **41**, 25–41.

Cosby, B. J., Whitehead, P. G. & Neale, R. 1986 A preliminary model of long-term changes in stream acidity in southwest Scotland. *J. Hydrol.* **84**, 381–401.

Flower, R. J. 1986 The relationship between surface sediment diatom assemblages and pH in 33 Galloway lakes: some regression methods for calculating pH and their application to sediment cores. *Hydrobiologia* **143**, 93–103.

Flower, R. J., Battarbee, R. W. & Appleby, P. G. 1987 The recent palaeolimnology of acid lakes in Galloway, south-west Scotland: diatom analysis, pH trends and the role of afforestation. *J. Ecol.* **75**, 797–824.

Fritz, S. C., Stevenson, A. C., Patrick, S. T., Appleby, P. G., Oldfield, F., Rippey, B., Darley, J. & Battarbee, R. W. 1986 *Palaeoecological evaluation of the recent acidification of Welsh lakes. 1. Llyn Hir, Dyfed*. Palaeoecology Research Unit, University College London, Research Paper no. 16.

Gibson, C. E. 1976 An investigation into the effects of forestry plantations on the water quality of upland reservoirs in Northern Ireland. *Wat. Res.* **10**, 995–998.

Harriman, R. 1978 Nutrient leaching from fertilized forest watersheds in Scotland. *J. appl. Ecol.* **15**, 933–942.

Harriman, R. & Morrison, B. R. S. 1982 Ecology of streams draining forested and non-forested catchments in an area of central Scotland subject to acid precipitation. *Hydrobiologia* **88**, 251–263.

Harriman, R., Morrison, B. R. S., Caines, L. A., Collen, P. & Watt, A. W. 1987 Long term changes in fish populations of acid streams in Galloway, south west Scotland. *Wat. Air Soil Pollut.* **32**, 89–112.

Henriksen, A., Lien, L., Traaen, T. S., Sevaldrud, I. S. & Brakke, D. F. 1988 Lake acidification in Norway – present and predicted chemical status. *Ambio* **17**, 259–266.

Hultberg, H. & Andersson, I. B. 1982 Liming of acid lakes; induced long-term changes. *Wat. Air Soil Pollut.* **18**, 311–331.

Liehu, A., Sandman, O. & Simola, H. 1986 Effects of peatbog ditching in lakes: problems in palaeolimnological interpretation. *Hydrobiologia* **143**, 417–424.

Rose, N. 1989 *A method for the extraction of carbonaceous particles from lake sediment*. Palaeoecology Research Unit, University College London. Research Paper no 33.

Stevenson, A. C., Patrick, S. T., Kreiser, A. & Battarbee, R. W. 1987 Palaeoecological evaluation of the recent acidification of susceptible lakes: methods utilized under DoE contract PECD7/7/139 and the Royal Society SWAP Project. Palaeoecology Research Unit, University College London, U.K. Research Paper no. 26.

ter Braak, C. J. F. 1986 Canonical Corespondence Analysis: a new eigenvector technique for multivariate direct gradient analysis. *Ecology* **67**, 1167–1179.

Underwood, J., Donald, A. P. & Stoner, J. H. 1987 Investigations into the use of limestone to combat acidification in two lakes in west Wales. *J. environ. Mgmt* **24**, 29–40.

Unsworth, M. H. 1984 Evaporation from forests in cloud enhances the effect of acid deposition. *Nature, Lond.* **312**, 262–264.

Phil. Trans. R. Soc. Lond. B **327**, 435–440 (1990)
Printed in Great Britain

Modelling long-term acidification: a comparison with diatom reconstructions and the implications for reversibility

By A. Jenkins[1], P. G. Whitehead[1], B. J. Cosby[2] and H. J. B. Birks[3]

[1] *Institute of Hydrology, Wallingford, Oxfordshire OX10 8BB, U.K.*

[2] *Department of Forestry and Environmental Studies, Duke University, Durham, North Carolina 22706, U.S.A.*

[3] *Botanical Institute, University of Bergen, Allégaten 41, N-5007 Bergen, Norway*

A model of long term acidification (MAGIC) is applied to a range of catchments in Scotland that are subject to different pollution inputs and land uses. The simulated historical trends in pH are compared with data from palaeolimnological reconstructions undertaken at the same sites. Both techniques produce similar historical acidification trends and, with some exceptions, closely match observed present day pH. The MAGIC model results indicate that pollution inputs and land-use, particularly afforestation, have significant effects on surface water acidification. Moreover, the model indicates that reversibility may be occurring at several sites. Reversibility of acidification is further explored by using the model in predictive mode under several scenarios for reduction deposition.

Introduction

In recent years many lakes and streams in upland Scotland have demonstrated increased surface water acidity (Harriman & Morrison 1981). This has been attributed to the effect of increased anthropogenic sulphur deposition since pre-industrial times in both moorland catchments and afforested systems (Flower *et al.* 1987). The timing of response of the surface water to increased input of anthropogenic sulphate is thought to be controlled by the physiochemical characteristics of the catchment, namely, bedrock, soils and vegetation. Evidence for the processes and mechanisms involved in the titration of acidity from catchment inputs to outputs is still being gathered, but a quantification of the change in water acidity and the timing of changes in acid status has been derived from two approaches: long-term hydrochemical simulation models and palaeolimnological reconstructions. The two approaches differ in that the palaeolimnological reconstruction may be viewed as a direct measure of a surrogate acidity indicator whereas the models, although having their roots in hydrochemical laws, draw largely on a conceptualized representation of the major processes thought to be operating, and so at best can only be regarded as a simplification of the catchment system. Given this situation, model hindcast simulations require validation against long-term water-quality data sets. Clearly, few data sets of sufficient time period exist with which to test and validate either approach but increased confidence in both techniques would be gained if the reconstructions from the two are found to be consistent. Furthermore, the international concern over the problem of surface water acidification and its ecological effects and a stated policy of promoting amelioration strategies (Mason & Seip 1985) demands that predictions of surface water quality are made to assess the ability of systems to reverse acidification under different emissions and land-use strategies.

We use the model of acidification of groundwater in catchments (MAGIC) to simulate historical water quality and to compare the pH reconstruction to those determined by diatom analysis of sediment cores from the same lake sites. Six sites are chosen to cover a range of deposition loadings, land-use and bedrock geology in Scotland (Battarbee & Renberg, this symposium). The results from the calibrated models are compared both historically and to present-day water chemistry; the models are run forward to assess reversibility under a range of scenarios for deposition reduction.

The study sites and data sources

The sites selected are Round Loch of Glenhead, Lochan Uaine, Loch Tinker, Loch Chon, Loch Doilet and Lochan Dubh (Battarbee & Renberg, this symposium). Rainfall amount and chemistry are taken, wherever possible, from nearby collectors operated by the Warren Springs Laboratory under the Department of the Environment monitoring network (Warren Spring Laboratory 1987). At L. Tinker and L. Uaine, because of the lack of a nearby D.O.E. collector, mean bulk precipitation data for 1987 for the L. Chon (Jenkins *et al.* 1989*a*) and Allt a Mharcaidh (Jenkins *et al.* 1988) catchments were used, respectively. Sea-salts dominate rainfall at the sites in the west and although sulphate concentrations are at a consistent level at all of the sites, rainfall quantity is substantially greater on the west coast thereby increasing the total loading. Mean present day observed water chemistry is taken from the SWAP Palaeolimnology Programme data-base (Munro *et al.*, this symposium).

To achieve a charge balance to both input and output it was necessary in some cases to add or subtract cations or anions. Where this was necessary concentrations of chloride or sodium, or both, were adjusted and the result of the changes generally improved the sea-salt ratio. In all cases, the changes implemented were within the annual variation in chemistry at each site.

Reconstruction techniques

Details of diatom analysis (Jones *et al.* and Kreiser *et al.*, this symposium), dating procedures (Appleby *et al.*, this symposium) and techniques for reconstructing historical pH (Birks *et al.*, this symposium) are fully documented in this volume. A full description of the MAGIC model is given by Cosby *et al.* (1985*a*, *b*, 1986) and details of the optimization and calibration procedure used for these applications are identical to those given in Jenkins and Cosby (1989). Partial pressure of CO_2 in soil and lake water was identical for all applications. Organic matter concentration in soil water was 100 mmol m^{-3} at all sites and proportional to measured total organic carbon (TOC) in the surface water.

Comparison of reconstruction techniques

The historical pH reconstructions at each site are given in figure 1. The MAGIC pH reconstruction is shown as an envelope curve, the width of which represents uncertainty in the model output; the 'true' pH value may lie anywhere within the envelope. These uncertainty bands encompass the range of variable values that were simulated given the specified uncertainty in the fixed parameter values and measured target values used in the optimization procedure (Jenkins & Cosby 1989). Values for pH inferred from the diatoms are represented

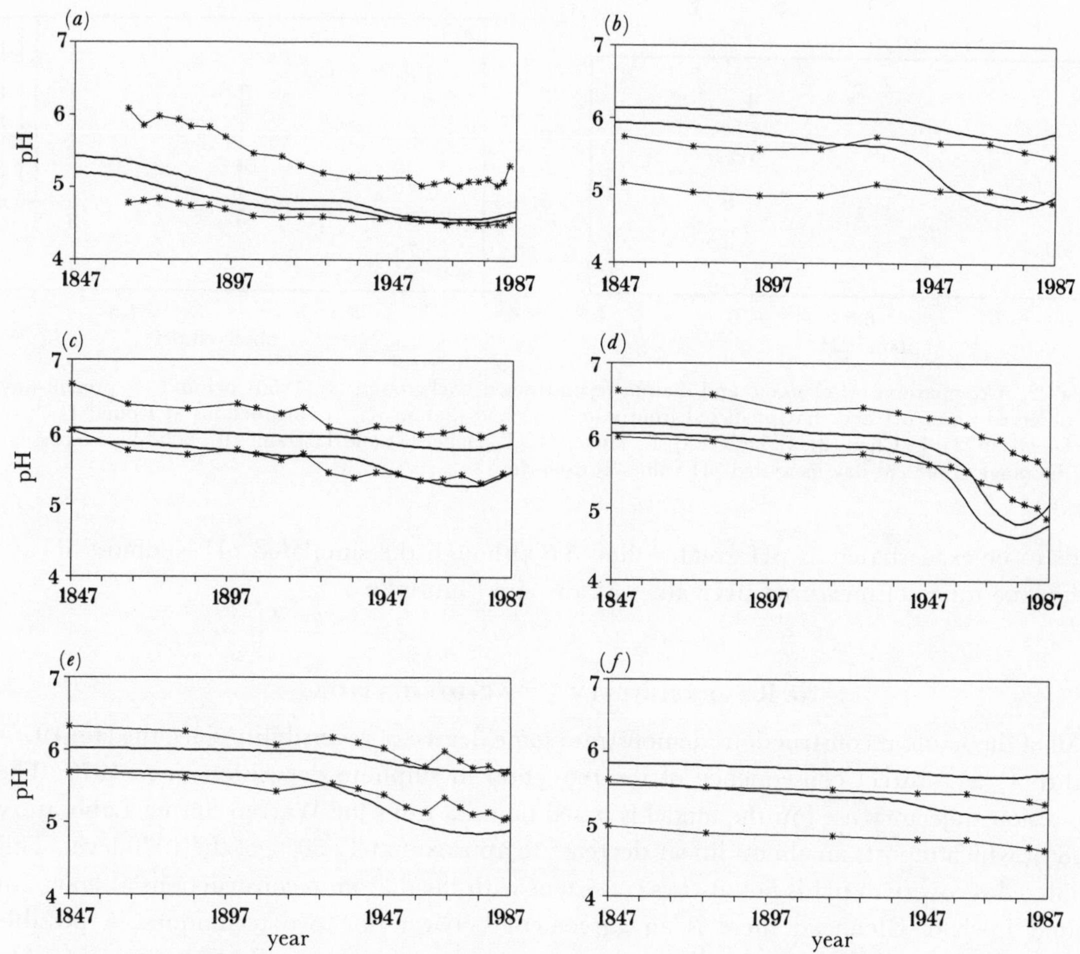

FIGURE 1. Historical pH trends reconstructed by MAGIC (thick lines) and diatoms (thin lines with asterisks) at (*a*) Round Loch of Glenhead, (*b*) Lochan Uaine, (*c*) Loch Tinker, (*d*) Loch Chon, (*e*) Loch Doilet and (*f*) Lochan Dubh.

as a series of points (asterisks), connected by thin lines. These represent the upper and lower standard errors of prediction for the weighted average pH reconstructions, estimated by bootstrapping (Birks *et al.*, this symposium). The overlap between the two reconstructions demonstrates a close agreement between the techniques in terms of the general pattern of historical acidification and timing of change. At L. Dubh and L. Uaine, however, the uncertainty bands from the two methods demonstrate the poorest agreement. These are high altitude sites where little pH change is predicted from a slightly acidic (pH 5.5–6.0) background (1847) level. At L. Uaine, MAGIC predicts a higher background pH although the uncertainty bands converge from 1940 onwards. At L. Dubh the diatom reconstructed pH is consistently lower than the MAGIC reconstruction. The predicted magnitude of pH change through the reconstruction period is consistent, however, being only *ca* 0.3 pH units for both methods. The background pH derived from both techniques for all lakes are in close agreement (figure 2*a*) and neither method shows a systematic bias. Comparison of observed and simulated present day pH (figure 2*b*), however, shows that both the MAGIC reconstructions, and to a lesser extent the diatom reconstructions, tend to underestimate observed mean pH. This problem

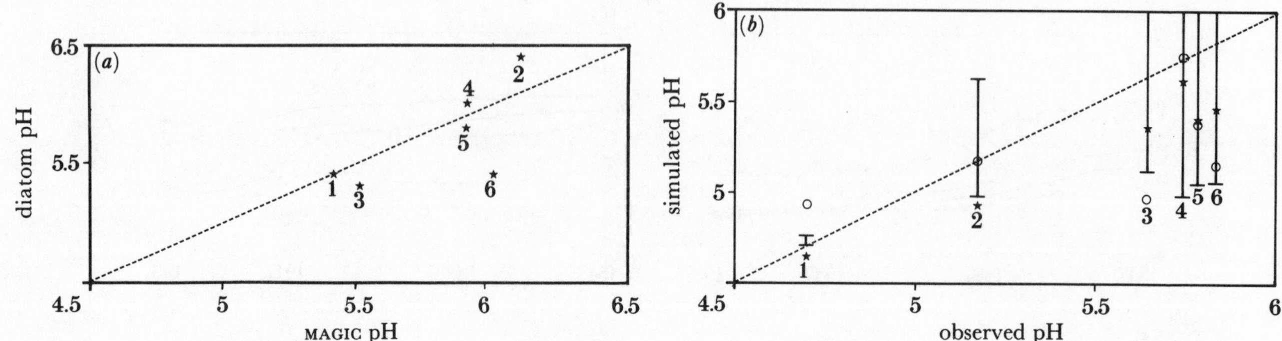

FIGURE 2. A comparison of (*a*) MAGIC and diatom reconstructed background (*ca.* 1850) pH and (*b*) present-day observed mean pH and that predicted from MAGIC (★) and diatom (○) reconstructions at Round Loch of Glenhead (1), L. Chon (2), L. Dubh (3), L. Tinker (4), L. Doilet (5) and L. Uaine (6). Solid bars represent the range of present-day measured pH values at each site.

tends to be exacerbated at pH greater than 5.5 although the simulated pH is almost always within the range of measured pH values at any site (figure 2*b*).

5. Reversibility of acidification

All of the MAGIC reconstructions demonstrate some degree of reversibility since the late 1970s (figure 1) as a direct consequence of the reduction in sulphate deposition since 1970. The deposition trajectory used in the model is based on data from the Warren Spring Laboratory (1987), which reports an almost linear decrease to approximately 50% of the 1970 level. This simulated recovery in pH is not always consistent with the diatom reconstructions although at Round Loch of Glenhead there is an agreement between the two techniques. A possible recovery is also indicated in the diatom reconstruction at L. Tinker. Battarbee *et al.* (1988) note a trend towards improved pH conditions at several other moorland sites in Scotland. The implication at the other four sites included in this analysis, however, is that the deposition trajectory is not applicable at all of the sites or that the pH change is as yet too small to be identified by diatom analysis.

It is predicted by MAGIC that under a range of deposition reduction scenarios reversibility of surface water acidification will continue and that greater deposition reductions will lead to increased surface water recovery (table 1). The simulations are run forward for 50 years to

TABLE 1. SIMULATIONS FROM MAGIC OF MEAN pH BY YEAR 2037 UNDER THREE FUTURE DEPOSITION REDUCTION SCENARIOS

(See text for details.)

	deposition reduction		
site	no reduction	30% reduction	70% reduction
Loch Doilet	5.0	5.2	5.4
Loch Chon	5.0	5.4	5.7
Lochan Dubh	5.2	5.3	5.4
Round Loch of Glenhead	4.7	4.8	5.0
Lochan Uaine	5.6	5.7	5.9
Loch Tinker	5.6	5.7	5.8

2037 on the basis of three different scenarios: no deposition reduction from the present day; a 30% linear reduction to the year 2000, then held constant at that level until 2037; a 70% reduction to the year 2000, then held constant until 2037. At Round Loch of Glenhead, L. Chon and L. Doilet, a decrease of 70% does not return the surface water to its background pH level and indeed, the predicted pH may still be too low for a self-sustaining fish population to be maintained (i.e. mean pH < 5.5) although this will depend on other chemical and biological factors. It is clear that at these sites further recovery of the surface water pH will only occur following more rapid recovery of the soil-base exchange capacity. A modelling analysis of the L. Chon system by Jenkins *et al.* (1989*b*) demonstrates that soil recovery occurs more slowly than surface water, even with relatively large reductions in sulphate input. At L. Chon and L. Doilet, however, the simulated pH reported in table 1 depends not only upon sulphate deposition levels but also on land management. The reported pH assumes that the forest, planted in the 1920s and 1950s at L. Doilet and L. Chon, respectively, remains in place for a further 50 years. This is unlikely in a commercial forest where trees are normally harvested after about 60 years. The surface water pH will then depend upon whether the forest is replanted or not and such considerations are detailed by Jenkins *et al.* (1989*b*). Furthermore, at L. Chon the high degree of recovery, simulated by MAGIC, in recent years (figure 1) and the level of future recovery (table 1) is greatly influenced by the very high calcium weathering rates, associated with a doleritic dyke, within the catchment. From this point of view L. Chon is not necessarily typical of forested catchments on bedrock with very low acid neutralizing capacity, which will recover only slowly (cf. L. Doilet).

Soil physical and chemical data were provided by Bob Ferrier, Bruce Walker, Basil Smith and Cyril Bown of the Macaulay Land Use Research Institute.

References

Battarbee, R. W., Flower, R. J., Stevenson, A. C., Jones, V. J., Harriman, R. & Appleby, P. G. 1988 Diatom and chemical evidence for reversibility of acidification of Scottish lochs. *Nature, Lond.* **332**, 530–532.

Cosby, B. J., Wright, R. F., Hornberger, H. M. & Galloway, J. N. 1985*a* Modelling the effects of acid deposition: assessment of a lumped parameter model of soil water and streamwater chemistry. *Wat. Res.* **21**, 51–63.

Cosby, B. J., Wright, R. F., Hornberger, G. M. & Galloway, J. N. 1985*b* Modelling the effects of acid deposition: estimation of long-term water quality responses in a small forested catchment. *Wat. Res.* **21**, 1591–1601.

Cosby, B. J., Hornberger, G. M., Wright, R. F. & Galloway, J. N. 1986 Modelling the effects of acid deposition: control of long-term sulfate dynamics by soil sulfate adsorption. *Wat. Res.* **22**, 1283–1291.

Flower, R. J., Battarbee, R. W. & Appleby, P. G. 1987 The recent palaeolimnology of acid lakes in Galloway, southwest Scotland: Diatom analysis, pH trends and the role of afforestation. *J. Ecol.* **75**, 797–824.

Harriman, R. & Morrison, B. R. S. 1981 Forestry, fisheries and acid rain in Scotland. *Scott. Forest.* **36**, 89–95.

Jenkins, A., Ferrier, R. C., Walker, T. A. B. & Whitehead, P. G. 1988 A modelling study of long term acidification in an upland Scottish catchment. *Wat. Air Soil Pollut.* **40**, 275–291.

Jenkins, A. & Cosby, B. J. 1989 Modelling surface water acidification using one and two soil layers and simple flow routing. In *Regional acidification models* (ed. J. Kamari, D. Brakke, A. Jenkins, S. Norton & R. Wright), pp. 253–267. Heidelberg: Springer-Verlag.

Jenkins, A., Cosby, B. J., Miller, J. D., Ferrier, R. C. and Walker, T. A. B. 1989*a* Modelling stream acidification in afforested catchments: long term reconstructions at two sites in central Scotland. *J. Hydrol.* (In the press).

Jenkins, A., Cosby, B. J., Ferrier, R. C., Walker, T. A. B. & Miller, J. D. 1989*b* Modelling stream acidification in afforested catchments: a comparison of the relative effects of acid deposition and afforestation. *J. Hydrol.* (In the press.)

Mason, B. J. & Seip, H. M. 1985 The current state of knowledge on acidification of surface waters and guidelines for further research. *Ambio* **14**, 45–51.

Warren Spring Laboratory 1987 *Acid deposition in the U.K.* Stevenage, U.K.: Warren Spring Laboratory.

Discussion

D. F. Charles (*Indiana University, Indiana, U.S.A.*). A concern has been raised at this meeting and elsewhere that computer models such as MAGIC do not account well for organic acids, especially for any change in output of organic acids from watersheds that may occur in response to increased acidic deposition.

A. Jenkins. The MAGIC model incorporates only a simple representation of the effects of organics on water chemistry. Organic matter concentrations for the soil water and stream water are specified, usually in proportion to TOC, together with dissociation constants derived from empirical relations. Organic concentrations are held constant at the specified level throughout the model simulation. In this form, the model has been applied to a Finnish lake (Liuhapuro) with high DOC (17.2 mg l^{-1}) and succesfully reproduces the pH decline indicated by palaeolimnological reconstruction. At present, the effect of increased acid deposition on the output of organic acid is not well documented and so cannot be represented in the model.

Phil. Trans. R. Soc. Lond. B **327**, 441–445 (1990)
Printed in Great Britain

Palaeolimnology and lake acidification: a summary

By K. Faegri

Botanical Institute, University of Bergen, Allégaten 41, *N*-5007 *Bergen, Norway*

When plans for the realization of the Surface Water Acidification Project (SWAP) were initially discussed, I advocated the inclusion of a palaeolimnological programme. One reason for that was personal: as a palaeobotanist, I wanted to see what palaeolimnology could contribute to solving problems that were, in principle, very similar to questions dealt with in other palaeobotanical research, but on a completely different timescale; years and decades instead of centuries or millennia.

More important, however, were the SWAP problems themselves, which seemed to beg for a palaeolimnological approach. The central problems of SWAP deal with ecophysical conditions in the so-called acidified lakes and mechanisms of their effect on biota. However, before considering such problems, the background should be studied by palaeolimnologists. In short: *did* anything happen, *what* happened, *when* and *why* did it happen? Naive questions indeed, but they demand answers: data about the simple existence and timing of the acidification are fundamental for further work.

The term 'acidification' used throughout is a general term that expresses a group of associated environmental conditions. Changes of pH may be the easiest observable and quantifiable parameter, but its actual physiological significance in relation to the biological phenomena observed may in itself be slight. However, within the general ecological framework it monitors the general status of the basins studied.

It is very simple to define in detail the immediate ecological status: ordinary ecochemical methods are well established and sufficient to confirm that waters are acid and also suffer from other deleterious influences, expressing themselves in fish death. But if we want to see how and when this came about such methods fail us: we have no historical data of this kind. Apart from anecdotal information, which should not be neglected as it is often the only information we possess, very few data are available, and those that may exist were collected for other purposes and provide poor comparative material.

Above all, there is one very important point: the very first, faint traces of a change cannot be pin-pointed in this manner because their manifestations are so indistinct as to be lost in the statistical 'noise'; at that time nobody would have had the foresight to realize what was going on and what could be used to provide us with a database for future reference.

For this purpose we need a monitoring system that is more robust against the 'noise', for example, by integrating it over time. It is then possible to trace the first beginning. Many organisms have this quality; they are, within their restricted field, both faster and more sensitive indicators than ecochemical measurements. Flowering of forest trees, as registered by pollen analysis, is one example: registering climatic deterioration almost instantaneously. However, the complicated physiological pathways of multicellular terrestrial organisms put them at a disadvantage in comparison with small, often unicellular aquatic organisms, the time-lag of whose reactions is very short. If, in addition, such organisms are specifically recognizable also after death and sufficiently resistant against decay and occur in large numbers, we have the ideal index fossils.

In evaluating such organisms it is important to realize that their reactions as observed are not always directly related to the primary ecochemical conditions, but may be mediated via other organisms, which may influence their occurrence. Indicator organisms may be liable to predation by other oganisms that are also dependent on acidification and that may not leave any recognizable traces behind. Such cases may be rather complicated.

Any palaeolimnological investigation that includes necessary and suitable marker oganisms immediately recognizes the onset of ecological change by changes in the numerical relation between groups of taxa with varying ecological niches. The basic reason for the change is usually chemical or physical. By studying ecophysiological characteristics of the organisms in question, they define quantitatively the influence of primary factors as they express themselves in the biota and may produce transfer data for quantifying the immediately observed qualitative manifestations.

This, more or less, was the basis for the palaeolimnological programme of SWAP, or, more correctly, of my understanding of the programme. Here I review the results of the programme that have led to two different types of study. One aims at answering our four basic questions directly. The others are calibration and methodological studies used to create the tools for answering the questions.

The answer to the first two questions is very clear: recently, there has been a change towards acidification in practically all lakes investigated that were situated in areas of high sulphur deposition. Both organisms and physical variables show the same picture. Indeed the only basins studies that did not register the effect are found in areas of low sulphur deposition in northwest Scotland and central Norway.

The timing of change also needed study. The usual dating method in Holocene palaeolimnology is by ^{14}C but this is unsuited to the dating of very recent sediments. Instead dating by ^{210}Pb and by fall-out radioisotopes has been used. These are beyond my field, but the results are consistent.

Diatom data pH calibration is more complicated, especially as organisms react holistically to all external conditions at the same time and reactions are far from being linearly related. Within a certain set of values one specific variable may be decisive, even given a monotonic reaction, but outside those limits other variables influence reactions and may over-ride the effects that we are studying.

As a group, diatoms may be the most versatile and reliable monitoring organisms available. They possess the qualities defined for the ideal index fossil. Also, they are relatively immune against predation (i) because the resistant remains are often preserved even after passage through the gut of a grazer and (ii) because they have an extremely high reproduction rate, indeed continuous reproduction given favourable ecological conditions. They are very sensitive to the quality of the water. In fresh water, pH is the dominating influence and has been studied earlier and very intensively under the SWAP programme. Interesting and penetrating studies have been done in the programme on the ecology of these organisms; for example, their relation to habitat, and in relation to their ecophysiology in acid waters. However the study material of palaeolimnology is thanatocenoses, remains of dead organisms brought together from a variety of habitats. Material from these habitats are inextricably mixed. In the constructions of pH transfer functions these assemblages are compared with average lake-water pH. I wonder what these average pH data actually mean. In some bodies of water, pH varies spatially, diurnally and seasonally even in response to short-term meterological conditions; it is far from certain that these variations are the same in basins of different characteristics. All the values from one body of water form a swarm around one central value, but the character of this swarm varies with ecological conditions. What are the relations between the pH of the statistical models and all those varying pH data out in nature? This is an important challenge for diatomists in the future to refine their methods to take such functions into account.

Another point is that the pH tolerance of a species need not be constant: it may be modifed by other influences especially nutrients. If the long-term 'acidification' of a lake is interrupted when the area has been opened by cultivation: is that only a pH effect, or does it mean that the changed nutrient status of the lake permits the diatoms to survive at lower pH, and some more demanding ones to immigrate into water that they would not tolerate at lower nutrient levels? Developing models to differentiate between such factors could also be a desirable future goal for diatomists.

Mutatis mutandis, I have a similar feeling with regard to some of the other groups studied, although to a smaller extent. I must admit that my practical knowledge of these groups is more superficial than with regard to diatoms. Chrysophytes seem to have many of the same qualities.

Certainly our knowledge of the ecology of diatoms has been greatly advanced by these studies, which have also given material for quantitative answers to SWAP problems.

It must also be stressed that by using catchment models as well as diatoms it has been possible to produce some tentative and not too cheerful predictions for the development of lakes under given conditions of sulphur deposition in the future.

The studies have not only given a convincing indication that the investigated lakes in contaminated areas have recently become more acid, but also that this acidification on the whole follows a pattern to be expected according to hypotheses (cf. below). The acidification is faintly foreshadowed since the middle of the 19th century, becoming strongly manifest during the post-war period.

The next question is whether the development thus observed and dated represents a unique event or (as maintained in discussions) it has occurred previously and for the same reasons. The answer is that even if some developments more or less resembling the recent one have been registered or postulated, the present event is unique and thus is confirmed not only by detailed studies in the SWAP programme but also by other work in the U.S.A., Finland, Sweden and the U.K.

Several studies in SWAP specifically address the last of our questions: why did acidification occur? Three hypotheses have been put forward.

1. Long-term acidification.
2. Effect of changes in land-use.
3. Effect of industrial pollution.

The hypotheses are not mutually exclusive and the effects may have been synergistic. Due to a vigorous defense of the land-use hypothesis from its originator, the land-use hypothesis was considered of central importance in 1984 when the SWAP study was designed and several sub-projects have dealt with this question.

Most of the studies gave a clear answer in favour of the acid deposition hypothesis, but some of the data may be interpreted in several ways.

In all cases the biological effects of land-use change according to hypothesis 2 would be very difficult to separate from those of atmospheric pollution. It is not easy to find deposits that register in such a way or under such circumstances that one of the competing hypotheses can be falsified but in the palaeolimnological programme two lines have been pursued that have given clear answers.

The reaction of diatoms and other biota to acidification is not influenced by the way in which this acidity has arisen, only on its existence. It is therefore necessary to find an indicator, the occurrence of which cannot be caused by one or the other influence. Spherical carbonaceous particles satisfy this condition. They are produced by modern, high-temperature combustion of fossil fuel; they are dispersed in the same way as the supposed atmospheric contaminants and they are very resistant. In cores, they are found from the mid-19th century and after 1940 the curve rises suddenly. The parallelism between acidification and the occurrence of these particles is a strong argument in favour of the atmospheric pollution hypothesis.

Another approach has been to find lakes in which land-use influence can be ruled out and to compare them with adjacent lakes that have been under influence of land-use. Several studies of such paired lakes have been done. An example is the 'perched' lake project, i.e. lakes situated in such a position (on the top plateau of hills) that they themselves constitute a major part of the catchment area, the rest of which is covered by, at most, a very scanty vegetation, and where no local agricultural or other human influence can have occurred during the period in question. Such lakes give a direct, almost unadulterated representation of precipitation. They present the same picture as the other lakes with a clear acidification after *ca.* 1850.

The 'perched' lakes and other similar projects in SWAP and reported in the literature thus falsify the land-use hypothesis. The carbonaceous particles and other indicators of atmospheric pollution give positive evidence for the atmospheric pollution hypothesis. The matter might therefore be considered settled, but even if acidification is registered under circumstances when land-use effects are excluded, I feel that it is not possible on the basis of the present material to say that land-use changes have not under certain circumstances also played a (probably minor) role in the acidification process. The influence of pollutant scavenging by coniferous forests is a case in point.

Comparisons have also been made with changes in lakes following the abandonment of cultivation in earlier epochs and with the natural immigration of spruce 2000–3000 years ago. Strict historical parallels do not exist but none of these studies so far have shown any effect comparable to today's acidification.

In the heated discussions of hypothesis 2 against hypothesis 3, number 1 has been less prominent. As compared to the effect of atmospheric pollution the effect of long-term changes is certainly very subordinate. Some long cores indicate such effect, others show a clear acidification after deglaciation and in the early part of the post-glacial period. But in any case over the last 5000 years the effect is so small that it could not conceivably produce the violent changes apparent in recent sediments.

Returning now to my original four problems: has the palaeolimnological sub-programme fulfilled its purpose and given answers to the questions? I feel that we may confidently say yes to that, and even more importantly, to the question of whether it was worth the effort; it was.

I should stress that no attempt has been intended nor made and no palaeolimnological data have been obtained that indicate the source of the atmospheric contamination: whether locally produced or coming into Scandinavia from the industrial areas to the south or the west, or both. This could be a worthwhile project for the future.

Finally, I want to point out very forcefully the role of taxonomy and taxonomists in this investigation. Where would we have been if it had not been possible to call upon and draw upon the expertise of a large body of taxonomic specialists in diatoms, chrysophytes, Cladocera and chironomids. Who would have done the monitoring? In today's university debate so-called progressive scientists have blown their own trumpets, with almost indecent volume, denigrating taxonomy and taxonomical expertise and, above all, the natural history museums. The SWAP palaeolimnology story shows what would have happened if they had had their way and if there had not existed museum material on which the taxonomists could support their identifications. I sincerely hope that it will also be possible in the future to localize the material upon which this study is based in the museums and compliment those taxonomists who in the beginning of these studies managed to align their diatom taxonomy to achieve the results obtained.

THE ROYAL SOCIETY

GUIDANCE ON SUBMISSION OF PAPERS: MATHEMATICAL AND PHYSICAL SCIENCES

Proceedings A

Papers in *Proceedings* A fall into two length categories, which determine their speed of publication after acceptance: papers that will occupy 10 printed pages or less ('rapid papers') will be published faster than longer papers. The normal maximum length of papers in *Proceedings* A is 25 printed pages.

Authors

1. **Three** copies of the typescript and figures are required. Authors are invited to indicate whether they wish the paper to be considered for rapid publication if it satisfies the length requirement.
2. Papers may be submitted (i) direct to the Society's editorial office at the address given below, (ii) through a Regional Editor of *Proceedings* A (addresses are given in the journal), or (iii) through a Fellow or Foreign Member of the Society, whose addresses are listed in the Society's *Year Book*.
3. Consideration of a paper will be accelerated if it is accompanied by a recommendation on its suitability for publication. The Editor will take a recommendation into account only if it is supported by a referee's report, prepared either by a Fellow, Foreign Member or Regional Editor, or at his or her request. Such papers may expect to receive priority in publication, irrespective of length. In addition, authors may suggest the names of possible referees, with the understanding that such suggestions will not necessarily be adopted.

Fellows, Foreign Members and Regional Editors receiving papers for submission

1. Fellows, Foreign Members and Regional Editors who are in receipt of a paper and wish to recommend it (see 3 above) are invited (i) to prepare or provide a referee's report before forwarding it to the Society's editorial office, marked for consideration for *Proceedings* A, and/or (ii) to suggest names of referees for the guidance of the Editor.
2. The report supporting a recommendation may not be prepared by an author of the paper.

Philosophical Transactions A

Authors

1. **Three** copies of the typescript and figures are required.
2. Papers may be submitted (i) direct to the Society's editorial office at the address given below, (ii) to the Editor or an Editorial Board member of *Transactions* A (addresses are given in the journal), or (iii) through a Fellow or Foreign Member of the Society, whose addresses are listed in the Society's *Year Book*.
3. Authors of review papers, Theme issue papers or Discussion Meeting papers will be given appropriate advice about submission.

Fellows and Foreign Members receiving papers for submission

1. The paper should be forwarded to the Society's editorial office, marked for consideration for *Transactions* A.
2. Fellows and Foreign Members are invited to suggest the names of possible referees for the guidance of the Editor.

Editorial Board members receiving papers for submission

1. The paper should be forwarded to the Society's editorial office with the names of two referees and, if possible, a reserve.

The role of Editorial Board members

1. The Editor may seek the advice of one or more members of the Editorial Board during the consideration of papers submitted to the Society's editorial office, via a Fellow or Foreign Member, or direct to the Editor.

For full details of the requirements of each journal the latest edition of the instructions to authors, published at the end of each volume of the relevant journal, should be consulted.

Editorial address: Editorial office, The Royal Society, 6 Carlton House Terrace, London SW1Y 5AG, U.K.

[January 1990

THE ROYAL SOCIETY

GUIDANCE ON SUBMISSION OF PAPERS: BIOLOGICAL SCIENCES

Proceedings B

Authors

1. **Four** copies of the typescript and figures are required. Papers should normally not exceed 4000 words (5 printed pages). The target publication time is three months from receipt.
2. Papers may be submitted (i) to an appropriate member of the Editorial Board, or a Corresponding Editor, of *Proceedings* B (addresses are given in the journal), (ii) to a Fellow or Foreign Member of the Society, whose addresses are listed in the Society's *Year Book*, or (iii) directly to the Editor at the address shown in the journal. Authors' telephone numbers, fax numbers and/or electronic mail addresses should be given.
3. Authors are advised to check with the intended recipient beforehand if they submit a paper by routes (i) or (ii), and to write to inform the Editor once the paper has been sent.

Fellows, Foreign Members, Editorial Board members and Corresponding Editors receiving papers for submission

1. To expedite publication, the Fellow, etc., should (i) immediately inform the Editor of receipt of the paper and (ii) arrange for its being refereed within two weeks of receipt. Reduced copies of the forms to be used for submission and refereeing of papers are printed in the *Year Book*; larger copies are printed in *Proceedings* B issues.
2. Referees should be sent typescripts and report forms, and appropriate action should be taken to ensure the provision of reports within two weeks.
3. The Fellow, etc., who receives the paper may act as one referee if he or she desires; however, an author may not referee his or her own paper.
4. If the referees judge a paper to be of very high quality but requiring attention, the Fellow, etc., should return it to the author for urgent revision and should check the revised version before sending it to the Editor. Otherwise the original version of the paper and reports should be sent to the Editor for action.

Philosophical Transactions B

Authors

1. **Three** copies of the typescript and figures are required. The normal maximum length of papers in *Transactions* B is 25 000 words. There is no lower length limit. The intended publication time is 5–7 months from receipt. The journal will publish papers in all branches of biological science (including clinical science), and will also accept review articles. Authors intending to submit review articles should consult the Editor, whose address is given in the journal.
2. Papers longer than 25 000 words will be considered exceptionally, and authors of such papers should consult the Editor well before submission, preferably at an early stage in preparation.
3. Papers may be submitted (i) direct to the Society's editorial office at the address given below, or (ii) through a Fellow or Foreign Member of the Society, whose addresses are listed in the Society's *Year Book*.
4. Authors of review papers or Discussion Meeting papers will be given appropriate advice about submission.

Fellows and Foreign Members receiving papers for submission

1. The paper should be forwarded to the Society's editorial office, marked for consideration for *Transactions* B.
2. Fellows and Foreign Members are invited to suggest the names of possible referees for the guidance of the Editor.

The role of Editorial Board members

1. The Editor may seek the advice of one or more members of the Editorial Board during the consideration of papers submitted to the Society's editorial office.
2. Papers should *not* be sent direct to Editorial Board members.

For full details of the requirements of each journal the latest edition of the instructions to authors, published at the end of each volume of the relevant journal, should be consulted.

Editorial address: Editorial office, The Royal Society, 6 Carlton House Terrace, London SW1Y 5AG, U.K.

[January 1990